Diane Nelson | President

Dan DiDio and Jim Lee | Co-Publishers

Geoff Johns | Chief Creative Officer

Amit Desai | Senior VP — Marketing & Global Franchise Management

Nairi Gardiner | Senior VP — Finance

Sam Ades | VP — Digital Marketing

Shelly Bond | VP & Executive Editor — Vertigo

Bobbie Chase | VP — Talent Development

Mark Chiarello | Senior VP — Art, Design & Collected Editions

John Cunningham | VP — Content Strategy

Anne DePies | VP — Strategy Planning & Reporting

Don Falletti | VP — Manufacturing Operations

John Ficarra | Senior VP & Executive Editor, MAD

Lawrence Ganem | VP — Editorial Administration & Talent Relations

Alison Gill | Senior VP — Manufacturing & Operations

Bob Harras | Senior VP — Editor-in-Chief, DC Comics

Hank Kanalz | Senior VP — Editorial Strategy & Administration

Kevin Kiniry | VP — Creative Services

Jay Kogan | VP — Legal Affairs

Derek Maddalena | Senior VP — Sales & Business Development

Jack Mahan | VP — Business Affairs

Dan Miron | VP — Sales Planning & Trade Development

Nick Napolitano | VP — Manufacturing Administration

Carol Roeder | VP — Marketing

Eddie Scannell | VP — Mass Account & Digital Sales

Courtney Simmons | Senior VP — Publicity & Communications

Jim (Ski) Sokolowski | VP — Comic Book Specialty & Newsstand Sales

Sam Viviano | VP — Art & Design, MAD

Sandy Yi | Senior VP — Global Franchise Management

DC ENTERTAINMENT ESSENTIAL GRAPHIC NOVELS 2016.
Published by DC Comics.
All Rights Reserved.

Copyright © 2016 DC Comics. All Rights Reserved. All books, products, titles, characters, character names, slogans, logos and related indicia are trademarks of and copyright of DC Comics or their respective owners. VERTIGO is a trademark of DC Comics. The stories, characters and incidents featured in this publication are entirely fictional. DC Comics does not read or accept unsolicited ideas, stories or artwork.

Cover art by Ivan Reis and Joe Prado

2900 W. Alameda Ave., Burbank, CA 91505

Printed by Transcontinental Interglobe, Beauceville, QC, Canada. 1/1/2016.
First Printing.
ISBN: 978-1-4012-6388-1
VERTIGO is a trademark of DC Comics.

FABLES ©BILL WILLINGHAM AND DC COMICS. ™ BILL WILLINGHAM.

Y: THE LAST MAN ™ & © BRIAN K. VAUGHAN AND PIA GUERRA.

DAYTRIPPER ™ & © GABRIEL BA AND FABIO MOON.

PREACHER ™ & © GARTH ENNIS AND STEVE DILLON.

GET JIRO! ©ANTHONY BOURDAIN, JOEL ROSE AND DC COMICS. ™ ANTHONY BOURDAIN AND JOEL ROSE.

PUNK ROCK JESUS ©SEAN MURPHY. ™ DC COMICS.

TRILLIUM ™ & © JEFF LEMIRE.

AMERICAN VAMPIRE ©SCOTT SNYDER, STEPHEN KING AND DC COMICS. ™ DC COMICS.

100 BULLETS©BRIAN AZZARELLO, EDUARDO RISSO AND DC COMICS. ™ DC COMICS.

DMZ ©BRIAN WOOD AND RICCARDO BURCHIELLI. ™ DC COMICS.

COFFIN HILL ™ & © CAITLIN KITTREDGE AND INAKI MIRANDA PANIAGUA.

EX MACHINA ™ & © BRIAN K. VAUGHAN AND TONY HARRIS.

FBP: FEDERAL BUREAU OF PHYSICS ©SIMON OLIVER AND ROBBI RODRIGUEZ. ™ DC COMICS.

IZOMBIE ©MONKEY BRAIN, INC. AND MICHAEL ALLRED. ™ DC COMICS.

SCALPED ©JASON AARON AND RAJKO MILOSOVIC. ™ DC COMICS.

SWEET TOOTH © JEFF LEMIRE. ™ DC COMICS.

TRANSMETROPOLITAN ™ & © WARREN ELLIS AND DARICK ROBERTSON.

THE UNWRITTEN ©MIKE CAREY AND PETER GROSS. ™ DC COMICS.

THE GIRL WITH THE DRAGON TATTOO ™ & © MOGGLIDEN AB.

PRIDE OF BAGHDAD ©BRIAN K. VAUGHAN AND NIKO HENRICHON. ™ DC COMICS.

THE ROYALS: MASTERS OF WAR ©ROB WILLIAMS AND SIMON COLEBY. ™ DC COMICS.

THE WAKE ™ & © SCOTT SNYDER AND SEAN MURPHY.

FAIREST ©BILL WILLINGHAM AND DC COMICS. ™ BILL WILLINGHAM.

THE LEAGUE OF EXTRAORDINARY GENTLEMEN ™ & © ALAN MOORE AND KEVIN O'NEILL.

JOE THE BARBARIAN ©GRANT MORRISON AND DC COMICS. ™ GRANT MORRISON.

THE INVISIBLES ™ & © GRANT MORRISON.

WE3 ™ & © GRANT MORRISON AND FRANK QUITELY.

THE FILTH ™ & © GRANT MORRISON AND CHRIS WESTON.

MAD ™ & © E.C. PUBLICATIONS, INC.

SPY VS. SPY ™ & © E.C. PUBLICATIONS, INC.

SCOOBY-DOO TEAM-UP ™ & © HANNA-BARBERA.

PEFC Certified
Printed on paper from sustainably managed forests and controlled sources
PEFC/01-31-106   www.pefc.org

TABLE OF CONTENTS

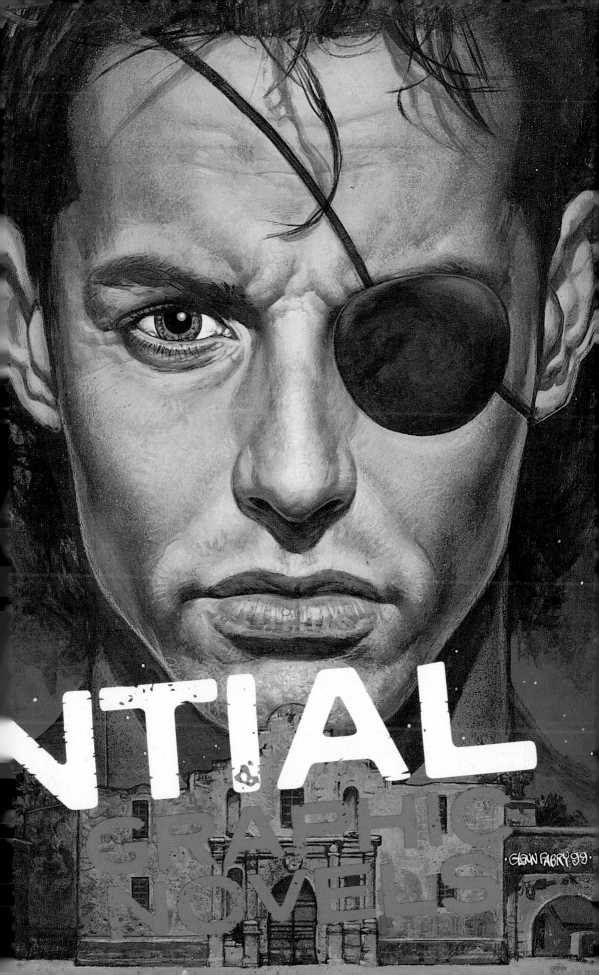

WATCHMEN

THE GREATEST GRAPHIC NOVEL OF ALL TIME

One of the most influential graphic novels of all time and a perennial bestseller, WATCHMEN is considered a gateway title to the entire graphic storytelling medium. Alan Moore and Dave Gibbons's seminal story is the benchmark against which all other graphic novels and comic books are judged.

A murder mystery turned nationwide conspiracy, WATCHMEN examines the lives of the eponymous superhero team as they seem to decay alongside the ever-darkening America around them. Rorschach, Nite Owl, the Silk Spectre, Dr. Manhattan and Ozymandias reunite to investigate who's behind a teammate's murder, but find that the truth may be even more grim than the world they seek to protect.

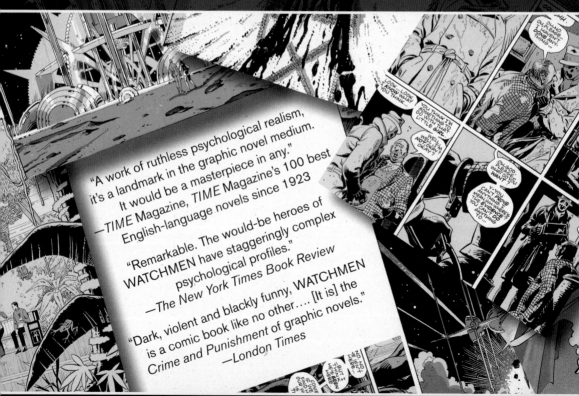

"A work of ruthless psychological realism, it's a landmark in the graphic novel medium. It would be a masterpiece in any."
—TIME Magazine, TIME Magazine's 100 best English-language novels since 1923

"Remarkable. The would-be heroes of WATCHMEN have staggeringly complex psychological profiles."
—The New York Times Book Review

"Dark, violent and blackly funny, WATCHMEN is a comic book like no other.... [It is] the Crime and Punishment of graphic novels."
—London Times

WATCHMEN

Writer: Alan Moore | Artist: Dave Gibbons | ISBN: 978-1-4012-4525-2 | Diamond Code: FEB140265 | Price: $19.99 /$23.99 CAN | Format: TP

BATMAN:
THE DARK KNIGHT RETURNS

THE GREATEST BATMAN STORY EVER TOLD

Ten years after an aging Batman has retired, Gotham City has sunk deeper into decadence and lawlessness. Now, when his city needs him most, the Dark Knight returns in a blaze of glory. Joined by Carrie Kelley, a teenage female Robin, Batman must take back the streets.

But for a man his age, a return to a life of crime-fighting is not easy. After facing off against two of his greatest enemies, the Joker and Two-Face, a haggard Batman finds himself in mortal combat with his former ally, Superman, in a battle that only one of them will survive.

Hailed as a comics masterpiece, THE DARK KNIGHT RETURNS is Frank Miller's (*300* and *SIN CITY*) reinvention of Gotham's legendary protector. It remains one of the most influential stories ever told in comics, and is a book cited by the filmmakers as an inspiration for the recent blockbuster Batman movies.

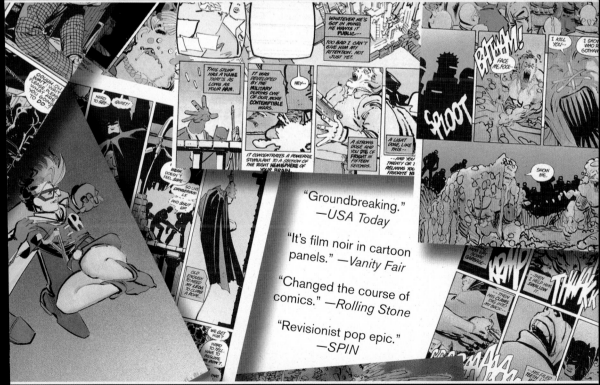

"Groundbreaking."
—*USA Today*

"It's film noir in cartoon panels." —*Vanity Fair*

"Changed the course of comics." —*Rolling Stone*

"Revisionist pop epic."
—*SPIN*

BATMAN: THE DARK KNIGHT RETURNS

Writer: Frank Miller | Artists: Frank Miller and Klaus Janson | ISBN: 978-1-4012-6311-9 | Diamond Code: NOV150279

Price: $19.99 /$23.99 CAN | Format: TP

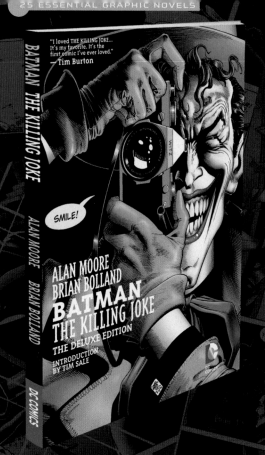

BATMAN:
THE KILLING JOKE

ALAN MOORE'S UNFORGETTABLE MEDITATION ON THE RAZOR-THIN LINE BETWEEN SANITY AND INSANITY, HEROISM AND VILLAINY, COMEDY AND TRAGEDY

In this groundbreaking work, Moore weaves together a twisted tale of insanity and human perseverance, featuring Batman's greatest foe, the Joker.

Looking to prove that any man can be pushed past his breaking point into madness, the Joker attempts to drive Commissioner Gordon insane. Refusing to give up even after suffering a tremendous personal tragedy, Gordon struggles to maintain his sanity with the help of Batman in a desperate effort to best the madman.

With art by one of comics' best illustrators, Brian Bolland, BATMAN: THE KILLING JOKE is a chilling introspection into the mind of fiction's most notorious villain.

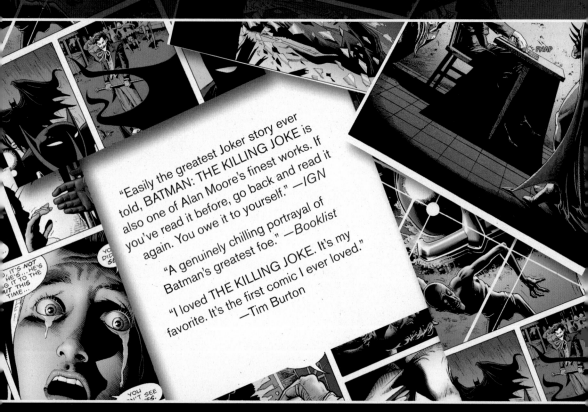

"Easily the greatest Joker story ever told, BATMAN: THE KILLING JOKE is also one of Alan Moore's finest works. If you've read it before, go back and read it again. You owe it to yourself." —IGN

"A genuinely chilling portrayal of Batman's greatest foe." —Booklist

"I loved THE KILLING JOKE. It's my favorite. It's the first comic I ever loved." —Tim Burton

BATMAN: THE KILLING JOKE: THE DELUXE EDITION

Writer: Alan Moore | Artist: Brian Bolland | ISBN: 978-1-4012-1667-2 | Diamond Code: NOV070226 | Price: $17.99 /$20.99 CAN | Format: HC

THE SANDMAN
OL. 1: PRELUDES & NOCTURNES

THE DEFINITIVE VERTIGO SERIES BY
THE LEGENDARY NEIL GAIMAN

The *New York Times* best-selling author Neil Gaiman's transcendent series THE SANDMAN is often labeled as not only the definitive Vertigo title, but also as one of the finest achievements in graphic storytelling. Gaiman created an unforgettable tale of the forces that exist beyond life and death by weaving ancient mythology, folklore and fairy tales with his own distinct narrative vision.

In THE SANDMAN VOLUME 1: PRELUDES & NOCTURNES, an occultist attempting to capture Death to bargain for eternal life traps her younger brother Dream instead. After his seventy-year imprisonment and eventual escape, Dream, also known as Morpheus, goes on a quest for his lost objects of power to reclaim his throne.

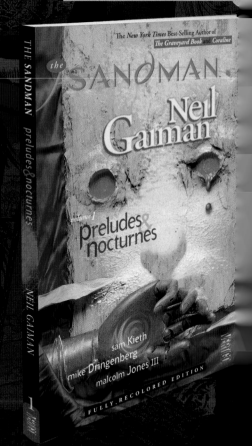

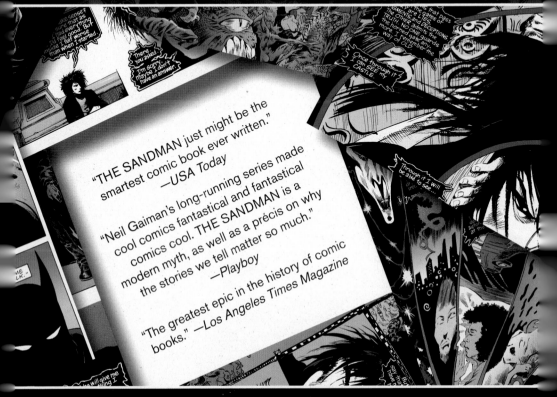

"THE SANDMAN just might be the smartest comic book ever written."
—USA Today

"Neil Gaiman's long-running series made cool comics fantastical and fantastical comics cool. THE SANDMAN is a modern myth, as well as a précis on why the stories we tell matter so much."
—Playboy

"The greatest epic in the history of comic books." —Los Angeles Times Magazine

THE SANDMAN VOL. 1: PRELUDES & NOCTURNES

Neil Gaiman | Artists: Sam Kieth, Malcolm Jones III & Mike Dringenberg | ISBN: 978-1-4012-2575-9 | Diamond Code: JUL100259 | Price: $19.99 /$23.99 CAN | Format: TP

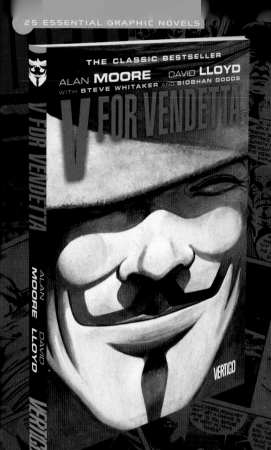

V FOR VENDETTA

A DARK PORTRAIT OF OPPRESSION AND RESISTANCE SET AGAINST THE BACKDROP OF DYSTOPIAN FUTURE ENGLAND

A visionary graphic novel that defines sophisticated story-telling, Alan Moore's best-selling V FOR VENDETTA is a ter-rifying portrait of totalitarianism and resistance, superbly illustrated by artist David Lloyd.

Set in a futuristic totalitarian England, a country without freedom or faith, a mysterious man in a white porcelain mask strikes back against the oppressive overlords on behalf of the voiceless. This powerful story detailing the loss and fight for individuality has become a cultural touchstone and an enduring allegory for current events.

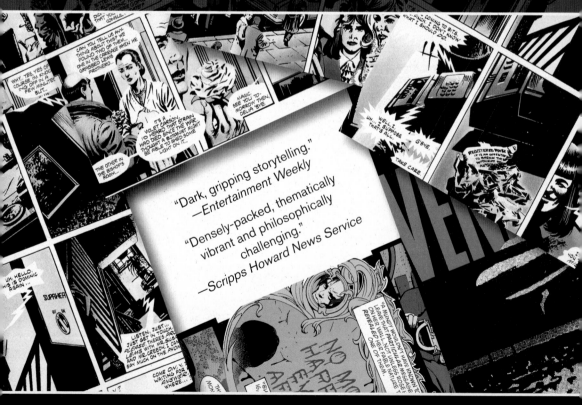

"Dark, gripping storytelling."
—*Entertainment Weekly*

"Densely-packed, thematically vibrant and philosophically challenging."
—*Scripps Howard News Service*

V FOR VENDETTA

Writer: Alan Moore | Artist: David Lloyd | ISBN: 978-1-4012-0841-7 | Diamond Code: SEP088030 | Price: $19.99 /$23.99 CAN | Format: TP

JUSTICE LEAGUE
VOL 1: ORIGIN

DC COMICS' FLAGSHIP TITLE! GEOFF JOHNS AND JIM LEE UNITE FOR THE FIRST TIME TO LAUNCH THE BOLD NEW BEGINNING OF THE DC UNIVERSE'S PREMIER SUPER-TEAM!

It's the dawn of a new age of superheroes, frightening to the world at large. Superman. Batman. The Flash. Wonder Woman. Green Lantern. Aquaman. Cyborg. Though young and inexperienced, brash and overconfident, each one alone is a powerful force in the battle of good against evil. Together, they may be the only thing on Earth that can stop the alien warlord Darkseid from claiming our planet as his own. Together they will become the Justice League!

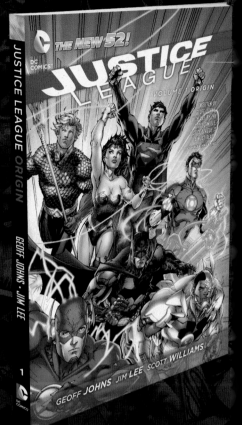

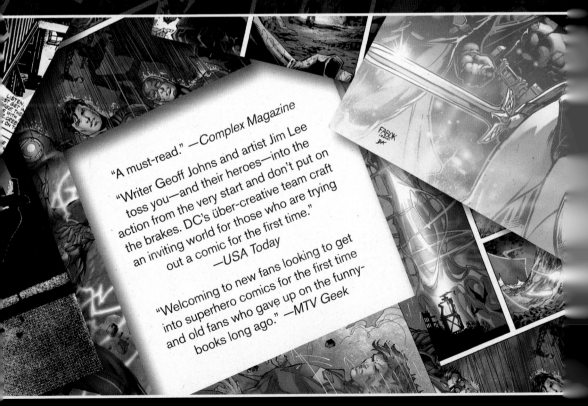

"A must-read." —Complex Magazine

"Writer Geoff Johns and artist Jim Lee toss you—and their heroes—into the action from the very start and don't put on the brakes. DC's über-creative team craft an inviting world for those who are trying out a comic for the first time."
—USA Today

"Welcoming to new fans looking to get into superhero comics for the first time and old fans who gave up on the funny-books long ago." —MTV Geek

JUSTICE LEAGUE VOL. 1: ORIGIN

Writer: Geoff Johns | Artist: Jim Lee | ISBN: 978-1-4012-3788-2 | Diamond Code: OCT120252 | Price: $16.99 /$19.99 CAN | Format: TP

BATMAN: YEAR ONE

THE TIMELESS ORIGIN STORY OF THE DARK KNIGHT

In 1986, Frank Miller and David Mazzucchelli produced this groundbreaking reinterpretation of the origin of Batman— who he is, and how he came to be. Sometimes careless and naive, this Dark Knight is far from the flawless vigilante he is today. In his first year on the job, Batman feels his way through a Gotham City far darker than when he left it. His solemn vow to extinguish the town's criminal element is only half the battle; along with Lieutenant James Gordon, the Dark Knight must also fight a police force more corrupt than the scum in the streets.

BATMAN: YEAR ONE stands alongside BATMAN: THE DARK KNIGHT RETURNS on the mantel of greatest Batman graphic novels of all time. Timeless in its appeal, Frank Miller and David Mazzucchelli's masterpiece would stand apart from the crowded comics field even today.

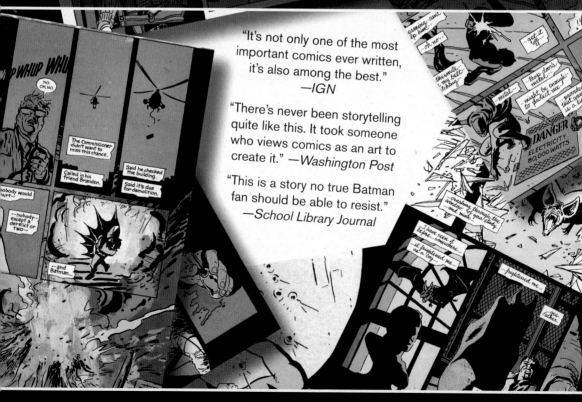

"It's not only one of the most important comics ever written, it's also among the best."
—IGN

"There's never been storytelling quite like this. It took someone who views comics as an art to create it." —Washington Post

"This is a story no true Batman fan should be able to resist."
—School Library Journal

BATMAN: YEAR ONE

Writer: Frank Miller | Artist: David Mazzucchelli | ISBN: 978-1-4012-0752-6 | Diamond Code: OCT060163 | Price: $14.99 /$17.99 CAN | Format: TP

FABLES VOL. 1:
LEGENDS IN EXILE

FOLKLORE COMES TO LIFE AS THESE REAL-LIFE FAIRY TALE CHARACTERS ARE EXILED IN MODERN-DAY NEW YORK CITY

No longer just children's tales, writer Bill Willingham has created a new world for these beloved fables ... one that exists within our own.

When a savage creature known only as the Adversary conquered the homeland of legends and myth, all of the infamous inhabitants of folklore were forced into exile. Disguised among the normal citizens of modern-day New York, these magical characters created their own secret society called Fabletown. But when Snow White's party-girl sister, Rose Red, is apparently murdered, it us up to Bigby, the reformed Big Bad Wolf and Fabletown's sheriff, to find the killer.

FABLES VOLUME 1: LEGENDS IN EXILE is the critically acclaimed, best-selling first chapter of one of Vertigo's great watershed series.

"[A] wonderfully twisted concept." —*Washington Post*

"An epic, beautifully written story." —*The Onion*

"Great fun." —*Booklist*

FABLES VOL. 1: LEGENDS IN EXILE

Writer: Bill Willingham | Artist: Lan Medina | ISBN: 978-1-4012-3755-4 | Diamond Code: FEB120285 | Price: $12.99 /$15.99 | Format: TP

FOR MATURE READERS

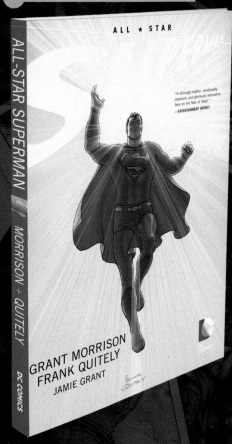

ALL-STAR SUPERMAN

THE CRITICALLY ACCLAIMED, GENRE-BENDING GRAPHIC NOVEL THAT HARKENS BACK TO THE GOLDEN AGE OF SUPERMAN

The Underverse ruled by Bizarros. The time-eating Chronovore. Jimmy Olsen, superhero?

Nothing is impossible in ALL-STAR SUPERMAN.

The unstoppable creative team of writer Grant Morrison and artist Frank Quitely (*We3, Flex Mentallo, JLA: Earth 2*) join forces once more to take Superman back to basics. In an emotionally and visually stunning graphic novel harkening back to a Golden Age of comics, ALL-STAR SUPERMAN creates a new, and at the same time familiar, take on the World's First Superhero.

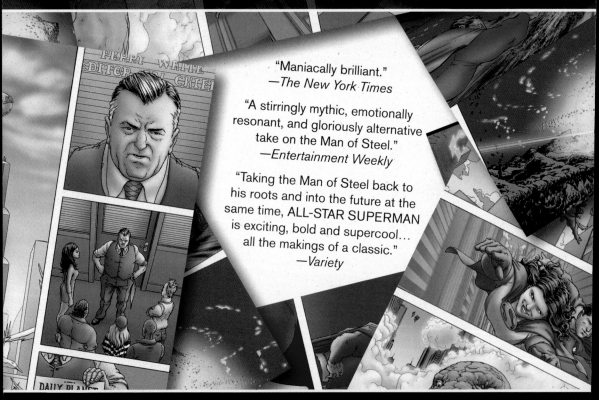

"Maniacally brilliant."
—*The New York Times*

"A stirringly mythic, emotionally resonant, and gloriously alternative take on the Man of Steel."
—*Entertainment Weekly*

"Taking the Man of Steel back to his roots and into the future at the same time, ALL-STAR SUPERMAN is exciting, bold and supercool... all the makings of a classic."
—*Variety*

ALL-STAR SUPERMAN

Writer: Grant Morrison | Artist: Frank Quitely | ISBN: 978-1-4012-3205-4 | Diamond Code: JUL110247 | Price: $29.99 /$35.00 CAN | Format: TP

BATMAN VOL. 1:
THE COURT OF OWLS

A NEW ERA FOR THE DARK KNIGHT AND GOTHAM CITY BEGINS HERE IN THIS #1 *NEW YORK TIMES* BESTSELLER!

Batman has heard tales of Gotham City's Court of Owls: That the members of this powerful cabal are the true rulers of Gotham. The Dark Knight dismissed the stories as rumors and old wives' tales. Gotham was *his* city. Until now.

A brutal assassin is sinking his razor-sharp talons into the city's best and brightest, as well as its most dangerous and deadly. If the dark legends are true, his masters are more powerful predators than the Batman could ever imagine.

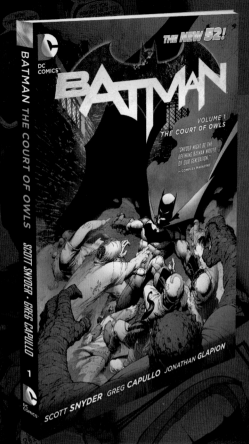

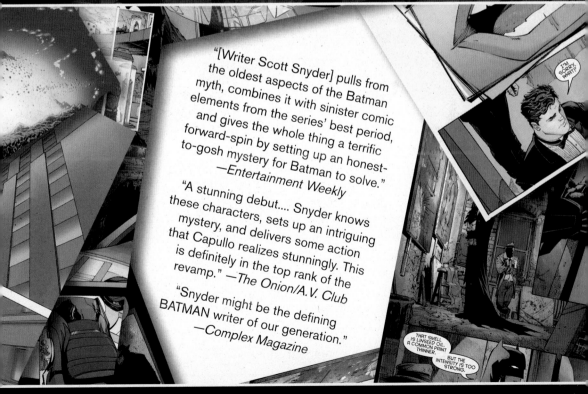

"[Writer Scott Snyder] pulls from the oldest aspects of the Batman myth, combines it with sinister comic elements from the series' best period, and gives the whole thing a terrific forward-spin by setting up an honest-to-gosh mystery for Batman to solve."
—Entertainment Weekly

"A stunning debut.... Snyder knows these characters, sets up an intriguing mystery, and delivers some action that Capullo realizes stunningly. This is definitely in the top rank of the revamp." —The Onion/A.V. Club

"Snyder might be the defining BATMAN writer of our generation."
—Complex Magazine

BATMAN VOL. 1: THE COURT OF OWLS

Writer: Scott Snyder | Artist: Greg Capullo | ISBN: 978-1-4012-3542-0 | Diamond Code: DEC120323 | Price: $16.99 /$19.99 CAN | Format: TP

PREACHER BOOK ONE

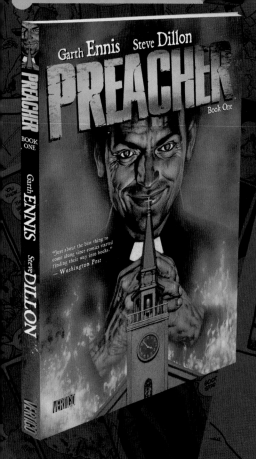

HEARTFELT AND UNAPOLOGETICALLY PROFANE, PREACHER FOLLOWS THE EPIC JOURNEY OF REVEREND JESSE CUSTER AS HE TRACKS DOWN A FUGITIVE GOD

Jesse Custer was just a small town-preacher in Texas, trying to help his fellow man. Until his congregation was flattened by powers beyond his control.

Now possessed by Genesis—the unholy coupling of an angel and demon—Jesse holds Word of God, an ability to command anyone or anything with a mere utterance. And he'll use this power to hold the lord accountable for the people he has forsaken.

From the ashes of a small-town church to the bright lights of New York City to the backwoods of Louisiana, Jesse Custer cuts a righteous path across the soul of America in his quest for the divine—an effort which will be met by every evil that Heaven and Earth can assemble. Joined by his gun-toting girlfriend Tulip and the hard-drinking Irish vampire Cassidy, Jesse will stop at nothing to fulfill his quest to find God.

Garth Ennis and Steve Dillon bring readers on a violent and riotous journey across the country in this award-winning Vertigo series.

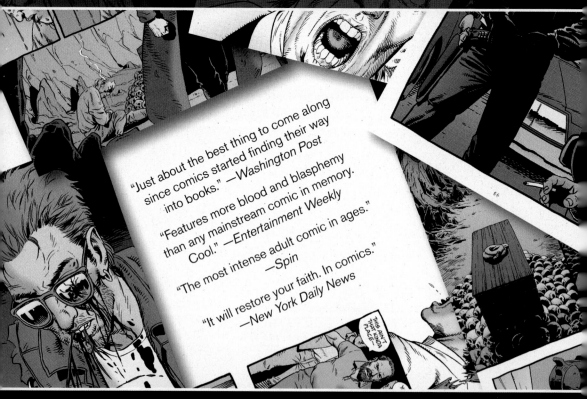

"Just about the best thing to come along since comics started finding their way into books." —Washington Post

"Features more blood and blasphemy than any mainstream comic in memory. Cool." —Entertainment Weekly

"The most intense adult comic in ages." —Spin

"It will restore your faith. In comics." —New York Daily News

PREACHER BOOK ONE

Writer: Garth Ennis | Artist: Steve Dillon | ISBN: 978-1-4012-4045-5 | Diamond Code: MAR130303 | Price: $19.99 /$23.99 CAN | Format: TP

Y: THE LAST MAN
BOOK ONE

WHAT WOULD YOU DO IF YOU WERE THE LAST MAN ON EARTH?

Y: THE LAST MAN is that rare example of a page-turner that is all at once humorous, socially relevant and endlessly surprising.

Written by Brian K. Vaughan (*Lost, Saga,* PRIDE OF BAGHDAD, EX MACHINA) and with art by Pia Guerra, this is the saga of Yorick Brown, the only human survivor of a planet-wide plague that instantly kills every mammal possessing a Y chromosome. Accompanied by a mysterious government agent, a brilliant young geneticist and his pet monkey, Ampersand, Yorick travels the world in search of his lost love and the answer to why he's the last man on Earth.

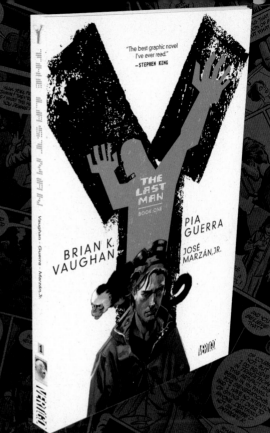

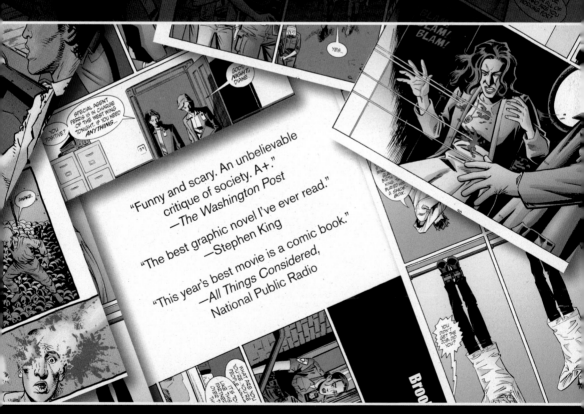

"Funny and scary. An unbelievable critique of society. A+."
—The Washington Post

"The best graphic novel I've ever read."
—Stephen King

"This year's best movie is a comic book."
—All Things Considered, National Public Radio

Y: THE LAST MAN BOOK ONE

Writer: Brian K. Vaughan | Artist: Pia Guerra | ISBN: 978-1-4012-5151-2 | Diamond Code: JUNE140312 | Price: $19.99 /$23.99 CAN | Format: TP

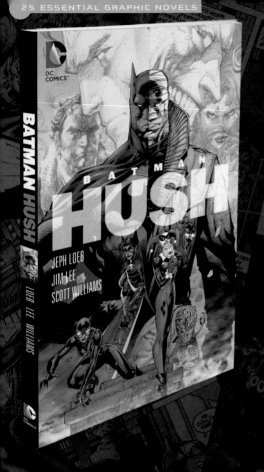

BATMAN: HUSH

BATMAN STALKS A NEW AND DEADLY VILLAIN WHO SEEMS TO KNOW MORE ABOUT BATMAN THAN ANYONE—HUSH!

Gotham City's worst criminals have emerged to throw Batman's life into utter chaos. However, these villains—Joker, Riddler, Ra's al Ghul, Clayface and others—are part of a much more elaborate, sinister scheme to destroy the Dark Knight once and for all. Pushed past his breaking point, Batman will need to use more than the world's greatest detective skills to uncover the true mastermind behind this murderous plot before those closest to Bruce Wayne suffer the consequences.

In this truly unforgettable story by two of comics' top talents, writer Jeph Loeb and DC Co-Publisher Jim Lee present the Caped Crusader's most personal case yet.

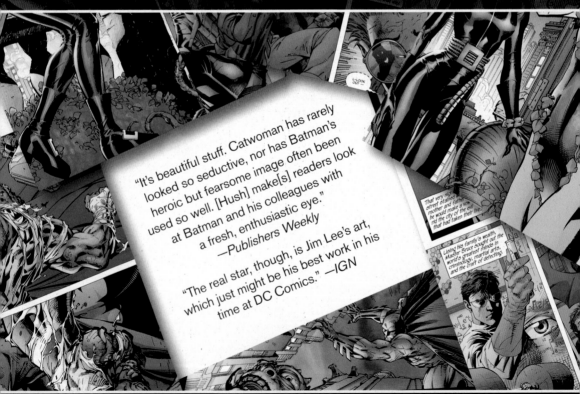

"It's beautiful stuff. Catwoman has rarely looked so seductive, nor has Batman's heroic but fearsome image often been used so well. [Hush] make[s] readers look at Batman and his colleagues with a fresh, enthusiastic eye."
—*Publishers Weekly*

"The real star, though, is Jim Lee's art, which just might be his best work in his time at DC Comics." —*IGN*

BATMAN: HUSH

Writer: Jeph Loeb | Artist: Jim Lee | ISBN: 978-1-4012-2317-5 | Diamond Code: MAY090178 | Price: $24.99 /$28.99 CAN | Format: TP

KINGDOM COME

OLD AND NEW ERAS OF SUPERHEROES ARE PITTED AGAINST EACH OTHER IN THIS EPIC GRAPHIC NOVEL

Winner of five Eisner and Harvey Awards, KINGDOM COME is the best-selling graphic novel from acclaimed writer Mark Waid and superstar painter Alex Ross.

Set in the not-so-distant future, the DC Universe is spinning inexorably out of control. The new generation of heroes has lost its moral compass, becoming just as reckless and violent as the villains its members fight. The previous regime of heroes—the Justice League—returns under the most dire of circumstances, setting up a battle of the old guard against these uncompromising protectors in a battle that will define what heroism truly is.

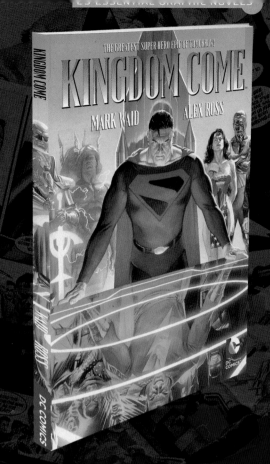

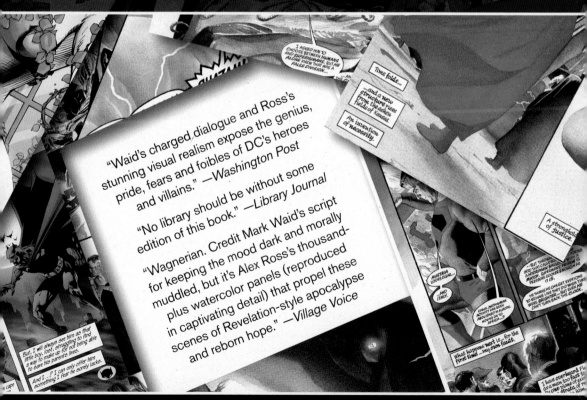

"Waid's charged dialogue and Ross's stunning visual realism expose the genius, pride, fears and foibles of DC's heroes and villains." —*Washington Post*

"No library should be without some edition of this book." —*Library Journal*

"Wagnerian. Credit Mark Waid's script for keeping the mood dark and morally muddled, but it's Alex Ross's thousand-plus watercolor panels (reproduced in captivating detail) that propel these scenes of Revelation-style apocalypse and reborn hope." —*Village Voice*

KINGDOM COME

Writer: Mark Waid | Artist: Alex Ross | ISBN: 978-1-4012-2034-1 | Diamond Code: SEP138294 | Price: $19.99 /$23.99 CAN | Format: TP

THE BEST-SELLING GRAPHIC NOVEL OF ALL TIME!

THE DEATH OF

SUPERMAN

Dan JURGENS
Jerry ORDWAY
Louise SIMONSON
Roger STERN
Jon BOGDANOVE
Tom GRUMMETT
Jackson GUICE
Brett BREEDING
Rick BURCHETT
Doug HAZLEWOOD
Dennis JANKE
Denis RODIER

THE DEATH OF SUPERMAN

DC COMICS

SUPERMAN:
THE DEATH OF SUPERMAN

THE BEST-SELLING PHENOMENON THAT REDEFINED THE MAN OF STEEL IN AN EARTH-SHATTERING SHOWDOWN WITH HIS MOST DEVASTATING THREAT OF ALL TIME

In this iconic overnight success, a team of legendary DC writers and artists render one of Superman's most expansive and emotional narratives to date—humanizing the Last Son of Krypton like never before.

The indomitable creature, Doomsday, breaks free from ancient imprisonment and razes a path of destruction headed straight for the heart of Metropolis. When all other superheroes fail to stop the colossus, only one hope remains—but even Superman may fall short. Expectations are obliterated as the Man of Steel is finally pushed to his limits in this unprecedented matchup of sheer physical force.

This graphic novel made national headlines, as the death of one of the most beloved characters in all of fiction made its way onto the nightly news, covers of dozens of magazines and into the bylines of newspapers across the country. SUPERMAN: THE DEATH OF SUPERMAN remains one of the most recognized stories in all of DC Comics lore to this day.

"It's not only one of the most important comics ever written, it's also among the best."
—IGN

"There's never been storytelling quite like this. It took someone who views comics as an art to create it." —Washington Post

"This is a story no true Batman fan should be able to resist."
—School Library Journal

SUPERMAN: THE DEATH OF SUPERMAN

Writers: Dan Jurgens, Jerry Ordway, Louise Simonson & Roger Stern | Artists: Dan Jurgens, Jackson Guice, Jon Bogdanove & Tom Grummett

BATMAN:
THE LONG HALLOWEEN

A CLASSIC BATMAN MURDER MYSTERY BY THE ICONIC CREATIVE TEAM OF JEPH LOEB AND TIM SALE

Set just after Batman's first year in Gotham City, the Dark Knight finds himself working alongside District Attorney Harvey Dent and Lieutenant James Gordon, trying to vanquish the criminal element. However, a serial killer known only as Holiday has been killing friend and foe each month. Batman races against the calendar trying to discover the assassin's identity, fighting the entirety of Gotham's rogues gallery along the way.

The magnificent creative team of Jeph Loeb and Tim Sale reach their apex in BATMAN: THE LONG HALLOWEEN, propelling the graphic novel to its place among comics' finest murder mystery stories.

THE NEW YORK TIMES BEST-SELLING CLASSIC

"THE LONG HALLOWEEN is more than a comic book. It's an epic tragedy."
— Christopher Nolan (director The Dark Knight Rises)

BATMAN THE LONG HALLOWEEN

LOEB SALE

FROM THE EISNER AWARD-WINNING CREATORS
JEPH LOEB
TIM SALE

DC COMICS

"The Long Halloween stretches beyond the normal boundaries of comics to create a legendary story of one man's crusade against an insane world." —IGN

"The Long Halloween is more than a comic book. It's an epic tragedy." —Christopher Nolan (director of Batman Begins, The Dark Knight and The Dark Knight Rises)

BATMAN: THE LONG HALLOWEEN

Writer: Jeph Loeb | Artist: Tim Sale | ISBN: 978-1-4012-3259-7 | Diamond Code: JUL110251 | Price: $24.99 /$28.99 CAN | Format: TP

SUPERMAN/BATMAN
VOL. 1

THE WORLD'S MOST ICONIC SUPERHEROES UNITE TO TAKE ON THE MOST DANGEROUS VILLAINS FROM THIS PLANET AND BEYOND

The Dark Knight. The Man of Steel. The world's finest team-up is here at last!

Superman and Batman square off against the greatest threats known to the DC Universe in this unforgettable graphic novel! Superman's arch-nemesis, Lex Luthor, is President of the United States and has launched a superpowered hunt for the Man of Tomorrow. Nearby in Gotham, Batman finds that Superman is not the last Kryptonian, as he discovers another survivor alive... Kal-El's cousin, Supergirl! However, behind this immense discovery may be the gravest threat of all: Darkseid.

Jeph Loeb, award-winning writer and celebrated television producer, along with Ed McGuinness and Michael Turner, two of the most popular artists in comics, pair two of the DC Universe's finest heroes for an epic, action-packed adventure.

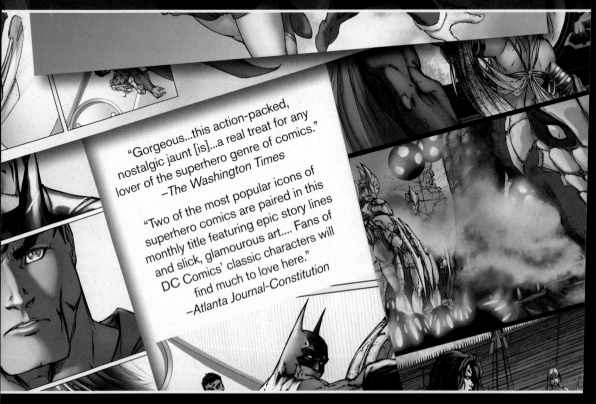

"Gorgeous...this action-packed, nostalgic jaunt [is]...a real treat for any lover of the superhero genre of comics."
—The Washington Times

"Two of the most popular icons of superhero comics are paired in this monthly title featuring epic story lines and slick, glamourous art.... Fans of DC Comics' classic characters will find much to love here."
—Atlanta Journal-Constitution

SUPERMAN/BATMAN VOL. 1

Writer: Jeph Loeb | Artists: Ed McGuinness & Michael Turner | ISBN: 978-1-4012-4818-5 | Diamond Code: JAN140354 | Price: $19.99 /$23.99 CAN | Format: TP

DAYTRIPPER

THIS EISNER AWARD-WINNING GRAPHIC NOVEL FOLLOWS BRAS DE OLIVA DOMINGOS DURING DIFFERENT PERIODS IN HIS LIFE, EACH WITH THE SAME ENDING: HIS DEATH

In DAYTRIPPER, the Eisner Award-winning twin brothers Fábio Moon and Gabriel Bá tell a magical, mysterious, and moving story about life itself—a hauntingly lyrical journey that uses the quiet moments to ask the big questions.

The miracle child of a world-famous Brazilian writer, Bras de Oliva Domingos spends his days penning other people's obituaries and his nights dreaming of becoming a successful author himself—writing the end of other people's stories, while his own has barely begun. Each day in Bras's life is like a page from a book. Each one reveals the people and things who have made him who he is: his mother and father, his child and best friend, his first love and the love of his life. And like all great stories, each has a twist he'll never see coming...

Truly one of the most unique and compelling graphic novels of the last decade, DAYTRIPPER is an affecting, memorable story that will stay with readers long after finishing.

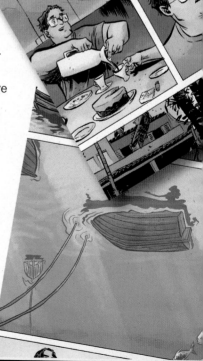

"Mixed with the expert craftsmanship of two artists in their prime telling a unique story in a remarkable way, the industry may have just crafted its latest WATCHMEN."
—*Pop Matters*

"DAYTRIPPER is absolutely breathtaking. Both the writing and the illustrations are beautiful, and the combination is powerful. Moon and Bá . . . create a masterpiece within the traditional constraints of the medium."
—*Wired/Geek Dad*

"DAYTRIPPER invites repeated, even recursive reading, as elements in early chapters find themselves echoed or entirely inverted as the book comes to a close." —*National Public Radio*

DAYTRIPPER

Writers: Gabriel Bá & Fábio Moon | Artists: Gabriel Bá & Fábio Moon | ISBN: 978-14012-2969-6 | Diamond Code: NOV100268 | Price: $19.99 /$23.99 CAN | Format: TP

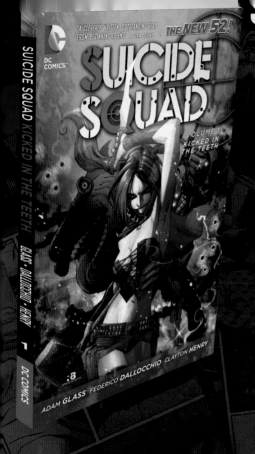

SUICIDE SQUAD VOL.
KICKED IN THE TEETH

AN ALL-NEW TEAM OF SUPER-VILLAINS TAKE ON HEROIC MISSIONS SO DANGEROUS — THEY'RE SHEER SUICIDE!

The Suicide Squad—a group of government-sanctioned super-villain convicts—has been defeated. Harley Quinn, Deadshot, Diablo, Captain Boomerang and company—has been caught, imprisoned, and is being interrogated about their most recent mission. Can they make it out alive without revealing who's pulling the strings behind their illegal operations? Who will be the first to crack under the pressure?

From *Supernatural* creator Adam Glass comes the *New York Times* best-selling series starring all the villains you love to hate in 2016's *Suicide Squad* film!

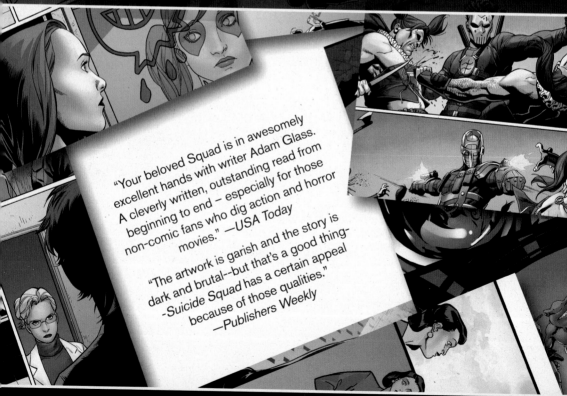

"Your beloved Squad is in awesomely excellent hands with writer Adam Glass. A cleverly written, outstanding read from beginning to end – especially for those non-comic fans who dig action and horror movies." —USA Today

"The artwork is garish and the story is dark and brutal--but that's a good thing- -Suicide Squad has a certain appeal because of those qualities." —Publishers Weekly

SUICIDE SQUAD VOL. 1: KICKED IN THE TEETH

Writer: Adam Glass | Artists: Federico Dallocchio & Clayton Henry | ISBN: 978-1-4012-3544-4 | Diamond Code: APR120250 | Price: $14.99 /$17.99 CAN | Format: TP

SUPERMAN:
RED SON

WHAT IF THE ROCKET FROM KRYPTON CARRYING THE INFANT SUPERMAN LANDED IN THE MIDST OF THE 1950S SOVIET UNION?

In this startling twist on a familiar tale, a certain Kryptonian rocketship crash-lands on Earth carrying an infant who will one day become the most powerful being on the planet. But his ship doesn't land in America. He is not raised by a kindly couple in Smallville, Kansas. Instead, he makes his new home on a collective in the Soviet Union. As the young alien becomes a symbol to the Soviet people, the world changes drastically from what we know—bringing Superman into conflict with Batman, Lex Luthor and more.

From the mind of Mark Millar, the best-selling writer of THE AUTHORITY and *Kick-Ass*, comes one of the most unique, critically acclaimed takes on the Superman mythos.

"One of the best stories in the history of the Man of Steel." –IGN

"I waited years to read this story, and Millar did not disappoint. Once again, Mark proves he has one of the most original voices in comics, not to mention a particularly distinct grasp of the comic book super-hero. And good God, is it gorgeous to look at, too." –Kevin Smith

"RED SON is one of those rare projects that bridges the gap between generations and illustrates why comics—and the movies based on them—are still fresh and full of surprises for new and old fans alike." –IFC

SUPERMAN: RED SON

Writer: Mark Millar | Artists: Dave Johnson & Killian Plunkett | ISBN: 978-1-4012-4711-9 | Diamond Code: JAN140353 | Price: $17.99 /$20.99 CAN | Format: TP

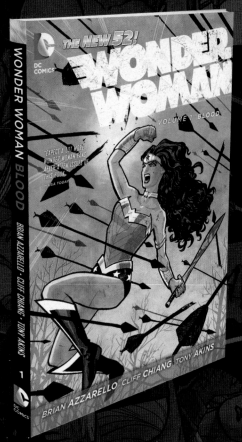

WONDER WOMAN
VOL. 1: BLOOD

CRITICALLY ACCLAIMED WRITER BRIAN AZZARELLO TEAMS WITH CLIFF CHIANG AND TONY AKINS TO CREATE A NEW WONDER WOMAN MYTHOLOGY

Experience a bold new beginning of the iconic character in WONDER WOMAN VOLUME 1: BLOOD in this critically acclaimed and best-selling series!

Wonder Woman's world is shattered when a secret her mother, Hippolyta, queen of the Amazons, kept all her life is revealed: Diana is not clay brought to life, but is in fact the child of Zeus! In this reimagining of Diana's history, super-heroics and mythology seamlessly blend as Brian Azzarello (JOKER, 100 BULLETS) creates a new direction for one of the world's best known heroes. With stunning art by Cliff Chiang and Tony Akins, Wonder Woman has never looked better.

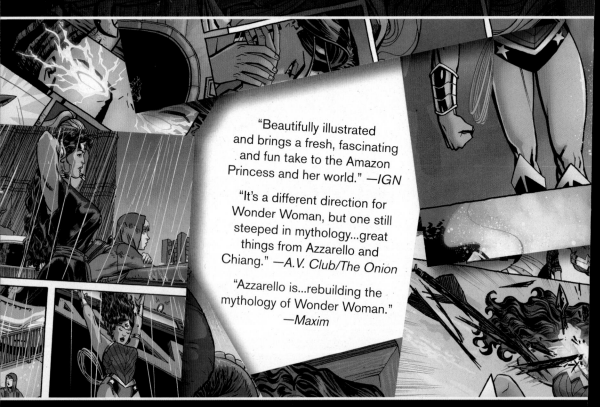

"Beautifully illustrated and brings a fresh, fascinating and fun take to the Amazon Princess and her world." —IGN

"It's a different direction for Wonder Woman, but one still steeped in mythology...great things from Azzarello and Chiang." —A.V. Club/The Onion

"Azzarello is...rebuilding the mythology of Wonder Woman." —Maxim

WONDER WOMAN VOL. 1: BLOOD

Writer: Brian Azzarello | Artists: Cliff Chiang & Tony Akins | ISBN: 978-1-4012-3562-8 | Diamond Code: OCT120256 | Price: $14.99 /$17.99 CAN | Format: TP

BATMAN: EARTH ONE

GEOFF JOHNS REIMAGINES THE DARK KNIGHT'S ORIGIN STORY IN THIS #1 *NEW YORK TIMES* BESTSELLER

Batman is not a hero. He is just a man. Fallible, vulnerable and angry.

In Gotham City, where friend and foe are indistinguishable, Bruce Wayne's path toward becoming the Dark Knight is riddled with more obstacles than ever before. Focused on punishing his parents' true killer and the corrupt police who allowed them to go free, Bruce Wayne's thirst for vengeance fuels his mad crusade, and no one, not even Alfred, can stop him.

In this #1 *New York Times* bestseller, writer Geoff Johns and artist Gary Frank reimagine a new mythology for the Dark Knight, where the familiar is no longer the expected in this original graphic novel.

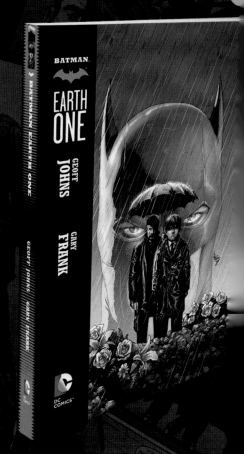

"Just when you thought there couldn't possibly be a fresh take on Batman, along come Johns and Frank to prove you extraordinarily wrong. Original, surprising and emotional, BATMAN: EARTH ONE is a must-read." —Damon Lindelof (Co-creator and Executive Producer of *Lost*)

"This isn't just about capes and tights. This is stuff that, like the best of fiction, goes beyond the parameters of its particular genre." —MTV Geek!

"Geoff Johns, the chief creative officer at DC Comics, has written us a Batman for Earth One that will knock your socks off." —*Huffington Post*

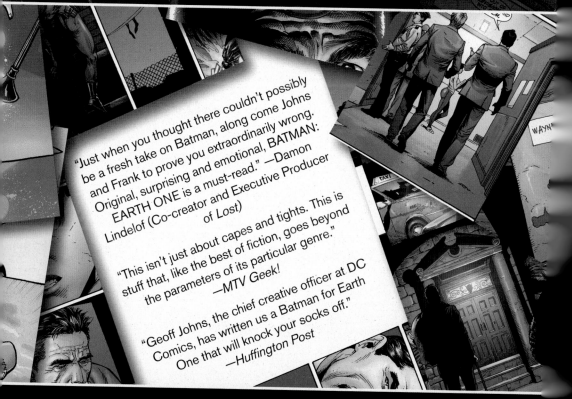

BATMAN: EARTH ONE

Writer: Geoff Johns | Artist: Gary Frank | ISBN: 978-1-4012-3209-2 | Diamond Code: MAY140376 | Price: $12.99 /$17.99 CAN | Format: TP

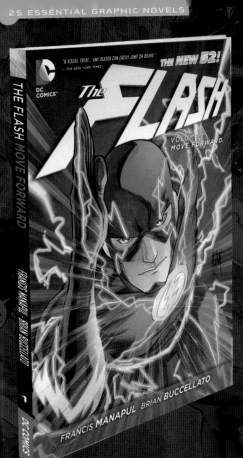

THE FLASH
VOL. 1: MOVE FORWARD

A BOLD NEW VISION OF THE SCARLET SPEEDSTER, BREATHTAKINGLY RENDERED BY ONE OF COMICS' BEST ARTISTS

Struck by a bolt of lightning and doused in chemicals, Central City police scientist Barry Allen was transformed into the Fastest Man Alive. But there are some things even the Flash can't outrun. Trying to solve his mother's murder since his youth, Barry has often ignored what was in front of his very eyes. And that personal grudge might end up affecting the Flash just as much as his alter ego.

Written and gorgeously illustrated by the creative tag team of Francis Manapul and Brian Buccellato, THE FLASH VOL. 1: MOVE FORWARD is the perfect vision of the Scarlet Speedster brought to life. This stunning graphic novel is one of the fastest and easiest entry points into DC Comics' vast library.

"THE FLASH is simply comics at its finest."
—*Pop Matters*

"A visual treat…any reader can easily jump on board."
—*The New York Times*

"This is why comic books are awesome."
—*Craveonline*

INJUSTICE: GODS AMONG US VOL. 1

THE #1 *NEW YORK TIMES* BESTSELLING PREQUEL TO THE SMASH-HIT VIDEO GAME.

You've played the game, but you don't know the whole story. Forget everything you think you know about the Man of Steel. Tradition is tossed aside and chaos erupts as Superman struggles to shoulder blame for the death of Lois Lane and their unborn child. Undone by grief and rage, he abandons his renowned moral code in favor of an unforgiving brand of justice.

As Superman's staunchest allies are divided by his stark transformation, conflicting visions of a new world order soon arise—and the looming crisis threatens to ignite when Batman emerges as his most vocal challenger.

In this epic prelude to the smash-hit video game phenomenon, INJUSTICE: GODS AMONG US VOL. 1 pits two longtime allies—Batman and Superman—as the DC Universe is torn in half!

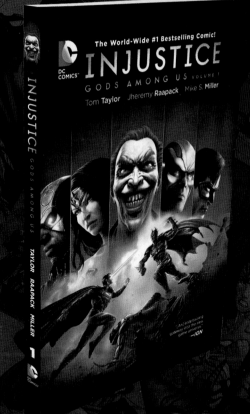

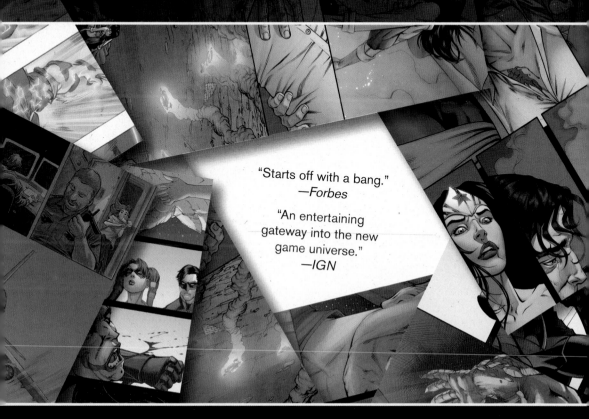

"Starts off with a bang."
—*Forbes*

"An entertaining gateway into the new game universe."
—*IGN*

INJUSTICE: GODS AMONG US VOL. 1

Writer: Tom Taylor | Artists: Jheremy Raapack & Mike S. Miller | ISBN: 978-1-4012-4843-7 | Diamond Code: MAR140265

AQUAMAN VOL. 1:
THE TRENCH

LEGENDARY CREATIVE DUO GEOFF JOHNS AND IVAN REIS RE-TEAM TO LAUNCH THE KING OF ATLANTIS BACK INTO PROMINENCE

Aquaman is back to challenge his status as a second-tier superhero. Maligned for years as the man who talks to fish, Arthur Curry stakes his claim as one of the most powerful heroes in the DC Universe in AQUAMAN VOL. 1: THE TRENCH. As the King of the Seven Seas, Aquaman has sworn to protect his ocean home, and there's been no greater threat to date than what's to come.

They are called The Trench. And they are hungry.

As thousands of carnivorous beasts emerge from the ocean's depths, can Aquaman protect his people from this deadly new threat? And also the surface world that he now calls home?

This is Aquaman's Renaissance—a cutting-edge revival of the King of the Seven Seas featuring the creative team behind The *New York Times* best-selling graphic novels BLACKEST NIGHT and JUSTICE LEAGUE: THRONE OF ATLANTIS!

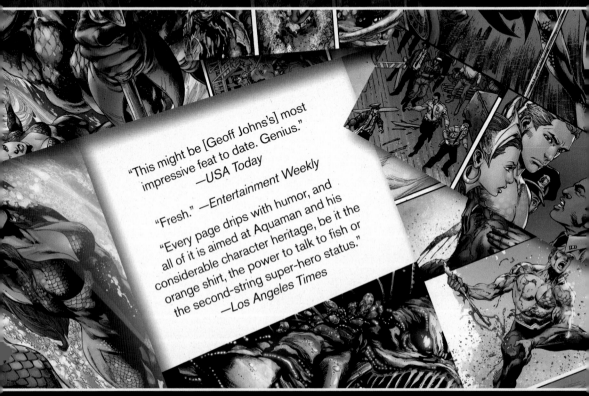

"This might be [Geoff Johns's] most impressive feat to date. Genius."
—USA Today

"Fresh." —Entertainment Weekly

"Every page drips with humor, and all of it is aimed at Aquaman and his considerable character heritage, be it the orange shirt, the power to talk to fish or the second-string super-hero status."
—Los Angeles Times

AQUAMAN VOL. 1: THE TRENCH

Writer: Geoff Johns | Artists: Ivan Reis & Joe Prado | ISBN: 978-1-4012-3710-3 | Diamond Code: FEB130206 | Price: $14.99 /$17.99 CAN | Format: TP

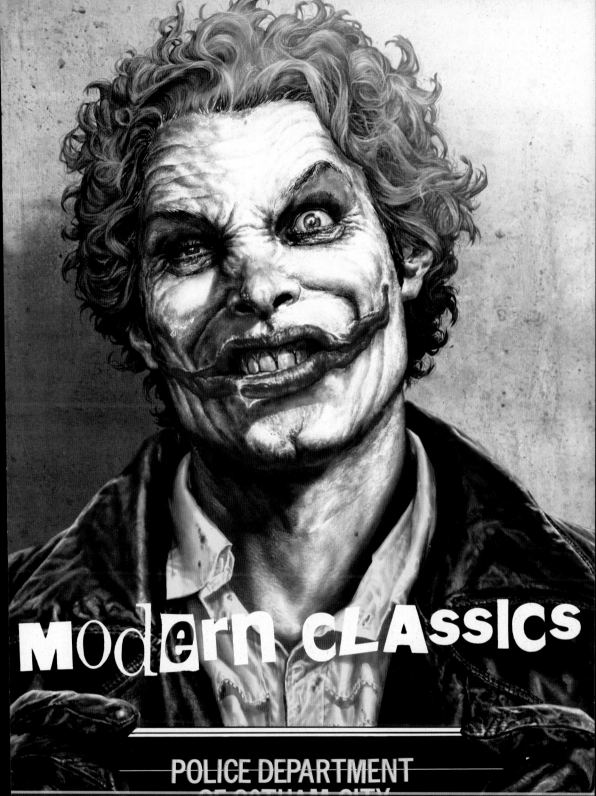

MOdern cLAssics

POLICE DEPARTMENT

Literary, unconventional, and noteworthy, these modern classics from DC Comics and Vertigo are graphic novels that rise above the rest. Top creators of recent years deliver innovative, poignant stories demonstrating that comics aren't just for superheroes, and superheroes aren't just for children. Pushing the boundaries of their respective genres and using the comic medium to maximum effect, each of these titles is a contemporary masterpiece in its own way.

BATGIRL VOL. 1: BATGIRL OF BURNSIDE

The red-hot creative team of Cameron Stewart, Brenden Fletcher and Babs Tarr reinvent Batgirl for a new generation.

Smart, savvy, chic and resourceful, Barbara Gordon is ready for a fresh start. That's exactly what the classic character gets—a new look, a new crew of friends and a fresh voice—in this vibrant and unexpected series overhaul. But when Batgirl starts trending as Gotham's first viral vigilante, she also attracts a new wave of enemies looking to steal her social media spotlight.

"This is a must-buy series." —*The New York Times*

Writers: Brenden Fletcher & Cameron Stewart | Artist: Babs Tarr | ISBN: 978-1-4012-5798-9 | Diamond Code: DEC148636 | Price: $14.99 /$17.99 CAN | Format: TP

BATMAN: ARKHAM ASYLUM 25TH ANNIVERSARY EDITION

The psychologically twisted celebration of Batman's Rogues Gallery that launched Grant Morrison's career and inspired one of the hottest video games of all time.

After striking a deal with the Joker to free a group of hostages, Batman is lobbed out of his comfort zone on the streets of Gotham and locked away with Arkham's most psychotic inmates. Surrounded by a fortress of grit and an onslaught of his most deranged enemies, the Dark Knight faces an unprecedented fight to stay in control of both body and mind.

"[A] darkly poetic, psychologically rich tale." —*Rolling Stone*

Writer: Grant Morrison | Artist: Dave McKean | ISBN: 978-1-4012-5124-6 | Diamond Code: JUN140278 | Price: $19.99/ $23.99 CAN | Format: TP

BATMAN: THE BLACK MIRROR

Eisner Award-winning writer Scott Snyder launches into comics superstardom with his #1 *New York Times* best-selling debut work on the Dark Knight.

A series of brutal murders pushes Batman's detective skills to the limit and forces him to confront one of Gotham City's oldest evils. Helpless and trapped in the deadly Mirror House, Batman must fight for his life against a villain from his past that he never sees coming.

"One of the best new collaborations in comics...this is a worthy spiritual successor to BATMAN: YEAR ONE." —*MTV Geek*

Writer: Scott Snyder | Artists: Jock & Francesco Francavilla | ISBN: 978-1-4012-3207-8 | Diamond Code: NOV120268 | Price: $16.99 /$17.99 CAN | Format: TP

BLACKEST NIGHT

Geoff Johns and Ivan Reis craft an unforgettable ensemble of undead superheroes in this highly anticipated and shockingly stylized blockbuster brawl.

The Black Lanterns are the scourge of the universe—and they won't stop at gravedigging to secure dominance. Led by Nekron and Black Hand, the Lanterns look to boost their sinister ranks by resurrecting and assembling an army of fallen superheroes—from Aquaman and Superman to Green Arrow—to support a vicious crusade against humankind.

"If you've read a superhero comic book published by DC Comics within the last few years, and were completely blown away by it, there's a good chance that it was something written by Geoff Johns." —*Washington Examiner*

Writer: Geoff Johns | Artist: Ivan Reis | ISBN: 978-1-4012-2953-5 | Diamond Code: APR110192 | Price: $19.99 /$23.99 CAN | Format: TP

DC: THE NEW FRONTIER

This Eisner, Harvey and Shuster Award-winning series takes readers on an epic journey from the end of the Golden Age of heroes to the beginnings of the legendary Justice League of America.

Welcome to 1950s America—a land of promise and paranoia, of glittering cities and segregated slums, of dizzying scientific progress and simmering Cold War conflict. A land where heroes have been outlawed. Those icons who do still fight on—Superman, Wonder Woman, Batman—must operate under hidden agendas and dueling ideologies.

"Composed from equal parts affection and ambition...Cooke creates a classic of his own." — *A.V. Club/The Onion*

Writer: Darwyn Cooke | Artist: Darwyn Cooke | ISBN: 978-1-4012-4888-8 | Diamond Code: OCT140355 | Price: $16.99 /$19.99 CAN | Format: HC

FINAL CRISIS

Writer Grant Morrison transforms the DC Universe in this monumental crossover event years in the making.

Evil has finally won. Darkseid and his legion have claimed a devastating victory in a time-bending war between light and dark, forcing Batman, Superman and the Justice League to face the fallout and adjust to a new apocalyptic reality. Experimental, vivid and relentless, this epic explores what happens when the world's most imposing superheroes are stripped of their powers—and their hope.

"The fertile mind of writer Grant Morrison...this [is] the event to trump all events." —*Entertainment Weekly*

Writer: Grant Morrison | Artists: J.G. Jones, Doug Mahnke & Carlos Pacheco | ISBN: 978-1-4012-4517-7 | Diamond Code: JAN140352 | Price: $19.99/$23.99 CAN | Format: TP

FLASHPOINT

The course of comics was forever changed in this graphic novel that set the stage for a new era in the DC Universe.

In a world where Wonder Woman and Aquaman have plunged millions into war, where no human has ever wielded the Green Lantern's light and no one has heard of Superman, Barry Allen—a.k.a. Flash—is the only man that remembers the world as it should be. How can the Fastest Man Alive bring his reality back? And what price will he pay?

"Heroic comic-book art at its finest." —*Entertainment Weekly/Shelf Life*

Writer: Geoff Johns | Artist: Andy Kubert | ISBN: 978-1-4012-3338-9 | Diamond Code: OCT138324 | Price: $16.99 /$19.99 CAN | Format: TP

FOREVER EVIL

Acclaimed creators Geoff Johns and David Finch spearhead this *New York Times* bestselling, universe-wide crossover event in a groundbreaking transformation of villains into antiheroes.

The Crime Syndicate—twisted villainous versions of the Justice League—has taken over the world in search of new recruits. With the Justice League eliminated, it's up to Lex Luthor, Batman and his legion of super-villains to protect the planet from falling to an even greater evil in this giant crossover event!

"Geoff Johns' best work since the New 52 began... a blast to read." — *Nerdist*

Writer: Geoff Johns | Artist: David Finch | ISBN: 978-1-4012-1581-1 | Diamond Code: FEB150254 | Price: $19.99 /$23.99 CAN | Format: TP

GET JIRO!

Anthony Bourdain, top chef and star of the hit travel show *No Reservations*, and Joel Rose co-write this *New York Times* best-selling graphic novel send-up of food culture and society.

In a not-too-distant future L.A. where master chefs rule the town like crime lords and people literally kill for a seat at the best restaurants, a bloody culinary war is raging. When a renegade and ruthless sushi chef named Jiro is sought after by the warring factions, no chef may be left alive!

"Get Jiro! is one of the year's most unusual comic-book projects, and also one of the most fun." —*A.V. Club/The Onion*

Writers: Anthony Bourdain & Joel Rose | Artist: Langdon Foss | ISBN: 978-1-4012-2828-6 | Diamond Code: FEB130242 | Price: $14.99/$17.99 CAN | Format: TP

GREEN ARROW VOL. 4: THE KILL MACHINE

The Emerald Archer is brought back to his roots by the indomitable creative team of Jeff Lemire and Andrea Sorrentino.

Oliver Queen thought he had it all figured out. As the heroic archer Green Arrow, he'd finally found a sense of purpose, friends to aid him, even a place in the Justice League of America. But when a mysterious enemy from his past comes to the surface, everything Oliver thought he knew about himself and his family is thrown into the fire.

"Jeff Lemire and Andrea Sorrentino hit the bulls-eye perfectly with GREEN ARROW." —*Craveonline*

Writer: Jeff Lemire | Artist: Andrea Sorrentino | ISBN: 978-1-4012-4690-7 | Diamond Code: DEC130306 | Price: $16.99 /$19.99 CAN | Format: TP

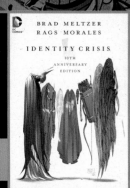

IDENTITY CRISIS

***New York Times* best-selling novelist Brad Meltzer teams with critically acclaimed artist Rags Morales to deliver one of the most intimate and heartbreaking graphic novels of all time.**

After a grisly murder rocks the DC Universe, the entire superhero community searches for the killer. But before the mystery is solved, a number of long-buried secrets will threaten to divide the Justice League.

"The IDENTITY CRISIS mystery involves the biggest DC heroes and will use all of Mr. Meltzer's skills as a thriller novelist." —*The New York Times*

Writer: Brad Meltzer | Artist: Rags Morales | ISBN: 978-1-4012-0458-7 | Diamond Code: AUG118125 | Price: $17.99 /$23.99 CAN | Format: TP

JOKER

Eisner Award-winner Brian Azzarello and Lee Bermejo's original graphic novel masterpiece with a never-before-told perspective on the most vile, dangerous and unpredictable inmate of Arkham—the Joker!

The Joker has been mysteriously released from Arkham Asylum, and he's not too happy about what's happened to his town while he's been away. What follows is a harrowing night of revenge, murder and manic crime, as he brutally takes back his stolen assets from the Penguin, Riddler, Two-Face, Killer Croc, and, of course, the Batman.

"Disturbing, violent, oddly psychological and insanely wonderful." —*USA Today*

Writer: Brian Azzarello | Artist: Lee Bermejo | ISBN: 978-1-4012-1581-1 | Diamond Code: JUL080124 | Price: $19.99 /$23.99 CAN | Format: HC

LUCIFER BOOK ONE

From the pages of Neil Gaiman's THE SANDMAN comes the irreverent stand-alone smash that inspired this year's hit new TV series on Fox.

What does the devil do when Hell itself becomes a bore? He packs his bags for Los Angeles. Lucifer Morningstar abdicates his top billing in the kingdom of sin to live it up in the City of Angels, but his luxurious new life as proprietor of an upscale piano bar is interrupted—and the balance of Heaven and Hell is disturbed—when he's recruited to complete a holy mission with the promise of unparalleled reward.

"Mike Carey's LUCIFER is even more manipulative, charming and dangerous than I ever could have hoped." — Neil Gaiman

Writers: Mike Carey | Artists: Peter Gross & Scott Hampton | ISBN: 978-1-4012-4026-4 | Diamond Code: FEB130247 | Price: $29.99/$35.00 CAN | Format: TP

THE MULTIVERSITY

Visionary Grant Morrison's expansive introduction to the alternate Earths of the DC Multiverse!

Travel beyond the familiar DC Universe and come face to face with the Vampire League of Earth-43, the Justice Riders of Earth-18, Superdemon, Doc Fate, the super-sons of Superman and Batman, the rampaging Retaliators of Earth-8, the Atomic Knights of Justice, Dino-Cop, and more. In this cosmos-spanning, soul-shaking saga, you're on the frontline in the battle for all creation against the demonic destroyers known as the Gentry.

"Doing 'big' and 'grand' is Morrison's greatest strength as a writer, and THE MULTIVERSITY is the opus he's been working on now for over five years." — *Nerdist*

Writer: Grant Morrison | Artists: Frank Quitely, Ivan Reis, Jim Lee, et al. | ISBN: 978-1-4012-5682-1 | Diamond Code: JUN150291 | Price: $49.99 /$58.00 | Format: HC

PUNK ROCK JESUS

Written and illustrated by Sean Murphy (THE WAKE), PUNK ROCK JESUS brilliantly deconstructs modern society, embraces the punk aesthetic, and takes readers on an epic, emotional ride, three chords at a time.

J2 has created the ultimate reality show stunt: create a human clone from DNA lifted off the Shroud of Turin, implant it in the womb of a virginal teen mom--and give birth, on live TV, to a boy who could be the second coming of Jesus Christ Himself.

"PUNK ROCK JESUS is amazing. The series has been incredible right from the beginning and it ends in a spectacular fashion. It's brilliant and heartbreaking, epic and emotional.... This is a book that makes you think." —*IGN*

Writer: Sean Murphy | Artist: Sean Murphy | ISBN: 978-1-4012-3768-4 | Diamond Code: JAN130330 | Price: $16.99 /$19.99 CAN | Format: TP

THE SANDMAN: OVERTURE

The widely acclaimed, must-read prequel to Neil Gaiman's legendary Sandman series.

Twenty-five years after THE SANDMAN changed the landscape of modern comics, Neil Gaiman returns to his monumental series and answers lingering questions about the origins of Morpheus and his siblings: Death, Desire, Despair, Delirium, Destruction and Destiny. Accompanied by breathtaking artwork by J.H. Williams III, this final chapter is an essential addition to any casual or serious collector's bookshelves.

"A sweeping and extravagant prequel." —*Entertainment Weekly*

Writer: Neil Gaiman | Artist: J.H. Williams III | ISBN: 978-1-4012-4896-3 | Diamond Code: JUL150333 | Price: $24.99/$29.99 CAN | Format: HC

TRILLIUM

Eisner Award-nominated writer/artist Jeff Lemire (SWEET TOOTH) reinvents the concept of a love story in the medium in this visually innovative and mind-expanding tale.

Two disparate souls are separated by thousands of years and hundreds of millions of miles. Yet they will fall in love and, as a result, bring about the end of the universe. Even though reality is unraveling all around them, nothing can pull them apart. This isn't just a love story: it's the last love story ever told.

"I'm bewildered and intrigued by the tale that's unfolding, in awe of Lemire's writing and art, and excited by the structural playfulness at work." —*MTV Geek*

Writer: Jeff Lemire | Artist: Jeff Lemire | ISBN: 978-1-4012-4900-7 | Diamond Code: MAY140407 | Price: $16.99 /$19.99 CAN | Format: TP

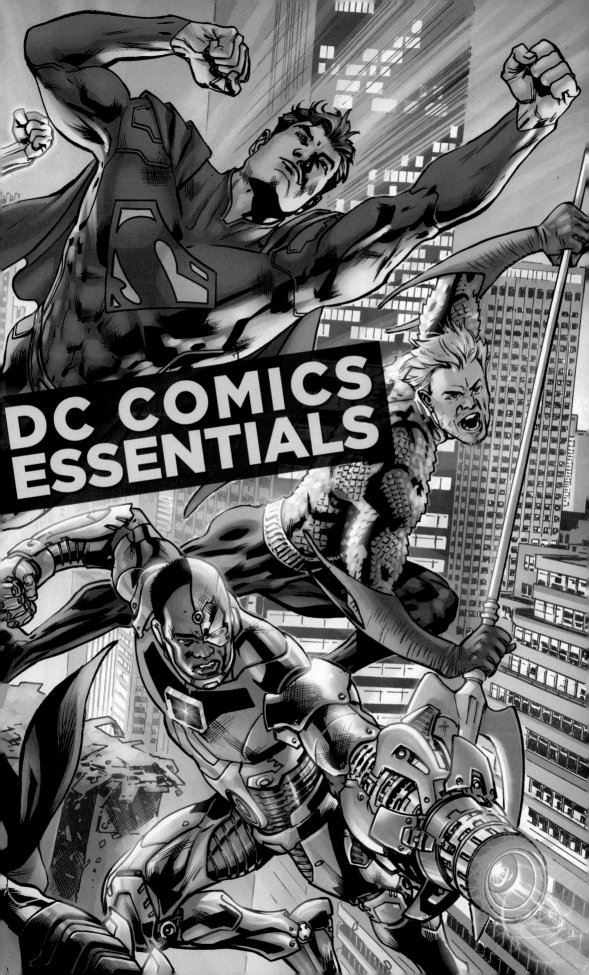

BATMAN

Dark Knight. Caped Crusader. World's Greatest Detective. Whatever you know him as, Batman shows us that you don't need superpowers to be a superhero—a point he proves again when he holds his own against the Man of Steel in this year's *Batman v Superman: Dawn of Justice*. As a child, Bruce Wayne watched helplessly as his parents were brutally murdered in front of him. From that day forth, he vowed to wage a one-man war on crime, donning the cape and the cowl to become Batman and redeem Gotham City. Created by Bob Kane and Bill Finger in 1939, Batman made his debut in the pages of DETECTIVE COMICS #27 and now dominates as one of the world's most iconic figures in popular culture.

BATMAN: YEAR ONE

Frank Miller's genre-defining graphic novel detailing a rookie Dark Knight's first year in Gotham City.

Writer: Frank Miller | Artist: David Mazzucchelli
ISBN: 978-1-4012-0752-6 | Diamond Code: OCT060163 | Price: $14.99/$17.99 CAN | Format: TP

BATMAN: THE LONG HALLOWEEN

A Batman murder mystery written by Jeph Loeb with art by Tim Sale, set during the Dark Knight's early days as he must race against the calendar to discover the identity of the serial killer Holiday.

Writer: Jeph Loeb | Artist: Tim Sale
ISBN: 978-1-4012-3259-7 | Diamond Code: JUL110251 | Price: $24.99/$28.99 CAN | Format: TP

BATMAN: DARK VICTORY

In this sequel to BATMAN: THE LONG HALLOWEEN, Batman faces another seemingly unsolvable mystery, as the Hangman runs through a murder spree in Gotham City.

Writer: Jeph Loeb | Artist: Tim Sale
ISBN: 978-1-4012-4401-9 | Diamond Code: NOV130237 | Price: $24.99/$28.99 CAN | Format: TP

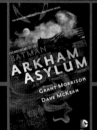

BATMAN: ARKHAM ASYLUM 25th ANNIVERSARY EDITION

Grant Morrison and Dave McKean's psychological horror story from Arkham Asylum, home to Gotham City's most deranged super-criminals.

Writer: Grant Morrison | Artist: Dave McKean
ISBN: 978-1-4012-5124-6 | Diamond Code: JUN140278 | Price: $19.99/$23.99 CAN | Format: TP

BATMAN: THE KILLING JOKE

The Joker, Batman's greatest adversary, in his definitive origin story by Alan Moore with breathtaking art by Brian Bolland. FOR MATURE READERS

Writer: Alan Moore | Artist: Brian Bolland
ISBN: 978-1-4012-1667-2 | Diamond Code: NOV070226 | Price: $17.99/$20.99 CAN | Format: HC

BATMAN: KNIGHTFALL VOL. 1

Batman's entire rogues gallery is freed from Arkham Asylum by the villainous Bane, who tests the Dark Knight mentally and physically as never before.

Writers: Various | Artists: Various
ISBN: 978-1-4012-3379-2 | Diamond Code: JAN120303 | Price: $29.99/$35.00 CAN | Format: TP

BATMAN: HUSH

The all-star team of Jeph Loeb and Jim Lee traces the tale of Batman as he seeks to stop a new and deadly villain who seems to know more about Batman than anyone—Hush!

Writer: Jeph Loeb | Artist: Jim Lee
ISBN: 978-1-4012-2317-5 | Diamond Code: MAY090178 | Price: $24.99/$28.99 CAN | Format: TP

BATMAN: HUSH ACTION FIGURE 3-PACK

Batman, Harley Quinn and the Joker—together as one? Believe it. No need to choose sides when you take home this 3-pack of fan favorites.

Diamond Code: MAY130272 | Price: $50.00

BATMAN: UNDER THE RED HOOD

The Red Hood returns to Gotham City, and his shocking actions—as well as his identity—will change Batman forever.

Writer: Judd Winick | Artist: Doug Mahnke
ISBN: 978-1-4012-3145-3 | Diamond Code: MAY110241 | Price: $29.99/$35.00 CAN | Format: TP

BATMAN AND SON

In Grant Morrison's epic Batman run, Bruce discovers that he's sired a son, Damian Wayne. Also included is BATMAN: THE BLACK GLOVE by Morrison with art by J.H. Williams III.

Writer: Grant Morrison | Artists: Andy Kubert, J.H. Williams III & Tony S. Daniel
ISBN: 978-1-4012-4402-6 | Diamond Code: OCT130238 | Price: $19.99/$23.99 CAN | Format: TP

BATMAN: R.I.P.

Grant Morrison continues his grand Batman story line, pitting the Dark Knight against the Black Glove in a prelude to FINAL CRISIS.

Writer: Grant Morrison | Artist: Tony S. Daniel
ISBN: 978-1-4012-2576-6 | Diamond Code: MAR100237 | Price: $14.99/$17.99 CAN | Format: TP

BATMAN & ROBIN VOL. 1: BATMAN REBORN

The dynamic duo is reborn, with Dick Grayson donning the cowl along with new Robin Damian Wayne.

Writer: Grant Morrison | Artist: Frank Quitely
ISBN: 978-1-4012-2987-0 | Diamond Code: DEC100246 | Price: $14.99/$17.99 CAN | Format: TP

BATMAN INCORPORATED

Batman deputizes different "Batmen" in nations around the globe, creating the indomitable Batman Incorporated.

Writer: Grant Morrison | Artist: Yanick Paquette
ISBN: 978-1-4012-3827-8 | Diamond Code: OCT120258 | Price: $19.99 /$23.99 CAN | Format: TP

BATMAN: THE BLACK MIRROR

The past comes back to haunt Commissioner Gordon and Batman by way of a diabolic murder mystery in this dark graphic novel that launched writer Scott Snyder into superstardom.

Writer: Scott Snyder | Artists: Jock & Francesco Francavilla
ISBN: 978-1-4012-3206-1 | Diamond Code: NOV120268 | Price: $16.99/$34.99 CAN | Format: TP

BATMAN: DETECTIVE COMICS VOL. 1: FACES OF DEATH

Writer/artist Tony S. Daniel's take on Batman's infamous rogues gallery.

Writer: Tony S. Daniel | Artist: Tony S. Daniel
ISBN: 978-1-4012-3467-6 | Diamond Code: JAN130296 | Price: $16.99/$19.99 CAN | Format: TP

BATMAN INCORPORATED VOL. 1: DEMON STAR

Batman and his allies must strengthen their resolve as Leviathan moves to take Gotham City.

Writer: Grant Morrison | Artist: Chris Burnham
ISBN: 978-1-4012-4263-3 | Diamond Code: AUG130293 | Price: $16.99 | Format: TP

BATMAN VOL. 1: THE COURT OF OWLS

A new era for the Dark Knight and Gotham City begins here from writer Scott Snyder and artist Greg Capullo, as Batman and the Bat-Family continue their quest to protect the people of Gotham.

Writer: Scott Snyder | Artist: Greg Capullo
ISBN: 978-1-4012-3542-0 | Diamond Code: DEC120323 | Price: $16.99/$19.99 CAN | Format: TP

DC COMICS DESIGNER SERIES: GREG CAPULLO

Clear your shelves for a legend! Greg Capullo's jaw-dropping artwork is brought to life beyond the page with these three impeccably detailed action figures from the bestselling Batman series.

BATMAN ACTION FIGURE
Diamond Code:
NOV130284
Price: $25.00

NIGHTWING ACTION FIGURE
Diamond Code:
NOV130286
Price: $25.00

TALON ACTION FIGURE
Diamond Code:
NOV130285
Price: $25.00

BATMAN VOL. 2: THE CITY OF OWLS

NIGHT OF THE OWLS continues here! Batman must stop the TALONS that have breached the Batcave in order to save an innocent life ... and Gotham City!

Writer: Scott Snyder | Artists: Greg Capullo & Rafael Albuquerque
ISBN: 978-1-4012-3778-3 | Diamond Code: JUL130235 | Price: $16.99/$19.99 CAN | Format: TP

BATMAN VOL. 3: DEATH OF THE FAMILY

After having his face sliced off one year ago, the Joker makes his horrifying return to Gotham City! How can Batman protect his city and those he's closest to?

Writer: Scott Snyder | Artist: Greg Capullo & Jock
ISBN: 978-1-4012-4602-0 | Diamond Code: FEB140248 | Price: $16.99/$19.99 CAN | Format: TP

BATMAN VOL. 4: ZERO YEAR – SECRET CITY

Scott Snyder and Greg Capullo present an astonishing new vision of the Dark Knight's origin—and his first encounters with the Riddler, the Red Hood and others!

Writer: Scott Snyder | Artist: Greg Capullo
ISBN: 978-1-4012-4933-5 | Diamond Code: JUL140237 | Price: $16.99/$19.99 CAN | Format: TP

BATMAN VOL. 5: ZERO YEAR - DARK CITY

Scott Snyder and Greg Capullo conclude their amazing new take on the Dark Knight's beginnings!

Writer: Scott Snyder | Artist: Greg Capullo
ISBN: 978-1-4012-5335-6 | Diamond Code: JAN150363 | Price: $16.99/$19.99 CAN | Format: TP

BATMAN VOL. 6: GRAVEYARD SHIFT

In the wake of the death of his son Damian, Batman is in danger of losing his humanity.

Writer: Scott Snyder | Artist: Greg Capullo
ISBN: 978-1-4012-5753-8 | Diamond Code: JUN150290 | Price: $16.99/$19.99 CAN | Format: TP

BATMAN VOL. 7: ENDGAME

The Joker is out to finally destroy Batman for good as Scott Snyder and Greg Capullo tell their definitive Joker story with an ending you have to see to believe!

Writer: Scott Snyder | Artist: Greg Capullo
ISBN: 978-1-4012-6116-0 | Diamond Code: DEC150331 | Price: $19.99/$19.99 CAN | Format: TP

COVER NOT FINAL

BATMAN VOL. 8: SUPERHEAVY

In the most daring chapter of their best-selling run, Snyder and Capullo bring an all-new Batman on the scene in Gotham City.

Writer: Scott Snyder | Artist: Greg Capullo
ISBN: 978-1-4012-5969-3 | Diamond Code: NOV150271 | Price: $24.99/$28.99 CAN | Format: HC

BATMAN ETERNAL VOL. 1

In the wake of FOREVER EVIL, the world looks at heroes in a different light, creating tension between Batman, his allies, and the Gotham City Police Department.

Writers: Scott Snyder, Tim Seeley, James Tynion IV, Ray Fawkes & Kyle Higgins | Artist: Jason Fabok
ISBN: 978-1-4012-5173-4 | Diamond Code: SEP140302 | Price: $39.99 /$47.99 CAN | Format: TP

COVER NOT FINAL

BATMAN & ROBIN ETERNAL VOL. 1

Starring the Dark Knight and Dick Grayson, this new series unearths a horrifying case from Batman's past.

Writers: Scott Snyder, James Tynion IV, Tim Seeley, Genevieve Valentine, Steve Orlando, et al. | Artists: Tony S. Daniel, et al.
ISBN: 978-1-4012-5967-9 | Diamond Code: DEC150341 | Price: $24.99/$29.99 CAN | Format: TP | Available March 15, 2016

READ THESE STAND-ALONE BATMAN GRAPHIC NOVELS

BATMAN: EARTH ONE VOL. 1

Geoff Johns reimagines the Dark Knight's origin story in this #1 *New York Times* bestseller.

Writer: Geoff Johns | Artist: Gary Frank | ISBN: 978-1-4012-3209-2
Diamond Code: JUL158202 | Price: $14.99 /$17.99 CAN | Format: TP

BATMAN: EARTH ONE VOL. 2

Writer Geoff Johns and artist Gary Frank continue their astonishing new take on the Dark Knight as the Riddler attacks Gotham City.

Writer: Geoff Johns | Artist: Gary Frank | ISBN: 978-1-4012-6251-8
Price: $14.99/$17.99 CAN | Format: TP

BATMAN: THE DARK KNIGHT RETURNS

Frank Miller's classic and gritty take on the return of Gotham's hero.

Writer: Frank Miller | Artists: Frank Miller and Klaus Janson | ISBN: 978-1-4012-6311-9
Diamond Code: NOV150279 | Price: $19.99/$23.99 CAN | Format: TP

BATMAN: THE DARK KNIGHT STRIKES AGAIN

The sequel to BATMAN: THE DARK KNIGHT RETURNS, in which Batman must come back once more to save a rapidly decaying world.

Writer: Frank Miller | Artist: Frank Miller | ISBN: 978-1-5638-9929-4
Diamond Code: FEB058404 | Price: $19.99/$23.99 CAN | Format: TP

EXPLORE ALL CORNERS OF GOTHAM WITH THESE GRAPHIC NOVELS!

BATGIRL VOL. 1: BATGIRL OF BURNSIDE

It's a reinvention of Batgirl from the boots up, by the incredible creative team of Cameron Stewart, Brenden Fletcher and rising star Babs Tarr.

Writers: Cameron Stewart & Brenden Fletcher | Artist: Babs Tarr
ISBN: 978-1-4012-5798-9 | Diamond Code: DEC148636 | Price: $14.99/$17.99 CAN | Format: TP

BATMAN & ROBIN VOL. 1: BORN TO KILL

Trained by the vicious League of Assassins, Damian Wayne, Batman's long-lost son, has instincts of a natural-born killer. But when he takes over the mantle of the new Boy Wonder, Damian must prove to his father--as well as his previous mantle-holders--that he's worthy of being the newest sidekick to the Dark Knight.

Writer: Peter J. Tomasi | Artist: Patrick Gleason
ISBN: 978-1-4012-3838-4 | Diamond Code: MAR130270 | Price: $16.99/$19.99 CAN | Format: TP

ALSO AVAILABLE:
BM& R VOL. 2-7

BLACK CANARY VOL. 1: KICKING AND SCREAMING

Spinning off from the pages of BATGIRL, Black Canary stars in her own series as a superhero by night, and a rock star singer later that night.

Writer: Brenden Fletcher | Artist: Annie Wu | ISBN: 978-1-4012-6117-7
Diamond Code: DEC150319 | Price: $14.99/$17.99 CAN | Format: TP | Available March 8, 2016

COVER NOT FINAL

CATWOMAN VOL. 1: THE GAME

Catwoman Selina Kyle is addicted to stealing...and Batman.

Writer: Judd Winick | Artist: Guillem March | ISBN: 978-1-4012-3464-5
Diamond Code: FEB120248 | Price: $14.99 /$17.99 CAN | Format: TP

ALSO AVAILABLE:
CATWOMAN VOL. 2-7

GOTHAM ACADEMY VOL. 1: WELCOME TO GOTHAM ACADEMY

Welcome to Gotham Academy! It's got a spooky campus, oddball teachers and rich benefactors always dropping by...like that weirdo Bruce Wayne. But nothing is as strange as the students!

Writers: Becky Cloonan & Brenden Fletcher | Artist: Karl Kerschl
ISBN: 978-1-4012-5472-8 | Diamond Code: MAR150269 | Price: $14.99/$17.99 CAN | Format: TP

JOKER

A never-before-told perspective on the most vile, dangerous and unpredictable inmate of Arkham—the Joker!

Writer: Brian Azzarello | Artist: Lee Bermejo
ISBN: 978-1-4012-1581-1 | Diamond Code: JUL080124 | Price: $19.99/$23.99 CAN | Format: HC

NIGHTWING VOL. 1: TRAPS AND TRAPEZES

Dick Grayson, once Batman's sidekick Robin, has grown up and become the high-flying Nightwing. Every bit the hero as his Caped Crusader mentor, he pursues justice on his own path, from costumed heroics in Gotham City to his new identity: secret agent of Spyral known only as Grayson!

Writer: Kyle Higgins | Artist: Eddy Barrows | ISBN: 978-1-4012-3705-9
Diamond Code: JUL120214 | Price: $14.99/$17.99 CAN | Format: TP

ALSO AVAILABLE:
NIGHTWING VOL. 2-5

GRAYSON VOL. 1: AGENTS OF SPYRAL

Faking his death amidst FOREVER EVIL, the one-time Boy Wonder Dick Grayson ditches his superhero gig as Nightwing for life as a double agent when he infiltrates the mysterious agency known as Spyral.

Writers: Tim Seeley & Tom King | Artist: Mikel Janin
ISBN: 978-1-4012-5759-0 | Diamond Code: OCT150253 | Price: $14.99/$17.99 CAN | Format: TP

RED HOOD AND THE OUTLAWS VOL. 1: REDEMPTION

Former Robin Jason Todd finds himself in an unlikely partnership with fellow misfits Arsenal and the exiled alien princess Starfire.

Writer: Scott Lobdell | Artist: Kenneth Rocafort | ISBN: 978-1-4012-3712-7
Diamond Code: AUG120248 | Price: $14.99/$17.99 CAN | Format: TP

ALSO AVAILABLE: RED HOOD
AND THE OUTLAWS VOL. 2-6

RED HOOD/ARSENAL VOL. 1: OPEN FOR BUSINESS

Best friends and teammates Red Hood and Arsenal break out in their very own series.

Writer: Scott Lobdell | Artist: Denis Medri | ISBN: 978-1-4012-6154-2
Diamond Code: DEC150322 | Price: $16.99 /$19.99 CAN | Format: TP | Available April 5, 2016

COVER NOT FINAL

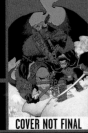

ROBIN: SON OF BATMAN VOL. 1: YEAR OF BLOOD

The Son of Batman is back in his first-ever solo series! Damian Wayne embarks on a globe-spanning quest to atone for the sins of his past.

Writer: Patrick Gleason | Artist: Patrick Gleason
ISBN: 978-1-4012-6155-9 | Price: $22.99/$27.99 CAN | Format: HC | Available March 29, 2016

COVER NOT FINAL

WE ARE ROBIN VOL. 1: THE VIGILANTE BUSINESS

The teenagers of Gotham City have adopted the "R" and made it their own. A new Robin? No, hundreds of new Robins!

Writer: Lee Bermejo | Artists: Jorge Corona & Khary Randolph | ISBN: 978-1-4012-5982-2
Diamond Code: DEC150326 | Price: $14.99/$17.99 CAN | Format: TP | Available April 5, 2016

COVER NOT FINAL

SUPERMAN

Since his debut in 1938's ACTION COMICS #1, Superman has achieved mythic folk hero status. Rocketed to Earth from the dying planet Krypton, baby Kal-El was raised on Earth by a kind-hearted farming couple. Clark Kent, as he was renamed, discovered that he had extraordinary and unmatched powers. Combining these abilities with the strong moral values his adoptive parents instilled in him, he became Superman. Created by Joe Shuster and Jerry Siegel, the Man of Steel was the first—and is now the most recognized—superhero in pop culture.

SUPERMAN: BIRTHRIGHT

SUPERMAN: FOR ALL SEASONS

CRISIS ON INFINITE EARTHS

MAN OF STEEL VOL. 1

SUPERMAN: THE DEATH OF SUPERMAN

WORLD WITHOUT SUPERMAN

THE RETURN OF SUPERMAN

SUPERMAN/BATMAN VOL. 1

SUPERMAN: THE GOLDEN AGE VOL. 1

Back to where it all began: Superman's very first, historic stories are now collected in one place, including the Man of Tomorrow's origin story and first battles against evil!

Writers: Jerry Siegel & Joe Shuster | Artists: Various | ISBN: 978-1-4012-6109-2
Diamond Code: DEC150348 | Price: $19.99/$23.99 CAN | Format: TP | Available March 22, 2016

SUPERMAN: WHATEVER HAPPENED TO THE MAN OF TOMORROW?

Alan Moore's quintessential Superman story.

Writer: Alan Moore | Artists: Curt Swan & George Pérez
ISBN: 978-1-4012-2731-9 | Diamond Code: APR100219 | Price: $14.99/$17.99 CAN | Format: TP

SUPERMAN: THE MAN OF STEEL VOL. 1

The first retelling of Superman's epic origin!

Writer: John Byrne | Artist: John Byrne
ISBN: 978-0-9302-8928-7 | Diamond Code: JUL058226 | Price: $14.99 /$17.99 CAN | Format: TP

SUPERMAN: FOR ALL SEASONS

The tale of Clark Kent's transformation from country boy to Metropolis's Superman as told by the acclaimed duo of Jeph Loeb and Tim Sale.

Writer: Jeph Loeb | Artist: Tim Sale
ISBN: 978-1-4012-5078-2 | Diamond Code: AUG140342 | Price: $17.99 /$20.99 CAN | Format: TP

THE DEATH OF SUPERMAN

The story that shocked the world! Superman pays the ultimate price to stop the killing machine Doomsday.

Writers: Various | Artists: Various
ISBN: 978-1-4012-4182-7 | Diamond Code: OCT120269 | Price: $14.99/$17.99 CAN | Format: TP

SUPERMAN/BATMAN VOL. 1

The iconic superheroes must unite to stop longtime Superman enemy Lex Luthor in this team-up tale from superstar writer Jeph Loeb (BATMAN: THE LONG HALLOWEEN).

Writer: Jeph Loeb | Artists: Ed McGuinness & Michael Turner
ISBN: 978-1-4012-4818-5 | Diamond Code: JAN140354 | Price: $19.99/$23.99 CAN | Format: TP

LUTHOR

The all-star team of Brian Azzarello and Lee Bermejo explores the mind of Superman's greatest villain, Lex Luthor.

Writer: Jeph Loeb | Artists: Ed McGuinness & Michael Turner
ISBN: 978-1-4012-4818-5 | Diamond Code: AUG150269 | Price: $19.99/$17.99 | Format: TP

SUPERMAN: FOR TOMORROW

A cataclysmic event has wiped out half the Earth's population, and no one is left unaffected, including Superman, in this graphic novel by the superstar team of Jim Lee and Brian Azzarello.

Writer: Brian Azzarello | Artist: Jim Lee
ISBN: 978-1-4012-3780-6 | Diamond Code: NOV120270 | Price: $24.99 /$28.99 CAN | Format: TP

SUPERMAN: SECRET ORIGIN

The origin of Superman as told by the *New York Times* best-selling team of Geoff Johns and Gary Frank.

Writer: Geoff Johns | Artist: Gary Frank
ISBN: 978-1-4012-3299-3 | Diamond Code: SEP110188 | Price: $19.99/$23.99 CAN | Format: TP

SUPERMAN: LAST SON OF KRYPTON

Film director Richard Donner and Geoff Johns pit the Man of Steel against General Zod and Brainiac in these stories illustrated by Adam Kubert and Gary Frank.

Writers: Geoff Johns & Richard Donner | Artists: Adam Kubert & Gary Frank
ISBN: 978-1-4012-3779-0 | Diamond Code: OCT120270 | Price: $19.99/$23.99 CAN | Format: TP

SUPERMAN — ACTION COMICS VOL. 1: SUPERMAN AND THE MEN OF STEEL

Grant Morrison returns to the Man of Steel, joined by sensational artist Rags Morales, to bring you the story of the early days of Superman.

Writer: Grant Morrison | Artists: Rags Morales & Andy Kubert | ISBN: 978-1-4012-3547-5
Diamond Code: FEB130215 | Price: $16.99 /$19.99 CAN | Format: TP

ALSO AVAILABLE: SUPERMAN — ACTION COMICS VOL. 2-8

SUPERMAN VOL. 1: WHAT PRICE TOMORROW?

The Man of Steel flies into the new DC Universe with a new status quo but a continued quest for truth and justice!

Writer: George Pérez | Artists: Jesus Merino & Nicola Scott
ISBN: 978-1-4012-3686-1 | Diamond Code: MAR130274 | Price: $14.99/$17.99 CAN | Format: TP

ALSO AVAILABLE: SUPERMAN VOL. 2-6

SUPERMAN: DOOMED

A league of comics' top talents presents this most epic Superman event. Doomsday is back, and it's bigger and deadlier than ever.

Writers: Charles Soule, Greg Pak & Scott Lobdell | Artists: Aaron Kuder, Tony S. Daniel & Ken Lashley
ISBN: 978-1-4012-5769-9 | Diamond Code: SEP150305 | Price: $29.99/$35.00 CAN | Format: TP

SUPERMAN/WONDER WOMAN VOL. 1: POWER COUPLE

This bold new series dives deep into the relationship between the Man of Steel and the Amazon Princess.

Writer: Charles Soule | Artists: Tony S. Daniel & Paulo Siqueira
ISBN: 978-1-4012-5346-2 | Diamond Code: DEC140383 | Price: $16.99/$19.99 CAN | Format: TP

BATMAN/SUPERMAN VOL. 1: CROSS WORLD

Discover how two of the World's Finest Superheroes met for the first time in this ultimate team-up.

Writer: Greg Pak | Artists: Jae Lee & Ben Oliver | ISBN: 978-1-4012-4934-2
Diamond Code: AUG140333 | Price: $14.99/$17.99 CAN | Format: TP

ALSO AVAILABLE: BATMAN/
SUPERMAN VOL. 2-4

SUPERMAN UNCHAINED

All-star creators Scott Snyder and Jim Lee unite for the first time to take on the Man of Steel in this graphic novel blockbuster!

Writer: Scott Snyder | Artists: Jim Lee & Dustin Nguyen
ISBN: 978-1-4012-4522-1 | Price: $24.99/$29.99 CAN | Format: TP

SUPERMAN: THE MEN OF TOMORROW

Comics legends Geoff Johns and John Romita Jr. team up to launch an all-new era of Superman!

Writer: Geoff Johns | Artist: John Romita Jr.
ISBN: 978-1-4012-5868-9 | Price: $16.99/$19.99 CAN | Format: TP

COVER NOT FINAL

SUPERMAN VOL. 1: BEFORE TRUTH

The National Book of the Year-nominated author of American Born Chinese, Gene Luen Yang, joins John Romita Jr. as Superman's identity is revealed to the world!

Writer: Gene Luen Yang | Artist: John Romita, Jr. | ISBN: 978-1-4012-5981-5
Diamond Code: NOV150284 | Price: $24.99/$29.99 CAN | Format: HC | Available April 5, 2016

READ THESE STAND–ALONE SUPERMAN GRAPHIC NOVELS

SUPERMAN: EARTH ONE VOL. 1

The #1 *New York Times* best-selling original graphic novel that reimagines Superman as a brooding, reluctant hero in modern-day Metropolis.

Writer: J. Michael Straczynski | Artist: Shane Davis | ISBN: 978-1-4012-2469-1
Diamond Code: FEB130226 | Price: $12.99/$12.99 CAN | Format: TP

ALSO AVAILABLE: SUPERMAN: EARTH ONE VOL. 2-3

SUPERMAN: BIRTHRIGHT

Superstar writer Mark Waid updates the origin of the Man of Steel in this classic tale.

Writer: Mark Waid | Artist: Leinil Francis Yu
ISBN: 978-1-4012-0252-1 | Diamond Code: JUL050214 | Price: $19.99/$23.99 CAN | Format: TP

ALL-STAR SUPERMAN

The critically acclaimed series that harkens back to the Golden Age of Superman by superstar writer Grant Morrison and artist Frank Quitely.

Writer: Grant Morrison | Artist: Frank Quitely
ISBN: 978-1-4012-3205-4 | Diamond Code: JUL110247 | Price: $29.99/$35.00 CAN | Format: TP

SUPERMAN: RED SON

In this alternate take on the Man of Steel's origin, the ship carrying the infant who would grow up to become Superman lands in the midst of the 1950s Soviet Union.

Writer: Mark Millar | Artists: Dave Johnson & Killian Plunkett
ISBN: 978-1-4012-4711-9 | Diamond Code: JAN140353 | Price: $17.99/$20.99 CAN | Format: TP

SUPERGIRL VOL. 1: LAST DAUGHTER OF KRYPTON

Superman's teenage cousin mysteriously crash-lands on Earth decades after the destruction of Krypton.

Writers: Michael Green & Mike Johnson | Artist: Mahmud Asrar
ISBN: 978-1-4012-3680-9 | Diamond Code: JUL120216 | Price: $14.99/$17.99 CAN | Format: TP

ALSO AVAILABLE: SUPERGIRL VOL. 2-6

WONDER WOMAN

Wonder Woman reigns as the most famous superheroine of all time as she prepares to star in the upcoming 2017 blockbuster film *Wonder Woman*. She is Princess Diana of the immortal Amazons from Greek mythology, equipped with powers granted by the Gods of Olympus and an arsenal of iconic weapons, from her Lasso of Truth to her indestructible bracelets. Since her first appearance in 1941, Wonder Woman has been unparalleled in brains, beauty, and brawn—a warrior princess beyond worthy of her status as a pop culture icon.

WONDER WOMAN BY GEORGE PÉREZ

INFINITE CRISIS

FLASHPOINT

WONDER WOMAN VOL. 1: BLOOD

SUPERMAN/WONDER WOMAN VOL. 1

WONDER WOMAN VOL. 7: WAR-TORN

WONDER WOMAN VOL. 1: BLOOD

Superheroics and ancient myth meet, as critically acclaimed writer Brian Azzarello teams with Cliff Chiang and Tony Akins to begin a new chapter for the Amazon Princess.

Writer: Brian Azzarello | Artists: Cliff Chiang & Tony Akins
ISBN: 978-1-4012-3562-8 | Diamond Code: OCT120256 | Price: $14.99/$17.99 CAN | Format: TP

WONDER WOMAN VOL. 2: GUTS

Wonder Woman goes to hell! After playing Poseidon, Hades, and Hera against each other, Hades strikes back by kidnapping Zola and trapping her in the Underworld.

Writer: Brian Azzarello | Artists: Cliff Chiang & Tony Akins
ISBN: 978-1-4012-3810-0 | Diamond Code: JUN130271 | Price: $14.99/$17.99 CAN | Format: TP

WONDER WOMAN VOL. 3: IRON

As Wonder Woman digs deeper into her familial tree, she finds there are as many Gods that are willing to lend her a hand as there are those that would do her harm.

Writer: Brian Azzarello | Artists: Cliff Chiang & Tony Akins
ISBN: 978-1-4012-4607-5 | Diamond Code: DEC130308 | Price: $16.99/$19.99 CAN | Format: TP

WONDER WOMAN VOL. 4: WAR

Meet the new God of War: Wonder Woman!

Writer: Brian Azzarello | Artists: Cliff Chiang & Tony Akins
ISBN: 978-1-4012-4954-0 | Diamond Code: JUL140247 | Price: $14.99/$17.99 CAN | Format: TP

WONDER WOMAN VOL. 5: FLESH

Wonder Woman must decide if the path set out for her is one she wants to take after assuming the War's place in the pantheon.

Writer: Brian Azzarello | Artists: Cliff Chiang & Goran Sudzuka
ISBN: 978-1-4012-5349-3 | Diamond Code: JAN150375 | Price: $16.99/$19.99 CAN | Format: TP

WONDER WOMAN VOL. 6: BONES

Writer Brian Azzarello and artist Cliff Chiang's astonishing finale of their epic run! Olympus must fall, and its rightful ruler must be restored.

Writer: Brian Azzarello | Artists: Cliff Chiang & Goran Sudzuka
ISBN: 978-1-4012-5775-0 | Diamond Code: JUN150295 | Price: $14.99/$17.99 CAN | Format: TP

WONDER WOMAN VOL. 7: WAR-TORN

This bold new series dives deep into the relationship between the Man of Steel and the Amazon Princess.

Writer: Meredith Finch | Artist: David Finch
ISBN: 978-1-4012-6163-4 | Price: $16.99 /$19.99 CAN | Format: TP

COVER NOT FINAL

WONDER WOMAN VOL. 8: TWIST OF FATE

The Finches continue their take on the Amazonian Princess, as she faces one of her most personal challenges to date.

Writer: Meredith Finch | Artist: David Finch
ISBN: 978-1-4012-6164-1 | Diamond Code: JAN160338 | Price: $22.99 /$27.99 CAN | Format:HC | Available May 24, 2016

WONDER WOMAN: EARTH ONE VOL. 1

Comics masters Grant Morrison and Yanick Paquette continue the best-selling Earth One series with a provocative take on Wonder Woman for the modern world.

Writer: Grant Morrison | Artist: Yanick Paquette
ISBN: 978-1-4012-2978-8 | Diamond Code: DEC140384 | Price: $22.99 /$27.99 CAN | Format: HC | Available April 12, 2016

JUSTICE LEAGUE

Greater than the sum of their awe-inspiring parts, the Justice League handles threats too massive for any single hero. Made up of the World's Greatest Superheroes, the core line-up is known as the Big Seven: Superman, the most powerful hero in the world; Batman, the apex of physical and mental human achievement; Wonder Woman, the Amazon's princess and greatest warrior; Green Lantern, an intergalactic cop armed with his own power ring; the Flash, the fastest man alive; Aquaman, King of the Seven Seas; and Cyborg, a half-man, half-robot outfitted with the world's most advanced technology.

52

JUSTICE LEAGUE OF AMERICA: THE SILVER AGE VOL. 1

For the first time, JLA's first 20 adventures are collected in a single volume spanning 1960-1964.

Writers: Various | Artists: Various
ISBN: 978-1-4012-6111-5 | Diamond Code: NOV150283 | Price: $19.99/$23.99 CAN | Format: TP

CRISIS ON INFINITE EARTHS

Worlds will live and worlds will die in this, comics' original epic event story line by the legendary creative team of Marv Wolfman and George Pérez.

Writer: Marv Wolfman | Artist: George Pérez
ISBN: 978-1-5638-9750-4 | Diamond Code: AUG058162 | Price: $29.99/$35.00 CAN | Format: TP

ZERO HOUR: CRISIS IN TIME

The universe is being destroyed by an all-consuming force working its way from the future to the past! Heroes struggle to survive this crisis in time as the world they know changes around them.

Writer: Dan Jurgens | Artists: Dan Jurgens & Jerry Ordway
ISBN: 978-1-5638-9184-7 | Diamond Code: JUN068105 | Price: $17.99/$20.99 CAN | Format: TP

JLA VOL. 1

Grant Morrison relaunches the greatest team in the DC Universe—returning the powerhouse lineup of Superman, Batman, Wonder Woman, the Flash, Green Lantern, Aquaman and Martian Manhunter!

Writer: Grant Morrison | Artists: Howard Porter & Oscar Jimenez
ISBN: 978-1-4012-3314-3 | Diamond Code: JUN110276 | Price: $19.99 /$23.99 CAN | Format: TP

ALSO AVAILABLE:
JLA VOL. 2 -7

INFINITE CRISIS

It's the DCU's darkest day, and long-lost heroes from the past return to make things right in this epic sequel to CRISIS ON INFINITE EARTHS.

Writer: Geoff Johns | Artist: Phil Jimenez
ISBN: 978-1-4012-1060-1 | Diamond Code: FEB118149 | Price: $17.99/$20.99 | Format: TP

IDENTITY CRISIS

Geoff Johns, Grant Morrison, Greg Rucka and Mark Waid pen the weekly, yearlong series that redefined not only the DC Universe but what exactly it means to be a hero.

Writer: Brad Meltzer | Artist: Rags Morales
ISBN: 978-1-4012-0458-7 | Diamond Code: AUG118125 | Price: $17.99/$23.99 CAN | Format: TP

FINAL CRISIS

Grant Morrison takes the DC Universe on a battle through the Multiverse that will leave both hero and villain changed forever.

Writer: Grant Morrison | Artists: J.G. Jones, Doug Mahnke & Carlos Pacheco
ISBN: 978-1-4012-4517-7 | Diamond Code: JAN140352 | Price: $19.99/$23.99 CAN | Format: TP

BLACKEST NIGHT

Hal Jordan and the Green Lantern Corps lead DC's champions into battle to save the universe from an army of undead Black Lanterns!

Writer: Geoff Johns | Artist: Ivan Reis
ISBN: 978-1-4012-2953-5 | Diamond Code: APR110192 | Price: $19.99/$23.99 CAN | Format: TP

FLASHPOINT

Heroes become villains in an alternate universe tale that changed the DC Universe forever!

Writer: Geoff Johns | Artist: Andy Kubert
ISBN: 978-1-4012-3338-9 | Diamond Code: OCT138324 | Price: $16.99 /$17.99 | Format: TP

JUSTICE LEAGUE VOL. 1: ORIGIN

In one of the most game-changing titles in comic industry history, Geoff Johns and Jim Lee reimagine the Justice League for the 21st century.

Writer: Geoff Johns | Artist: Jim Lee
ISBN: 978-1-4012-3788-2 | Diamond Code: OCT120252 | Price: $16.99/$19.99 CAN | Format: TP

JUSTICE LEAGUE VOL. 2: THE VILLAIN'S JOURNEY

A villain from the League's past reemerges, and it all ends with one of the most surprising moments in DC history!

Writer: Geoff Johns | Artist: Jim Lee
ISBN: 978-1-4012-3765-3 | Diamond Code: JUN130261 | Price: $16.99/$19.99 CAN | Format: TP

JUSTICE LEAGUE VOL. 3: THRONE OF ATLANTIS

The armies of Atlantis attack the surface world, pitting the Justice League against one of their own.

Writer: Geoff Johns | Artists: Ivan Reis & Tony S. Daniel
ISBN: 978-1-4012-4698-3 | Diamond Code: JAN140339 | Price: $16.99/$19.99 CAN | Format: TP

JUSTICE LEAGUE VOL. 4: THE GRID

The Justice League becomes embroiled in a battle with the two other Justice Leagues—the Trinity War. But who is the real force behind it all?

Writer: Geoff Johns | Artist: Ivan Reis
ISBN: 978-1-4012-5008-9 | Diamond Code: JUN140272 | Price: $16.99/$19.99 CAN | Format: TP

JUSTICE LEAGUE: TRINITY WAR

When the three Justice Leagues go to war with one another, whose side will everyone be on? Allies will be born, friends will become enemies, and the DC Universe will never be the same.

Writers: Geoff Johns & Jeff Lemire | Artists: Ivan Reis, Doug Mahnke & Mikel Janin
ISBN: 978-1-4012-4944-1 | Diamond Code: AUG140331 | Price: $19.99 /$23.99 | Format: TP

The Justice League is dead! An evil version of the Justice League takes over the DC Universe, and no one stands in the way... no one except for Lex Luthor.

Writer: Geoff Johns | Artist: David Finch
ISBN: 978-1-4012-5338-7 | Diamond Code: FEB150254 | Price: $19.99/$23.99 CAN | Format: TP

JUSTICE LEAGUE VOL. 5: FOREVER HEROES

New York Times best-selling writer Geoff Johns continues the FOREVER EVIL event, as the Justice League must find a way to defeat their deadly mirror images—the Crime Syndicate!

Writer: Geoff Johns | Artists: Ivan Reis & Doug Mahnke
ISBN: 978-1-4012-5419-3 | Diamond Code: DEC140382 | Price: $14.99 /$17.99 | Format: TP

THE NEW 52: FUTURES END VOL. 1

Five years from now, the DC Universe is reeling from a war with another Earth, leaving the world unprepared for an approaching evil that threatens to destroy the future.

Writers: Jeff Lemire, Brian Azzarello, Dan Jurgens & Keith Giffen | Artists: Various
ISBN: 978-1-4012-5244-1 | Diamond Code: SEP140303 | Price: $39.99/$47.99 CAN | Format: TP

CONVERGENCE

Every DC Universe from the past, present and future collide here in this mega-event that will change the course of every story ever told in DC Comics history.

Writer: Jeff King & Scott Lobdell | Artists: Carlo Pagulayan & Stephen Segovia
ISBN: 978-1-4012-5686-9 | Diamond Code: JUL150293 | Price: $29.99/$35.00 CAN | Format: HC

JUSTICE LEAGUE VOL. 6: INJUSTICE LEAGUE

The Justice League roster you've never seen before, all led by the world's greatest hero—Lex Luthor!

Writer: Geoff Johns | Artists: Doug Mahnke & Jason Fabok
ISBN: 978-1-4012-5852-8 | Diamond Code: DEC150328 | Price: $19.99/$23.99 CAN | Format: TP

COVER NOT FINAL

JUSTICE LEAGUE VOL. 7: DARKSEID WAR PART 1

Darkseid and the Anti-Monitor—two of the most powerful beings in the universe—face off in one of the biggest Justice League story lines ever!

Writer: Geoff Johns | Artist: Jason Fabok | ISBN: 978-1-4012-5977-8
Price: $24.99/$29.99 CAN | Diamond Code: NOV150281 | Format: HC | Available March 15, 2016

JUSTICE LEAGUE OF AMERICA VOL. 1

Superstar Bryan Hitch returns to DC Comics to launch this all-new Justice League series!

Writer: Bryan Hitch | Artist: Bryan Hitch
ISBN: 978-1-4012-5976-1 | Diamond Code: APR150167 | Price: $24.99/$29.99 CAN | Format: HC

COVER NOT FINAL

FOLLOW THE ADVENTURES OF THE MEMBERS OF THE JUSTICE LEAGUE!

AQUAMAN VOL. 1: THE TRENCH

Superstar writer Geoff Johns re-teams with artist Ivan Reis to relaunch Aquaman as one of the most powerful and important heroes of the DC Universe.

Writer: Geoff Johns | Artist: Ivan Reis
ISBN: 978-1-4012-3710-3 | Diamond Code: FEB130206 | Price: $14.99/$17.99 CAN | Format: TP

ALSO AVAILABLE:
AQUAMAN VOL. 2-7

CYBORG VOL. 1: UNPLUGGED

Cyborg, fan-favorite Justice League member, finally stars in his own series!

Writer: David Walker | Artists: Ivan Reis & Joe Prado
ISBN: 978-1-4012-6119-1 | Diamond Code: DEC150318 | Price: $14.99/$17.99 CAN | Format: TP | Available April 19, 2016

COVER NOT FINAL

MARTIAN MANHUNTER VOL. 1: THE EPIPHANY

Martian Manhunter tries to stop ruthless alien terrorists from destroying everything, and no one can be trusted.

Writer: Rob Williams | Artist: Eddy Barrows
ISBN: 978-1-4012-6151-1 | Diamond Code: NOV150264 | Price: $16.99/$19.99 CAN | Format: TP

SHAZAM! VOL. 1

By shouting a wizard's name--Shazam!--young teen Billy Batson is mystically transformed into the powerhouse known as Captain Marvel.

Writer: Geoff Johns | Artist: Gary Frank
ISBN: 978-1-4012-4699-0 | Diamond Code: FEB140251 | Price: $16.99/$19.99 CAN | Format: TP

JUSTICE LEAGUE ACTION FIGURE 7-PACK

Complete your collection all at once with these seven classic, stunningly crafted Justice League heroes—united for the first time in the third dimension!

Diamond Code: NOV138235 | Price: $100.00

The FLASH

Young Barry Allen's life stopped the minute his mother was killed, and the mystery behind her murder drove him to become a forensic scientist. Years later, when a freak lightning bolt strikes a shelf of chemicals in his lab, Barry receives super-speed and becomes the fastest man alive—the Flash! Engaging and energetic, the Flash has been a fan favorite in the DC Universe since his inception in 1940 and is earning a new generation of followers with the wildly popular TV series on The CW, The Flash.

THE FLASH CHRONICLES VOL. 1

CRISIS ON INFINITE EARTHS

THE FLASH BY GEOFF JOHNS

THE FLASH: REBIRTH

THE FLASH: THE DASTARDLY DEATH OF THE ROGUES

THE FLASH: ROAD TO FLASHPOINT

FLASHPOINT

THE FLASH VOL. 1: MOVE FORWARD

THE FLASH: A CELEBRATION OF 75 YEARS

An anthology collection featuring the Scarlet Speedster, ranging over his seven decades as a mainstay in the DC Universe.

Writers: Various | Artists: Various
ISBN: 978-1-4012-5178-9 | Diamond Code: SEP140317 | Price: $39.99/$47.99 CAN | Format: HC

THE FLASH: REBIRTH

The explosive epic that reintroduces the newly returned Barry Allen as the Flash!

Writer: Geoff Johns | Artist: Ethan Van Sciver
ISBN: 978-1-4012-3001-2 | Diamond Code: JAN110329 | Price: $14.99/$17.99 CAN | Format: TP

THE FLASH: THE DASTARDLY DEATH OF THE ROGUES

The Fastest Man Alive must solve the murder of one of his greatest villains and protect his other foes from an elusive killer.

Writer: Geoff Johns | Artist: Francis Manapul
ISBN: 978-1-4012-3195-8 | Diamond Code: OCT110249 | Price: $14.99/$17.99 CAN | Format: TP

THE FLASH: ROAD TO FLASHPOINT

Make way for Hot Pursuit—the latest speedster to come out of the Speed Force in this super-charged story that ties directly into Flashpoint!

Writer: Geoff Johns | Artist: Francis Manapul
ISBN: 978-1-4012-3448-5 | Diamond Code: JUN120245 | Price: $14.99/$17.99 CAN | Format: TP

FLASHPOINT

Heroes become villains in an alternate-universe tale that changed the DC Universe forever!

Writer: Geoff Johns | Artist: Andy Kubert
ISBN: 978-1-4012-3338-9 | Diamond Code: OCT138324 | Price: $16.99/$19.99 CAN | Format: TP

THE FLASH VOL. 1: MOVE FORWARD

The Fastest Man Alive returns as Central City's greatest protector.

Writers: Francis Manapul & Brian Buccellato | Artist: Francis Manapul
ISBN: 978-1-4012-3554-3 | Diamond Code: MAY130224 | Price: $16.99/$19.99 CAN | Format: TP

THE FLASH VOL. 2: ROGUES REVOLUTION

The Flash's Rogues Gallery is back—more powerful than ever, they're each looking to take down the Fastest Man Alive!

Writers: Francis Manapul & Brian Buccellato | Artist: Francis Manapul
ISBN: 978-1-4012-4273-2 | Diamond Code: NOV130229 | Price: $16.99/$19.99 CAN | Format: TP

THE FLASH VOL. 3: GORILLA WARFARE

The Flash will have to turn to his former enemies, the Rogues, if he wants to defeat the invading hordes of Gorilla Grodd.

Writers: Francis Manapul & Brian Buccellato | Artist: Francis Manapul
ISBN: 978-1-4012-4712-6 | Diamond Code: MAY140367 | Price: $16.99/$19.99 CAN | Format: TP

THE FLASH VOL. 4: REVERSE

Brian Buccellato and Francis Manapul continue their critically acclaimed run on THE FLASH as Barry Allen confronts his most deadly foe: the Reverse-Flash!

Writers: Francis Manapul & Brian Buccellato | Artist: Francis Manapul
ISBN: 978-1-4012-4949-6 | Diamond Code: OCT140357 | Price: $16.99/$19.99 CAN | Format: TP

THE FLASH VOL. 5: HISTORY LESSONS

The Flash faces a mystical serial killer who might be responsible for his mother's murder!

Writer: Brian Buccellato | Artist: Patrick Zircher
ISBN: 978-1-4012-4950-2 | Diamond Code: OCT140358 | Price: $14.99/$17.99 CAN | Format: HC

THE FLASH VOL. 6: OUT OF TIME

A brand-new era for the Scarlet Speedster from Robert Venditti, Van Jensen and artist Brett Booth.

Writers: Van Jensen & Robert Venditti | Artist: Brett Booth
ISBN: 978-1-4012-5427-8 | Diamond Code: FEB150256 | Price: $24.99/$28.99 CAN | Format: HC

THE FLASH VOL. 7: SAVAGE WORLD

The Flash is trapped in a bizarre, unknown land terrorized by castaways from the past, present and future.

Writers: Van Jensen & Robert Venditti | Artist: Brett Booth
ISBN: 978-1-4012-5875-7 | Diamond Code: SEP150296 | Price: $22.99/$27.99 CAN | Format: HC

EXPLORE *THE WORLD OF* THE TV SHOW

THE FLASH: SEASON ZERO

An all-new series that ties in directly to the world of the hit TV show *The Flash* on The CW.

Writer: Andrew Kreisberg | Artist: Phil Hester & Marcus To
ISBN: 978-1-4012-5771-2 | Diamond Code: JUN150297 | Price: $19.99/$23.99 CAN | Format: TP

Oliver Queen had it all: movie-star good looks, his own billion-dollar company, and a destructive attitude. Everything changed the day an accident left him marooned on a dangerous island. Forced to survive the island's harsh environment and countless unexpected threats, Oliver became proficient in the use of the bow and arrow and learned what it meant to have to fight for freedom. Now back home, he has become the hero known as Green Arrow. Also starring in The CW's TV show *Arrow*, the Green Arrow fights for others against the worst criminals Starling City has to offer.

GREEN ARROW: YEAR ONE

Oliver's first year donning the quiver as Green Arrow!

Writer: Andy Diggle | Artist: Jock
ISBN: 978-1-4012-1743-3 | Diamond Code: JAN090227 | Price: $14.99/$17.99 CAN | Format: TP

GREEN ARROW: THE LONGBOW HUNTERS

A gritty take on a vigilante Emerald Archer in this essential Green Arrow story by Mike Grell.

Writer: Mike Grell | Artist: Mike Grell
ISBN: 978-1-4012-3862-9 | Diamond Code: JUN120250 | Price: $14.99/$17.99 CAN | Format: TP

GREEN ARROW: THE ARCHER'S QUEST

Oliver Queen returns to discover and recover secrets from his past in this graphic novel by *New York Times* best-selling novelist Brad Meltzer.

Writer: Brad Meltzer | Artist: Phil Hester
ISBN: 978-1-4012-5525-1 | Diamond Code: APR150294 | Price: $14.99/$17.99 CAN | Format: HC

GREEN ARROW VOL. 4: THE KILL MACHINE

Jeff Lemire and Andrea Sorrentino begin their groundbreaking saga!

Writer: Jeff Lemire | Artist: Andrea Sorrentino
ISBN: 978-1-4012-4690-7 | Diamond Code: DEC130306 | Price: $16.99/$19.99 CAN | Format: TP

GREEN ARROW VOL. 5: THE OUTSIDERS WAR

Green Arrow had finally found a sense of purpose, friends to aid him, and even a place in the Justice League of America. Now, he's not even sure where he came from...or who he came from.

Writer: Jeff Lemire | Artist: Andrea Sorrentino
ISBN: 978-1-4012-5044-7 | Diamond Code: JUL140242 | Price: $16.99/$19.99 CAN | Format: TP

GREEN ARROW VOL. 6: BROKEN

Everything about Oliver Queen's past comes to the surface, as his life and those of the people he loves, are all on the line in Jeff Lemire's concluding story line.

Writer: Jeff Lemire | Artist: Andrea Sorrentino
ISBN: 978-1-4012-5474-2 | Diamond Code: JAN150370 | Price: $14.99/$17.99 CAN | Format: TP

GREEN ARROW VOL. 7: KINGDOM

From the showrunner of the TV hit *Arrow* comes the DC Universe adventures of the Emerald Archer.

Writers: Andrew Kreisberg & Ben Sokolowski | Artist: Daniel Sampere
ISBN: 978-1-4012-5762-0 | Diamond Code: AUG150270 | Price: $14.99/$17.99 CAN | Format: TP | Available July 12, 2016

GREEN ARROW VOL. 8

Oliver Queen meets his match when he investigates the world of the supernatural.

Writers: Benjamin Percy | Artist: Patrick Zircher
COVER NOT FINAL
ISBN: 978-1-4012-6255-6 | Price: $14.99/$17.99 CAN | Format: TP | Available July 12, 2016

DEATHSTROKE VOL. 1: GODS OF WAR

Slade Wilson, the world's deadliest assassin, stars in this new solo series from writer and artist Tony S. Daniel.

Writer: Tony S. Daniel | Artist: Tony S. Daniel | ISBN: 978-1-4012-5471-1 | Diamond Code: MAR150267 | Price: $14.99/$17.99 CAN | Format: TP

EXPLORE THE WORLD OF THE TV SHOW

ARROW VOL. 1

Directly from the hit CW television series ARROW come these digital-first adventures by show creators Andrew Kreisberg and Marc Guggenheim.

Writers: Marc Guggenheim & Andrew Kreisberg
Artist: Mike Grell
ISBN: 978-1-4012-4299-2 |
Diamond Code: JUN130265
Price: $16.99 /$19.99 CAN
Format: TP

GREEN LANTERN

When a dying alien crashes on Earth, reckless test pilot Hal Jordan is chosen to be its successor in the universal peacekeeping force known as the Green Lantern Corps. Armed with a power ring that has the ability to create anything he can imagine, the newest Green Lantern now faces his greatest fears and the most dangerous villains in the universe.

GREEN LANTERN: A CELEBRATION OF 75 YEARS

This anthology collects Green Lantern's greatest stories throughout seven decades as a DC Universe superhero.

Writers: Various | Artists: Various
ISBN: 978-1-4012-5819-1 | Diamond Code: MAY150241 | Price: $39.99/$48.99 CAN | Format: HC

GREEN LANTERN: REBIRTH

A jaw-dropping epic that reintroduces the quintessential Green Lantern, Hal Jordan!

Writer: Geoff Johns | Artist: Ethan Van Sciver
ISBN: 978-1-4012-2755-5 | Diamond Code: FEB100185 | Price: $14.99/$17.99 CAN | Format: TP

GREEN LANTERN: THE SINESTRO CORPS WAR

Sinestro—Hal Jordan's former mentor and archnemesis—has gathered an army of soldiers fueled by the fear to wage war with the Green Lantern Corps.

Writers: Geoff Johns, Dave Gibbons & Peter J. Tomasi | Artists: Ethan Van Sciver, Ivan Reis & Patrick Gleason
ISBN: 978-1-4012-3301-3 | Diamond Code: JUN110275 | Price: $29.99/$35.00 CAN | Format: TP

GREEN LANTERN: SECRET ORIGIN

Witness the beginnings of the greatest Green Lantern of all.

Writer: Geoff Johns | Artist: Ivan Reis
ISBN: 978-1-4012-3086-9 | Diamond Code: JAN110337 | Price: $14.99/$17.99 CAN | Format: TP

BLACKEST NIGHT

Hal Jordan and the Green Lantern Corps lead DC's champions into battle to save the universe from an army of undead Black Lanterns!

Writer: Geoff Johns | Artist: Ivan Reis
ISBN: 978-1-4012-2953-5 | Diamond Code: APR110192 | Price: $19.99/$23.99 CAN | Format: TP

BLACKEST NIGHT: GREEN LANTERN

The must-read companion graphic novel to the epic BLACKEST NIGHT.

Writer: Geoff Johns | Artist: Doug Mahnke
ISBN: 978-1-4012-2952-8 | Diamond Code: APR110193 | Price: $19.99/$23.99 CAN | Format: TP

GREEN LANTERN VOL. 1: SINESTRO

Hal Jordan has been stripped of his ring. Left is an unexpected new Green Lantern in town: Sinestro!

Writer: Geoff Johns | Artist: Doug Mahnke
ISBN: 978-1-4012-3455-3 | Diamond Code: OCT120257 | Price: $14.99/$17.99 CAN | Format: TP

GREEN LANTERN VOL. 2: THE REVENGE OF BLACK HAND

Now teaming up with his former foe, Hal Jordan and Sinestro find themselves investigating a crime that leads them deep into the homeworld of the Indigo Tribe.

Writer: Geoff Johns | Artist: Doug Mahnke
ISBN: 978-1-4012-3767-7 | Diamond Code: JUL130229 | Price: $14.99 /$17.99 CAN | Format: TP

GREEN LANTERN VOL. 3: THE END

Geoff Johns ends his monumental run on Green Lantern.

Writer: Geoff Johns | Artist: Doug Mahnke
ISBN: 978-1-4012-4684-6 | Diamond Code: JAN140338 | Price: $19.99/$23.99 CAN | Format: TP

GREEN LANTERN VOL. 4: DARK DAYS

New writer Robert Venditti creates an all-new direction with the new leader of the Green Lantern Corps: Hal Jordan!

Writer: Robert Venditti | Artist: Billy Tan
ISBN: 978-1-4012-4942-7 | Diamond Code: JUL140243 | Price: $16.99/$19.99 CAN | Format: TP

GREEN LANTERN VOL. 5: TEST OF WILLS

Hal Jordan has lost everything and war threatens to dismantle the Green Lantern Corps. Will Hal be able to bring together a team and take down this new deadly enemy?

Writer: Robert Venditti | Artist: Billy Tan
ISBN: 978-1-4012-5416-2 | Diamond Code: FEB150255 | Price: $17.99/$20.99 CAN | Format: TP

GREEN LANTERN VOL. 6: THE LIFE EQUATION

Having staked their claim to the emotional spectrum, the New Gods plan to redefine the universe in their image.

Writer: Robert Venditti | Artist: Billy Tan & Francis Portela
ISBN: 978-1-4012-5846-7 | Diamond Code: JAN160317 | Price: $16.99/$19.99 CAN | Format: TP

GREEN LANTERN/NEW GODS: GODHEAD

The epic crossover that reintroduces the New Gods to the DC Universe!

Writers: Robert Venditti & Van Jensen | Artist: Billy Tan
ISBN: 978-1-4012-6127-6 | Price: $24.99/$29.99 CAN | Format: HC

GREEN LANTERN VOL. 7: RENEGADE

Hal Jordan begins a new chapter as he becomes the universe's most wanted outlaw!

Writer: Robert Venditti | Artist: Billy Tan | ISBN: 978-1-4012-6125-2
Diamond Code: DEC150333 | Price: $22.99/$27.99 CAN | Format: HC | Available April 24, 2016

COVER NOT FINAL

GREEN LANTERN 1:1 SCALE POWER BATTERY PROP WITH RING

Suit up alongside Green Lantern and take home two of the most iconic symbols in the DC Universe. This replica battery and accompanying power ring are classic conversation pieces—and a call to action.
Diamond Code: FEB130261 | Price: $200.00

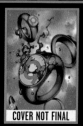

COVER NOT FINAL

GREEN LANTERN: LOST ARMY VOL. 1

Lost in a strange, unfamiliar universe, John Stewart and a small group of Green Lanterns must team up with one of their greatest enemies to get back home.

Writer: Cullen Bunn
Artist: Jesus Saiz
ISBN: 9781401261269
Diamond Code: APR150193
Price: $16.99 /$19.99 CAN
Format: TP
Available April 12, 2016

SINESTRO VOL. 1: THE DEMON WITHIN

The deadliest villain in the Green Lantern mythos gets his own solo series for the first time!

Writer: Cullen Bunn
Artist: Dale Eaglesham
ISBN: 978-1-4012-5050-8
Diamond Code: OCT140359
Price: $14.99/$17.99 CAN
Format: TP

TEEN TITANS

Robin. Superboy. Beast Boy. Kid Flash. Wonder Girl. They're the protégés of the World's Greatest Superheroes, but they are first and foremost an extended family of friends. They help each other cope with the pressure of being the most powerful adolescents on the planet as they face off against super-villains, super-calamities—and sometimes even super-hormones.

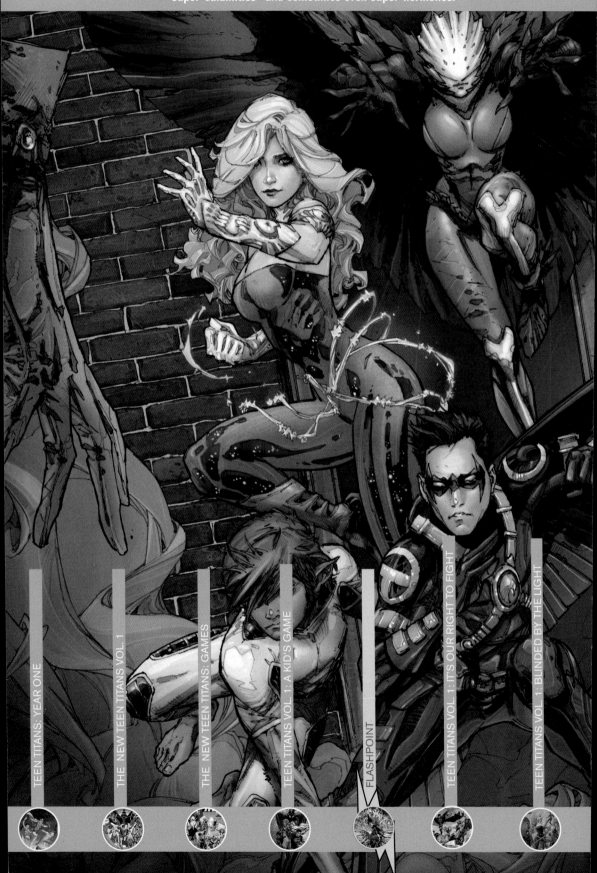

THE NEW TEEN TITANS VOL. 1

Crafted by comics legends Marv Wolfman and George Pérez, this all-new super-team featured greater dangers, fiercer emotions and more tangled relationships than ever before.

Writer: Marv Wolfman | Artist: George Pérez
ISBN: 978-1-4012-5143-7 | Diamond Code: JUN140283 | Price: $19.99/$23.99 CAN | Format: TP

ALSO AVAILABLE:
NEW TEEN TITANS VOL. 2-4

TEEN TITANS VOL. 1: A KID'S GAME

Witness the gathering of a new team of Teen Titans from superstar writer Geoff Johns and their initial battle against an old, familiar foe: Deathstroke!

Writer: Geoff Johns | Artist: Mike McKone
ISBN: 978-1-4012-0308-5 | Diamond Code: SEP148048 | Price: $16.99 /$19.99 CAN | Format: TP

TEEN TITANS VOL. 1: IT'S OUR RIGHT TO FIGHT

Scott Lobdell and Brett Booth launch an all-new Teen Titans into new and action-packed adventures!

Writer: Scott Lobdell | Artist: Brett Booth
ISBN: 978-1-4012-3698-4 | Diamond Code: JUN120239 | Price: $14.99 /$17.99 CAN | Format: TP

ALSO AVAILABLE:
TEEN TITANS VOL. 2-5

TEEN TITANS VOL. 1: BLINDED BY THE LIGHT

Red Robin, Wonder Girl, Raven, Bunker and Beast Boy offer bold, exciting and sometimes dangerous ideas on how to protect a world full of superpowered teenagers.

Writer: Will Pfeifer | Artist: Kenneth Rocafort
ISBN: 978-1-4012-5237-3| Diamond Code: MAY150249 | Price: $16.99 /$19.99 CAN | Format: TP

READ THESE STAND-ALONE TEEN TITANS GRAPHIC NOVELS

TEEN TITANS: EARTH ONE VOL. 1

Critically acclaimed creators Jeff Lemire and Terry Dodson reinvent DC's youngest heroes, with an all-new mythos in an all-new world.

Writer: Jeff Lemire | Artist: Terry Dodson
ISBN: 978-1-4012-5908-2 | Diamond Code: JUL150302 | Price: $14.99/$17.99 CAN | Format: TP

TEEN TITANS: EARTH ONE VOL. 2

Jeff Lemire and Andy MacDonald return to the best-selling series with the adolescent super-team in the 21st century.

Writer: Jeff Lemire | Artist: Andy MacDonald | ISBN: 978-1-4012-5906-8
Price: $22.99/$27.99 CAN | Format: HC | Available August 16, 2016

COVER NOT FINAL

FROM PAGE

Can't get enough of your favorite characters in movies and TV shows? Get even more of all the heroes and villains you can't stop watching with this guide to the comics and graphic novels that introduce these stars and take them on their most wild adventures. Between prequels and hit video games, continuations of classic and modern TV shows, story-lines familiar from movies and more, there are plenty of ways to be a comics fan.

↳ TO SCREEN ↲

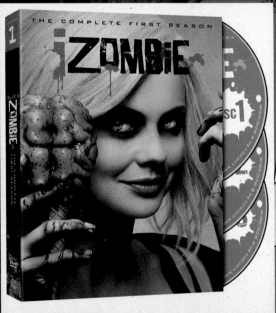

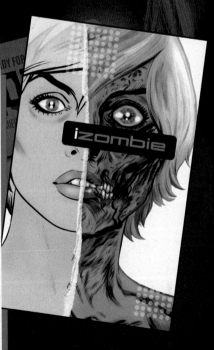

THE CW'S HIT SERIES *ARROW* FEATURES CHARACTERS FROM GRAPHIC NOVELS LIKE *GREEN ARROW: YEAR ONE* AND THE *GREEN ARROW* SERIES. NOW FILL IN ALL THE BREAKS BETWEEN EPISODES WITH *ARROW* VOLUMES 1 AND 2, AND *ARROW SEASON 2.5.*

GREEN ARROW: YEAR ONE

Writer: Andy Diggle
Artist: Jock
ISBN: 978-1-4012-1743-3
Diamond Code: JAN090227
Price: $14.99/$17.99 CAN | Format: TP

GREEN ARROW VOL. 4: THE KILL MACHINE

Writer: Jeff Lemire
Artist: Andrea Sorrentino
ISBN: 9781401246907
Diamond Code: DEC130306
Price: $16.99/$19.99 CAN | Format: TP

ARROW VOL. 1

Writer: Marc Guggenheim
& Andrew Kreisberg | Artist: Mike Grell
ISBN: 978-1-4012-4299-2
Diamond Code: JUN130265
Price: $16.99/$19.99 CAN | Format: TP

ARROW: THE COMPLETE THIRD SEASON [BLU-RAY]

SRP: $60.10
UPC: 883929445172

ARROW VOL. 2

Writer: Various | Artist: Various
ISBN: 978-1-4012-4603-7
Diamond Code: JAN140347
Price: $16.99/$19.99 CAN | Format: TP

ARROW: SEASON 2.5

Writer: Marc Guggenheim
Artist: Joe Bennett
ISBN: 978-1-4012-5748-4
Diamond Code: JUN150296
Price: $19.99 /$23.99 CAN | Format: TP

OLIVER QUEEN AND HIS COHORTS COME TO LIFE WITH THESE EPIC ACTION FIGURES

ARROW ACTION FIGURE
Diamond Code: OCT140411
Price: $25.00

DEATHSTROKE ACTION FIGURE
Diamond Code: OCT140412
Price: $25.00

OLIVER QUEEN/DEATHSTROKE ACTION FIGURE 2-PACK
Diamond Code: NOV130293
Price: $50.00

CATCH UP WITH BARRY ALLEN AND ALL HIS FRIENDS AND FOES IN THESE GROUNDBREAKING STORIES OF *THE* SCARLETT SPEEDSTER, FEATURING HIS QUICKEST AND MOST DARING ADVENTURES. THE FASTEST MAN ALIVE ALSO STARS IN HIS OWN HUGELY POPULAR TV SERIES, THE CW'S *THE FLASH*, SPINNING OFF INTO THE PAGES OF THE TV CONTINUITY SERIES THE FLASH: SEASON ZERO.

THE FLASH: THE DASTARDLY DEATHS OF THE ROGUES

Writer: Geoff Johns
Artist: Francis Manapul
ISBN: 978-1-4012-3195-8
Diamond Code: OCT110249
Price: $14.99 /$17.99 CAN | Format: TP

THE FLASH VOL. 4: REVERSE

Writers: Francis Manapul
& Brian Buccellato
Artist: Francis Manapul
ISBN: 978-1-4012-4949-6
Diamond Code: OCT140357
Price: $16.99/$19.99 | Format: TP

THE FLASH VOL. 1: MOVE FORWARD

Writers: Francis Manapul
& Brian Buccellato
Artist: Francis Manapul
ISBN: 978-1-4012-3554-3
Diamond Code: MAY130224
Price: $16.99/$19.99 CAN | Format: TP

THE FLASH: THE COMPLETE FIRST SEASON [BLU-RAY]

SRP: $60.10
UPC: 883929463022

THE FLASH VOL. 2: ROGUES REVOLUTION

Writers: Francis Manapul & Brian Buccellato
Artist: Francis Manapul
ISBN: 978-1-4012-4273-2
Diamond Code: NOV130229
Price: $16.99/$19.99 CAN | Format: TP

THE FLASH: SEASON ZERO

Writer: Andrew Kreisberg
Artists: Phil Hester & Marcus To
ISBN: 978-14012-5771-2
Diamond Code: JUN150297
Price: $19.99/$23.99 CAN | Format: TP

HURRY UP AND BRING THE FASTEST MAN ALIVE HOME WITH THIS TIMELESS COLLECTIBLE OF THE FLASH HIMSELF!

THE FLASH VOL. 3: GORILLA WARFARE

Writers: Francis Manapul
& Brian Buccellato
Artist: Francis Manapul
ISBN: 978-1-4012-4712-6
Diamond Code: MAY140367
Price: $16.99/$19.99 CAN | Format: TP

THE FLASH ACTION FIGURE

Hurry up and bring the fastest man alive home with this timeless collectible of The Flash himself!
Diamond Code: MAY120340
Price: $25.00

DC's LEGENDS OF TOMORROW

A CAST OF UNEXPECTED AND UNFORGETTABLE SUPERHEROES COME TOGETHER IN THE CW'S DEBUT TV SHOW *DC'S LEGENDS OF TOMORROW*. TAKING PLACE IN THE SAME UNIVERSE AS HIT SHOWS *ARROW* AND *THE FLASH*, RECOGNIZABLE HEROES LIKE FIRESTORM, HAWKGIRL, CAPTAIN COLD AND MORE JOIN THE TIME–TRAVELING RIP HUNTER ON A WHIRLWIND ADVENTURE TO SAVE TIME AND SPACE. SEE THE STARS OF THIS NEW SERIES IN THESE GREAT GRAPHIC NOVELS.

FROM PAGE TO SCREEN ↓

FOREVER EVIL

Writer: Geoff Johns
Artist: David Finch
ISBN: 978-1-4012-5338-7
Diamond Code: FEB150254
Price: $19.99 | Format: TP

BRIGHTEST DAY VOL. 1

Writer: Geoff Johns
Artist: Ivan Reis
ISBN: 978-1-4012-3276-4
Diamond Code: SEP110177
Price: $19.99 | Format: TP

ZERO HOUR: CRISIS IN TIME

Writer: Dan Jurgens
Artist: Dan Jurgens & Jerry Ordway
ISBN: 9781563891847
Diamond Code: JUN068105
Price: $17.99 | Format: TP

THE FURY OF FIRESTORM: THE NUCLEAR MEN VOL. 1: GOD PARTICLE

Writer: Ethan Van Sciver
Artist: Yildiray Cinar
ISBN: 9781401237004
Diamond Code: JUN120237
Price: $14.99 | Format: TP

THE FLASH: THE DASTARDLY DEATHS OF THE ROGUES

Writer: Geoff Johns
Artist: Francis Manapul
ISBN: 9781401231958
Diamond Code: OCT110249
Price: $14.99 | Format: TP

EARTH 2 VOL. 1: THE GATHERING

Writer: James Robinson
Artist: Nicola Scott
ISBN: 9781401242817
Diamond Code: JUL130241
Price: $14.99 | Format: TP

iZOMBIE

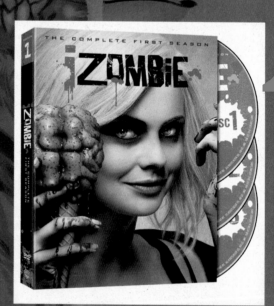

TUE ON **CW** THE

FROM PAGE TO SCREEN↓

CRAVING MORE OF THE CW'S *iZOMBIE*? GET EVEN MORE OF YOUR FAVORITE BRAIN—EATING GAL WITH THE ENTIRE *iZOMBIE* SERIES FROM VERTIGO.

iZOMBIE VOL. 1: DEAD TO THE WORLD

Writer: Chris Roberson
Artist: Michael Allred
ISBN: 978-1-4012-2965-8
Diamond Code: DEC100299
Price: $14.99 | Format: TP

iZOMBIE VOL. 2: uVAMPIRE

Writer: Chris Roberson
Artist: Michael Allred
ISBN: 978-1-4012-3296-2
Diamond Code: JUN110353
Price: $14.99 | Format: TP

iZOMBIE VOL. 3: SIX FEET UNDER AND RISING

Writer: Chris Roberson
Artist: Michael Allred
ISBN: 978-1-4012-3370-9
Diamond Code: NOV110232
Price: $14.99 | Format: TP

iZOMBIE VOL. 4: REPOSSESSED

Writer: Chris Roberson
Artist: Michael Allred
ISBN: 978-1-4012-3697-7
Diamond Code: SEP120261
Price: $19.99 | Format: TP

iZOMBIE: THE COMPLETE FIRST SEASON

SRP: $39.98 | UPC: 883929486526

GOTHAM

MON ON FOX

FROM PAGE TO SCREEN ↓

GO BACK TO THE BEGINNING WITH RISING DETECTIVE JIM GORDON AND THE SEEDY UNDERBELLY OF GOTHAM IN THESE PIVOTAL ORIGIN STORIES FEATURING THE HEROES AND VILLAINS OF FOX'S HIT SHOW *GOTHAM*.

BATMAN: YEAR ONE

Writer: Frank Miller
Artist: David Mazzucchelli
ISBN: 978-1-4012-0752-6
Diamond Code: OCT060163
Price: $14.99 | Format: TP

BATMAN: EARTH ONE

Writer: Geoff Johns
Artist: Gary Frank
ISBN: 978-1-4012-3209-2
Diamond Code: JUL158202
Price: $14.99 | Format: TP

BATMAN: EARTH ONE VOL. 2

Writer: Geoff Johns
Artist: Gary Frank
ISBN: 978-1-4012-6251-8
Price: $14.99
Format: TP

GOTHAM: THE COMPLETE FIRST SEASON

SRP: $60.10
UPC: 883929458943

GOTHAM CITY POLICE BADGE

Diamond Code: FEB150304
Price: $30.00

GET IN ON ALL THE ACTION WITH YOUR VERY OWN
GOTHAM CITY POLICE DEPARTMENT BADGE!

LUCIFER

FROM PAGE TO SCREEN ↓

WHAT HAPPENS WHEN SATAN GETS BORED OF HELL? IN FOX'S NEWEST SERIES *LUCIFER*, THE DEVIL HIMSELF TAKES UP RESIDENCE IN LA, THE CITY OF ANGELS, CHARMING WOMEN AND GETTING EVERYONE TO SPILL THEIR DARKEST TRUTHS. GET THE WHOLE STORY OF THE RETIRED RULER OF HELL IN VERTIGO'S *LUCIFER* SERIES. FROM THE PAGES OF THE SANDMAN, GET THE WHOLE STORY OF THE RETIRED RULER OF HELL IN VERTIGO'S ORIGINAL LUCIFER COMIC SERIES

MON ON **FOX**

LUCIFER BOOK ONE

Writer: Mike Carey
Artist: Peter Gross & Scott Hampton
ISBN: 978-1-4012-4026-4
Diamond Code: FEB130247
Price: $29.99 | Format: TP

LUCIFER BOOK TWO

Writer: Mike Carey
Artist: Peter Gross
ISBN: 978-1-4012-4260-2
Diamond Code: JUL130266
Price: $29.99 | Format: TP

LUCIFER BOOK FOUR

Writer: Mike Carey
Artist: Peter Gross
ISBN: 978-1-4012-4605-1
Diamond Code: MAY140408
Price: $29.99 | Format: TP

LUCIFER BOOK THREE

Writer: Mike Carey
Artist: Peter Gross
ISBN: 978-1-4012-4604-4
Diamond Code: DEC130345
Price: $29.99 | Format: TP

LUCIFER BOOK FIVE

Writer: Mike Carey
Artist: Peter Gross & Ryan Kelly
ISBN: 978-1-4012-4945-8
Diamond Code: SEP140346
Price: $29.99 | Format: TP

SUPERGIRL

FROM PAGE TO SCREEN ↓

MON ON ●CBS

THE MAN OF STEEL'S COUSIN MAKES HER TELEVISION DEBUT IN CBS'S SMASH-HIT SHOW *SUPERGIRL.* FOLLOW KARA ZOR-EL'S JOURNEY FROM KRYPTON TO EARTH AND BEYOND IN *THESE STELLAR SUPERGIRL* TITLES!

SUPERGIRL VOL. 1: LAST DAUGHTER OF KRYPTON

Writers: Michael Green & Mike Johnson

Artist: Mahmud Asrar

ISBN: 978-1-4012-3680-9

Diamond Code: JUL120216

Price: $14.99 | Format: TP

SUPERGIRL VOL. 2: GIRL IN THE WORLD

Writers: Michael Green & Mike Johnson

Artist: Mahmud Asrar

ISBN: 978-1-4012-4087-5

Diamond Code: APR130223

Price: $14.99 | Format: TP

SUPERGIRL VOL. 3: SANCTUARY

Writer: Mike Johnson

Artist: Mahmud Asrar

ISBN: 978-1-4012-4318-0

Diamond Code: NOV130235

Price: $16.99 | Format: TP

PREACHER

ANYTHING CAN HAPPEN IN THIS SMALL TEXAS TOWN AS THE LOCAL PREACHER IS POSSESSED BY POTENTIALLY THE MOST POWERFUL BEING EVER CREATED, AND HE THUS EMBARKS ON A JOURNEY TO LITERALLY FIND GOD IN THIS DARK AND THRILLING SERIES. THE POSSESSED PREACHER IS ALSO STARRING IN AMC'S NEWEST TV SERIES, *PREACHER*.

PREACHER
BOOK ONE

Writer: Garth Ennis
Artist: Steve Dillon
ISBN: 978-1-4012-4045-5
Diamond Code: MAR130303
Price: $19.99 | Format: TP

PREACHER
BOOK FOUR

Writer: Garth Ennis
Artist: Steve Dillon
ISBN: 978-1-4012-3094-4
Diamond Code: MAR140292
Price: $19.99 | Format: TP

PREACHER
BOOK TWO

Writer: Garth Ennis
Artist: Steve Dillon
ISBN: 978-1-4012-4255-8
Diamond Code: JUN130299
Price: $19.99 | Format: TP

PREACHER
BOOK FIVE

Writer: Garth Ennis
Artist: Steve Dillon
ISBN: 978-1-4012-5074-4
Diamond Code: MAY140409
Price: $19.99 | Format: TP

PREACHER
BOOK THREE

Writer: Garth Ennis
Artist: Steve Dillon
ISBN: 978-1-4012-4501-6
Diamond Code: OCT130293
Price: $19.99 | Format: TP

PREACHER
BOOK SIX

Writer: Garth Ennis
Artist: Steve Dillon
ISBN: 978-1-4012-5279-3
Diamond Code: JUL140282
Price: $19.99 | Format: TP

JUSTICE LEAGUE VOL. 1: ORIGIN

The Justice League begins again in the action-packed, animated adaptation of Geoff Johns and Jim Lee's best-selling graphic novel JUSTICE LEAGUE VOL. 1: ORIGIN.

Writer: Geoff Johns
Artist: Jim Lee
ISBN: 978-1-4012-3788-2
Diamond Code: OCT120252
Price: $16.99 | Format: TP

JUSTICE LEAGUE: WAR
BLU-RAY
UPC 883929318438; SRP | $24.98

JUSTICE LEAGUE VOL. 3: THRONE OF ATLANTIS

A revitalized Aquaman takes center stage as the Justice League faces off against otherworldly weapons and perilous odds in this adaptation of Geoff Johns's wildly popular JUSTICE LEAGUE series.

Writer: Geoff Johns
Artists: Ivan Reis & Tony S. Daniel
ISBN: 978-1-4012-4698-3
Diamond Code: JAN140339
Price: $16.99 | Format: TP

JUSTICE LEAGUE: THRONE OF ATLANTIS
BLU-RAY
UPC 883929366095; SRP | $24.98

BATMAN VOL. 1: THE COURT OF OWLS

Batman and Robin become one another's most dangerous adversaries in this dark and gripping animated film, adapting elements of Scott Snyder's groundbreaking BATMAN VOL. 1: THE COURT OF OWLS.

Writer: Scott Snyder
Artist: Greg Capullo
ISBN: 9781401235420
Diamond Code: DEC120323
Price: $16.99 | Format: TP

BATMAN VS. ROBIN
BLU-RAY
UPC 883929394074; SRP | $24.98

JUSTICE LEAGUE: GODS AND MONSTERS

Saviors or tyrants? In an alternate reality, the Justice League relies on brute force and intimidation to protect the planet with the comic book prequel to JUSTICE LEAGUE: GODS AND MONSTERS.

JUSTICE LEAGUE: GODS AND MONSTERS
BLU-RAY
UPC 883929406265; SRP | $24.98

BATMAN: THE DARK KNIGHT SAGA DELUXE EDITION

Writer: Frank Miller
Artists: Frank Miller and Klaus Janson
ISBN: 978-1-4012-5691-3
Diamond Code: MAY150234
Price: $49.99 /$58.00 CAN
Format: HC

BATMAN VS. SUPERMAN: THE GREATEST BATTLES

Writer: Various | Artist: Various
ISBN: 978-1-4012-5698-2
Diamond Code: SEP150285
Price: $9.99 /$11.99 CAN
Format: TP

BATMAN: THE DARK KNIGHT RETURNS ACTION FIGURE BOX SET

Diamond Code: OCT120313
Price: $60.00

JUSTICE LEAGUE VOL. 1: ORIGIN

Writer: Geoff Johns | Artist: Jim Lee
ISBN: 978-1-4012-3788-2
Diamond Code: OCT120252
Price: $16.99 /$19.99 CAN
Format: TP

SUPERMAN/WONDER WOMAN VOL. 1: POWER COUPLE

Writer: Charles Soule
Artists: Tony S. Daniel & Paulo Siqueira
ISBN: 978-1-4012-5346-2
Diamond Code: DEC140383
Price: $16.99 /$19.99 CAN | Format: TP

ALSO AVAILABLE: SUPERMAN/WONDER WOMAN VOL. 2-3

JLA VOL. 1

Writer: Grant Morrison
Artists: Howard Porter & Oscar Jimenez
ISBN: 978-1-4012-3314-3
Diamond Code: JUN110276
Price: $19.99/$23.99 CAN
Format: TP

PRE
FOR 2
MOS
BA

BATMAN

DAWN

IN THEATERS

LUTHOR

Writer: Brian Azzarello
Artist: Lee Bermejo
ISBN: 978-1-4012-2930-6
Diamond Code: AUG150269
Price: $14.99/$23.99 CAN
Format: TP

SUPERMAN/BATMAN VOL. 1

Writer: Jeph Loeb | Artists: Ed McGuinness & Michael Turner
ISBN: 978-1-4012-4818-5
Diamond Code: JAN140354
Price: $19.99 /$23.99 CAN
Format: TP

BATMAN: HUSH

Writer: Jeph Loeb
Artist: Jim Lee
ISBN: 978-1-4012-2317-5
Diamond Code: MAY090178
Price: $24.99 /$28.99 CAN
Format: TP

WONDER WOMAN VOLUME 1: BLOOD

Writer: Brian Azzarello
Artists: Cliff Chiang & Tony Akins
ISBN: 978-1-4012-3562-8
Diamond Code: OCT120256
Price: $14.99 /$17.99 CAN
Format: TP

BATMAN/SUPERMAN VOL. 1: CROSS WORLD

Writer: Greg Pak
Artists: Jae Lee & Ben Oliver
ISBN: 978-1-4012-4934-2
Diamond Code: AUG140333
Price: $14.99 /$17.99 CAN | Format: TP

ALSO AVAILABLE: BATMAN/SUPERMAN VOL. 2-4

INJUSTICE: GODS AMONG US VOL. 1

Writer: Tom Taylor
Artists: Jheremy Raapack & Mike S. Miller
ISBN: 978-1-4012-4843-7
Diamond Code: MAR140265
Price: $14.99 /$17.99 CAN
Format: TP

ARE
16'S
EPIC
LE!

SUPERMAN
JUSTICE
CH 25, 2016

cipated blockbuster event of the year. Throughout the decades, the Dark Knight and
e prepared to witness unforgettable transformations of these legendary powerhouses
stories featuring the stars of 2016's *Batman V Superman: Dawn of Justice.*

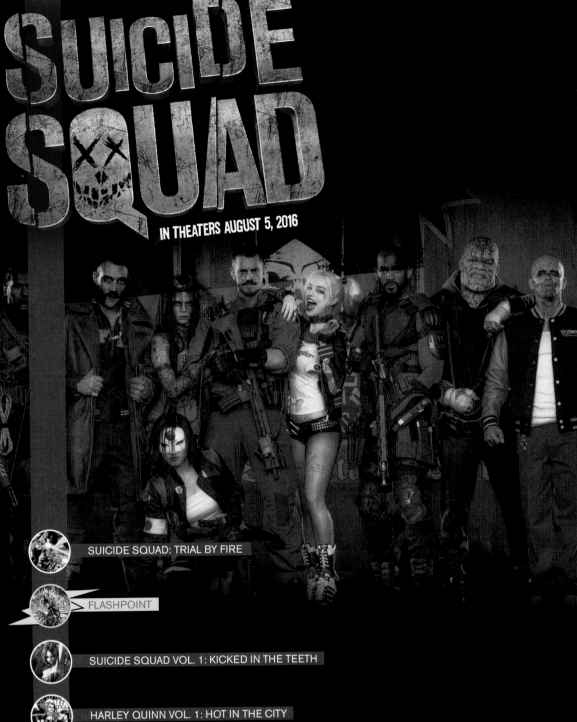

SUICIDE SQUAD

IN THEATERS AUGUST 5, 2016

Harley Quinn, Deadshot, Rick Flagg and Captain Boomerang headline the ultimate cult-favorite crew of criminal outcasts—and they're locked, loaded and ready for their explosive blockbuster debut Summer 2016's *Suicide Squad* film. Lethal, driven and completely unhinged, the Suicide Squad is a group of death row inmates assembled by iron-fisted agent Amanda Waller to carry out high-risk covert missions for the U.S. Government in exchange for their freedom. Conceptualized in 1959 and revived in modern form by John Ostrander in 1987, this unorthodox band of bad guys are at the helm of a hot new wave of antiheroes.

SUICIDE SQUAD VOL. 1: TRIAL BY FIRE

Just in time for the blockbuster film release, this collection is the definitive and explosive introduction to the Suicide Squad.

Writer: John Ostrander | Artist: Luke McDonnell
ISBN: 978-1-4012-5831-3 | Diamond Code: JUN150292 | Price: $19.99/$23.99 CAN | Format: TP

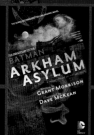

BATMAN: ARKHAM ASYLUM 25th ANNIVERSARY EDITION

Grant Morrison and Dave McKean's psychological horror story from Arkham Asylum, home to Gotham City's most deranged super-criminals.

Writer: Grant Morrison | Artist: Dave McKean
ISBN: 978-1-4012-5124-6 | Diamond Code: JUN140278 | Price: $19.99/$23.99 CAN | Format: TP

ALSO AVAILABLE:
SUICIDE SQUAD VOL. 2-5

BATMAN: THE KILLING JOKE

The Joker, Batman's greatest adversary, in his definitive origin story by Alan Moore with breathtaking art by Brian Bolland. FOR MATURE READERS

Writer: Alan Moore | Artist: Brian Bolland
ISBN: 978-1-4012-1667-2 | Diamond Code: NOV070226 | Price: $17.99/$20.99 CAN | Format: HC

BATMAN: HARLEY QUINN

Get reacquainted with the villain we all love to hate, Harley Quinn, just in time for her film debut!

Writer: Paul Dini | Artist: Neil Googe
ISBN: 978-1-4012-5517-6 | Diamond Code: APR150289 | Price: $19.99/$23.99 CAN | Format: TP

JOKER

Eisner Award-winner Brian Azzarello and Lee Bermejo's original graphic novel masterpiece with a never-before-told perspective on the most vile, dangerous and unpredictable inmate of Arkham—the Joker!

Writer: Brian Azzarello | Artist: Lee Bermejo
ISBN: 9781401215811 | Diamond Code: JUL080124 | Price: $19.99/$23.99 CAN | Format: HC

DEADSHOT: BULLETPROOF

The world's deadliest marksman is front and center in his own graphic novel!

Writer: Christos N. Gage | Artist: Steve Cummings
ISBN: 978-1-4012-5519-0 | Diamond Code: JAN150376 | Price: $14.99/$17.99 CAN | Format: TP

SUICIDE SQUAD VOL. 1: KICKED IN THE TEETH

A band of former super-villains are recruited by a shadowy government agency for missions so dangerous, it's suicide.

Writer: Adam Glass | Artists: Federico Dallocchio & Clayton Henry
ISBN: 978-1-4012-3544-4 | Diamond Code: APR120250 | Price: $14.99/$17.99 CAN | Format: TP

ALSO AVAILABLE:
SUICIDE SQUAD VOL. 2-5

NEW SUICIDE SQUAD VOL. 1: PURE INSANITY

The Joker's Daughter. Deadshot. Black Manta. Harley Quinn. Deathstroke. The world's most dangerous incarcerated super-villains are sent to carry out impossible missions on foreign soil in exchange for a commuted prison sentence.

Writer: Sean Ryan | Artist: Jeremy Roberts, Tom Derenick & Rob Hunter
ISBN: 978-1-4012-5238-0 | Diamond Code: APR150302 | Price: $16.99/$19.99 CAN | Format: TP

HARLEY QUINN VOL. 1: HOT IN THE CITY

The Cupid of Crime returns in her smash-hit solo series! Jimmy Palmiotti and Amanda Conner unleash Harley on an unsuspecting DC Universe, leaving no one unscathed in her wake.

Writers: Jimmy Palmiotti & Amanda Conner | Artist: Chad Hardin
ISBN: 978-1-4012-5415-5 | Diamond Code: JAN150369 Price: $16.99 /$19.99 CAN | Format: TP

BATMAN VOL. 7: ENDGAME

The Joker is out to finally destroy Batman for good as Scott Snyder and Greg Capullo tell their definitive Joker story with an ending you have to see to believe!

Writer: Scott Snyder | Artist: Greg Capullo
ISBN: 978-1-4012-6116-0 | Diamond Code: DEC150331 | Price: $19.99/$23.99 CAN | Format: TP

100 BULLETS BOOK ONE

Guaranteed full immunity, what would you do? Vertigo's seminal crime series features ordinary citizens who are given the opportunity to exact revenge on a person who has wronged them.

Writer: Brian Azzarello | Artist: Eduardo Risso | ISBN: 978-1-4012-5056-0
Diamond Code: JUL140274 | Price: $24.99 /$28.99 CAN | Format: TP

ALSO AVAILABLE: 100 BULLETS BOOKS TWO-FIVE

AMERICAN VAMPIRE VOL. 1

Scott Snyder and legendary novelist Stephen King's stirring take on the vampire mythology.

Writers: Stephen King & Scott Snyder | Artist: Rafael Albuquerque
ISBN: 978-1-4012-2974-0 | Diamond Code: JUL110284 | Price: $19.99 /$23.99 CAN | Format: TP

ALSO AVAILABLE: AMERICAN VAMPIRE VOL.

ANIMAL MAN VOL. 1

The bizarre adventures of Animal Man, a second-rate superhero struggling with real-life issues and moral dilemmas.

Writer: Grant Morrison | Artists: Chas Truog, Doug Hazlewood & Tom Grummett
ISBN: 978-1-5638-9005-5 | Diamond Code: OCT068037 | Price: $19.99 /$23.99 CAN | Format: TP

ALSO AVAILABLE: ANIMAL MAN VOL. 2-7

DMZ VOL. 1: ON THE GROUND

In the near future after a second American Civil War, Manhattan becomes a wasteland known as the DMZ. Matty Roth, a naive aspiring photojournalist, must cover the war zone from the inside...if he can survive.

Writer: Brian Wood | Artist: Riccardo Burchielli
ISBN: 978-1-4012-1062-5 | Diamond Code: OCT118125 | Price: $12.99 /$15.99 CAN | Format: TP

ALSO AVAILABLE: DMZ VOL. 2-12

EX MACHINA BOOK ONE

Tired of risking his life day-in and day-out, superhero Mitchell Hundred becomes the mayor of New York City in this thrilling graphic novel from the creator of Y: THE LAST MAN.

Writer: Brian K. Vaughan | Artist: Tony Harris
ISBN: 978-1-4012-4498-9 | Diamond Code: OCT130291 | Price: $19.99 /$23.99 CAN | Format: TP

ALSO AVAILABLE: EX MACHINA BOOKS 2-5

THE INVISIBLES VOL. 1: SAY YOU WANT A REVOLUTION

Throughout history, a secret society called the Invisibles has worked against dark forces conspiring to end mankind.

Writer: Grant Morrison | Artists: Steve Yeowell & Jill Thompson | ISBN: 978-1-5638-9267-7
Diamond Code: SEP068118 | Price: $19.99 /$23.99 CAN | Format: TP

ALSO AVAILABLE:
THE INVISIBLES VOL. 2-7

iZOMBIE VOL. 1: DEAD TO THE WORLD

Get even more of the undead star of The CW's *iZombie* with Vertigo's critically-acclaimed introduction to this charming brain-eater.

Writer: Chris Roberson | Artist: Michael Allred
ISBN: 978-1-4012-2965-8 | Diamond Code: DEC100299 | Price: $14.99 /$17.99 CAN | Format: TP

ALSO AVAILABLE:
iZOMBIE VOL. 2-4

JOHN CONSTANTINE, HELLBLAZER VOL. 1: ORIGINAL SINS

In the longest running Vertigo series ever, Earth's resident exorcist, demonologist and Master of the Dark Arts, John Constantine, is on the side of the angels, but is willing to make a deal with a demon to prevail.

Writer: Jamie Delano | Artist: John Ridgway, Alfredo Alcala, Rick Veitch & Tom Mandrake
ISBN: 978-1-4012-3006-7 | Diamond Code: DEC100302 | Price: $19.99/$23.99 CAN | Format: TP

ALSO AVAILABLE:
JOHN CONSTANTINE,
HELLBLAZER VOL. 2-13

THE LEAGUE OF EXTRAORDINARY GENTLEMEN VOL. 1

The best-known characters of 19th century literature band together in Alan Moore's award-winning graphic novel.

Writer: Alan Moore | Artist: Kevin O'Neill
ISBN: 978-1-5638-9858-7 | Diamond Code: MAY118167 | Price: $16.99 /$19.99 CAN | Format: TP

LUCIFER BOOK ONE

The ultimate bad boy is starring in The CW's *Lucifer*, and you can get even more of his dark and twisted antics in this Vertigo series.

Writer: Mike Carey | Artists: Peter Gross & Scott Hampton | ISBN: 978-1-4012-4026-4
Diamond Code: FEB130247 | Price: $29.99 / $35.00 CAN | Format: TP

ALSO AVAILABLE:
LUCIFER BOOKS TWO-FIVE

PREACHER BOOK ONE

Jesse Custer, a wayward preacher, begins a violent journey to find God (literally), joined by his girlfriend Tulip and the hard-drinking Irish vampire Cassidy.

Writer: Garth Ennis | Artist: Steve Dillon | ISBN: 978-1-4012-4045-5
Diamond Code: MAR130303 | Price: $19.99/$35.00 CAN | Format: TP

ALSO AVAILABLE:
PREACHER BOOKS TWO-SIX

SAGA OF THE SWAMP THING BOOK ONE

Alan Moore's take on the classic monster stretched the creative boundaries of the medium and became one of the most spectacular series in comic book history.

Writer: Alan Moore | Artist: Stephen Bissette
ISBN: 978-1-4012-2083-9 | Diamond Code: JAN120343 | Price: $19.99 /$23.99 CAN | Format: TP

ALSO AVAILABLE: SAGA OF THE SWAMP THING BOOKS TWO-SIX

SCALPED VOL. 1: INDIAN COUNTRY

Dashiell Bad Horse must return to the reservation he grew up in, determined to clean up the crime-ridden "rez" he left years ago, one way or another.

Writer: Jason Aaron | Artist: R.M. Guera
ISBN: 978-1-4012-1317-6 | Diamond Code: APR108251 | Price: $14.99 /$17.99 CAN | Format: TP

ALSO AVAILABLE:
SCALPED VOL. 2-10

SWEET TOOTH VOL. 1: OUT OF THE DEEP WOODS

Gus—a boy born with deer-like antlers—is left to survive in an American landscape devastated a decade earlier by an inexplicable pandemic.

Writer: Jeff Lemire | Artist: Jeff Lemire
ISBN: 978-1-4012-2696-1 | Diamond Code: AUG108007 | Price: $12.99 /$15.99 CAN | Format: TP

ALSO AVAILABLE:
SWEET TOOTH VOL. 2-6

TRANSMETROPOLITAN VOL. 1: BACK ON THE STREET

Mastermind writer Warren Ellis delivers this sharp, manic, anything-goes exploration of urban life about journalist/cult author Spider Jerusalem.

Writer: Warren Ellis | Artist: Darick Robertson
ISBN: 978-1-4012-2084-6 | Diamond Code: DEC080220 | Price: $14.99 /$17.99 CAN | Format: TP

ALSO AVAILABLE:
TRANSMETROPOLITAN VOL. 2-10

THE UNWRITTEN VOL. 1: TOMMY TAYLOR AND THE BOGUS IDENTITY

Tom Taylor, the inspiration for the boy wizard from the series of novels his father made famous, finds that the worlds of fiction and real life are crossing over into each other in this fantastic graphic novel.

Writer: Mike Carey | Artist: Peter Gross
ISBN: 978-1-4012-2565-0 | Diamond Code: APR128238 | Price: $12.99 /$17.99 CAN | Format: TP

ALSO AVAILABLE:
THE UNWRITTEN VOL. 2-11

Y: THE LAST MAN BOOK ONE

What would you do if you were the last man on Earth? Brian K. Vaughan's epic series made him a comics legend.

Writer: Brian K. Vaughan | Artist: Pia Guerra
ISBN: 978-1-4012-5151-2 | Diamond Code: JUN140312 | Price: $19.99 /$23.99 CAN | Format: TP

ALSO AVAILABLE:
Y: THE LAST MAN BOOKS TWO - FIVE

VERTIGO ESSENTIAL GRAPHIC NOVELS

COVER NOT FINAL

DARK NIGHT: A TRUE BATMAN STORY

In this autobiographical true story, *Batman: The Animated Series* creator Paul Dini recounts a harrowing near-death beating and the subsequent road to recovery through the eyes of the Dark Knight.

Writer: Paul Dini | Artist: Eduardo Risso | ISBN: 978-1-4012-4143-8
Price: $22.99 /$27.99 CAN | Format: HC | Available June 21, 2016

FOR MATURE READERS

DAYTRIPPER

This award-winning graphic novel follows Brás de Oliva Domingos during different periods in his life, each with the same ending: his death.

Writers: Gabriel Bá & Fabío Moon | Artists: Gabriel Bá & Fabío Moon
ISBN: 978-1-4012-2969-6 | Diamond Code: NOV100268 | Price: $19.99/$23.99 CAN | Format: TP

GET JIRO!

The star of TV's *No Reservations,* Anthony Bourdain slashes his way into comics with this outrageous action-adventure tale of katanas and sushi.

Writers: Anthony Bourdain & Joel Rose | Artist: Langdon Foss
ISBN: 978-1-4012-2828-6 | Diamond Code: FEB130242 | Price: $14.99/$17.99 CAN | Format: TP

MAD MAX: FURY ROAD

The same minds behind the blockbuster film present this series of prequel tales set within the world of *Mad Max.*

Writers: George Miller, Nico Lathouris & Mark Sexton | Artists: Leandro Fernandez, Riccardo Burchielli, Andrea Mutti, et al. ISBN: 978-1-4012-5905-1 | Diamond Code: MAY150271 | Price: $14.99 /$17.99 CAN | Format: TP

PRIDE OF BAGHDAD DELUXE EDITION

Inspired by true events, acclaimed writer Brian K. Vaughan brings readers a startlingly original look at life on the streets of Baghdad during the Iraq War.

Writer: Brian K. Vaughan | Artist: Niko Henrichon
ISBN: 978-1-4012-4894-9 | Diamond Code: AUG140360 | Price: $24.99 /$28.99 CAN | Format: HC

PUNK ROCK JESUS

A reality TV show starring a clone of Jesus Christ causes chaos across the U.S. of the near future in PUNK ROCK JESUS, a graphic novel written and drawn by Sean Murphy.

Writer: Sean Murphy | Artist: Sean Murphy
ISBN: 978-1-4012-3768-4 | Diamond Code: JAN130330 | Price: $16.99 /$19.99 CAN | Format: TP

TRILLIUM

Two disparate souls are separated by thousands of years and hundreds of millions of miles. Yet they will fall in love and, as a result, bring about the end of the universe.

Writer: Jeff Lemire | Artist: Jeff Lemire
ISBN: 978-1-4012-4900-7 | Diamond Code: MAY140407 | Price: $16.99 /$19.99 CAN | Format: TP

COVER NOT FINAL

THE TWILIGHT CHILDREN

Critically acclaimed creators Gilbert Hernandez and Darwyn Cooke team up to launch this surreal new miniseries, where a sleepy seaside village may be facing an alien invasion.

Writer: Gilbert Hernandez | Artist: Darwyn Cooke
ISBN: 978-1-4012-6245-7 | Price: $22.99 /$27.99 CAN | Format: HC | Available May 17, 2016

V FOR VENDETTA

Alan Moore's iconic tale set in a near-future dystopian London and its revolutionary hero "V."

Writer: Alan Moore | Artist: David Lloyd
ISBN: 978-1-4012-0841-7 | Diamond Code: SEP088030 | Price: $19.99 /$23.99 CAN | Format: TP

THE WAKE

The winner of the 2014 Eisner Award for Best Limited Series, this horrific new thriller confirms what we all suspected: that our greatest fears have come from the ocean's depths.

Writer: Scott Snyder | Artist: Sean Murphy
ISBN: 978-1-4012-5491-9 | Diamond Code: MAR150313 | Price: $17.99 /$20.99 CAN | Format: TP

WE3

Grant Morrison and Frank Quitely deliver the emotional journey of three house pets who are weaponized for lethal combat by the government.

Writer: Grant Morrison | Artist: Frank Quitely
ISBN: 978-1-4012-4302-9 | Diamond Code: NOV130270 | Price: $14.99 /$17.99 CAN | Format: TP

One of the most popular and critically acclaimed graphic novel series of all time, Neil Gaiman's award-winning masterpiece THE SANDMAN has set the standard for mature, lyrical fantasy in the comic book field. Illustrated by a rotating cast of the medium's most sought-after artists, the series is a rich blend of modern and ancient mythology into which contemporary fiction, historical drama and legend are seamlessly interwoven.

NEIL GAIMAN

THE SANDMAN: OVERTURE DELUXE EDITION

Twenty-five years since THE SANDMAN changed the landscape of modern comics, Neil Gaiman returns to the world of The Dreaming with this prequel story, brilliantly illustrated by J.H. Williams III.

Writer: Neil Gaiman | Artist: J.H. Williams III | ISBN: 978-1-4012-4896-3
Diamond Code: JUL150333 | Price: $24.99 /$29.99 CAN | Format: HC

THE SANDMAN VOL. 1: PRELUDES & NOCTURNES

The first chapter of Neil Gaiman's landmark graphic novel series sees the main character, Morpheus, reclaiming his throne as the King of Dreams.

Writer: Neil Gaiman | Artists: Mike Dringenberg, Sam Kieth & Malcolm Jones III
ISBN: 978-1-4012-2575-9 | Diamond Code: JUL100259 | Price: $19.99 /$23.99 CAN | Format: TP

ALSO AVAILABLE:
THE SANDMAN VOL. 2-10

THE SANDMAN: ENDLESS NIGHTS

Seven stories featuring the Sandman and his siblings, the Endless, with art from the industry's finest illustrators.

Writer: Neil Gaiman | Artists: Frank Quitely, Glenn Fabry, Bill Sienkiewicz, P. Craig Russell, et al.
ISBN: 978-1-4012-0113-5 | Diamond Code: DEC068187 | Price: $19.99 /$23.99 CAN | Format: TP

DEATH

The Sandman's sister stars in her own graphic novel with these poignant tales of the beginning, the middle and the end, as it appears to the living embodiment of Death.

Writer: Neil Gaiman | Artist: Chris Bachalo
ISBN 978-1-4012-4716-4 | Diamond Code: DEC130341 | Price: $19.99 /$23.99 CAN | Format: TP

FREE COUNTRY: A TALE OF THE CHILDREN'S CRUSADE

Neil Gaiman, alongside such creators as Toby Litt, Peter Gross, Chris Bachalo, Jamie Delano and others, presents a compelling tale of ancient history, stolen dreams and lost children.

Writers: Neil Gaiman, Toby Litt, Jamie Delano, et al. | Artists: Peter Gross, Chris Bachalo, Peter Snejbjerg, et al.
ISBN 978-1-4012-4241-1 | Diamond Code: MAY150258 | Price: $24.99 /29.99 CAN | Format: HC

Run out of their happily-ever-after homeworlds by a mighty conqueror known only as The Adversary, these universally recognized princes, princesses, talking animals, heroes, and villains now face a new challenge: adapting to a modern-day Manhattan filled with sex, violence, and lots of moral ambiguity.

FABLES VOL. 1: LEGENDS IN EXILE
Writer: Bill Willingham | Artist: Lan Medina
ISBN: 978-1-4012-3755-4
Diamond Code: FEB120285
Price: $12.99 /$15.99 CAN | Format: TP

FAIREST VOL. 1: WIDE AWAKE
Writer: Bill Willingham | Artist: Phil Jimenez
ISBN: 978-1-4012-3550-5
Diamond Code: AUG120283
Price: $14.99 /$17.99 CAN | Format: TP

BILL WILLINGHAM'S
FABLES

MAD

For fifty years, MAD has been a staple in bedrooms, living rooms, dorm rooms and recycling bins. Irreverent as ever, MAD continues to satirize and parody anything and everything about pop culture.

EPIC MAD

Your favorite MAD Magazine parodies and segments available in one low-priced compilation.

By: The Usual Gang Of Idiots
ISBN: 978-1-4012-3762-2 | Diamond Code: DEC118177 | Price: $12.99 /$15.99 CAN | Format: TP

AMAZINGLY STUPID MAD

Ripped from the pages of MAD Magazine, the "finest" moments designed for fans of the Cartoon Network show!

By: The Usual Gang Of Idiots
ISBN: 978-1-4012-3857-5 | Diamond Code: MAY120312 | Price: $12.99 /$15.99 CAN | Format: TP

EXTREMELY MORONIC MAD

More ridiculous hilarity from MAD!

By: The Usual Gang Of Idiots
ISBN: 978-1-4012-3861-2 | Diamond Code: JUL120238 | Price: $12.99 /$15.99 CAN | Format: TP

TOTALLY USELESS MAD

Insane, awesome and insanely awesome "best-of" features from MAD!

By: The Usual Gang Of Idiots | ISBN: 978-1-4012-3911-4
Diamond Code: JAN130326 | Price: $12.99 /$15.99 CAN | Format: TP

DISTURBINGLY AWFUL MAD

Haven't got enough? Here's more of the best of the worst of MAD.

By: The Usual Gang Of Idiots
ISBN: 978-1-4012-4190-2 | Diamond Code: MAY130245 | Price: $12.99 /$15.99 CAN | Format: TP

INTENSELY DUMB MAD

If you needed more MAD, look no further!

By: The Usual Gang Of Idiots
ISBN: 978-1-4012-4191-9 | Diamond Code: JUL130255 | Price: $12.99 /$15.99 CAN | Format: TP

MAD: SPY VS. SPY TOP SECRET FILES

The continuing adventures of the popular MAD Magazine feature by Peter Kuper.

Writer: Peter Kuper | Artist: Peter Kuper
ISBN: 978-1-4012-3527-7 | Diamond Code: AUG118124 | Price: $9.99 /$11.99 CAN | Format: TP

SPY VS. SPY: FIGHT TO THE FINISH

The diabolical duo of double-crosses and deceit (one dressed in black, the other in white) continue to one-up each other until death do they part.

Writer: Peter Kuper
Artist: Peter Kuper
ISBN: 978-1-4012-4814-7
Diamond Code: AUG138237
Price: $9.99 /$11.99 CAN
Format: TP

HIGHLIGHTING THE ART OF SOME OF THE GREAT ARTISTS IN MAD HISTORY!

THE MAD ART OF JACK DAVIS

ISBN: 9781401258993
Diamond Code: JUN150285
Price: $14.99/$17.99 CAN | Format: TP

THE MAD ART OF WALLY WOOD

ISBN: 9781401259013
Diamond Code: JUN150286
Price: $14.99/$17.99 CAN | Format: TP

THE MAD ART OF WILL ELDER

ISBN: 9781401259006
Diamond Code: JUN150287
Price: $14.99/$17.99 CAN | Format: TP

DC COMICS: ALL AGES

ALL-AGES GRAPHIC NOVELS RANGE FROM THE CRIME-FIGHTING TEAM-UPS IN *BATMAN: LI'L GOTHAM* TO THE MYSTERY-SOLVING MAYHEM OF *SCOOBY-DOO TEAM-UP*, AND NOW THE STUDENTS OF SUPER HERO HIGH WILL BE JUMPING IN ON THE ACTION TO KEEP THE THRILLS COMING!

DC SUPER HERO GIRLS

The girls of DC Super Hero High are here to save the world, just after they finish their homework!

Writer: Shea Fontana | ISBN: 978-1-4012-6247-1 | Price: $9.99 /$11.99 CAN | Format: TP | Available July 12, 2016

TINY TITANS: WELCOME TO THE TREEHOUSE

See what life is like for the very young heroes of Sidekick Elementary, and learn what could go wrong when the kids spend an afternoon in the Batcave in this all-ages graphic novel.

Written and illustrated by Art Baltazar & Franco | ISBN: 978-1-4012-2078-5 | Diamond Code: NOV080197 | Price: $12.99 /$15.99 CAN | Format:

TINY TITANS: RETURN TO THE TREEHOUSE

Superboy and Supergirl return to the treehouse to discover it's missing. Or is it just...really small? The Tiny Titans search for who could do such a thing!

Writer: Art Baltazar | Artist: Franco | ISBN: 978-1-4012-5492-6 | Diamond Code: DEC140398 | Price: $12.99 /$15.99 CAN | Format: TP

BATMAN: LI'L GOTHAM VOL. 1

Follow all of your favorite Gotham City characters throughout each holiday in these gorgeously drawn and painted all-ages tales!

Writers: Derek Fridolfs & Dustin Nguyen | Artist: Dustin Nguyen | ISBN: 978-1-4012-4494-1 | Diamond Code: NOV130255 | Price: $12.99 /$15.99 CAN | Format: TP

SCOOBY-DOO TEAM-UP

The Dynamic Duo of Batman and Robin team up with Scooby-Doo and Mystery Inc.!

Writer: Sholly Fisch | Artist: Dario Brizuel | ISBN: 978-1-4012-4946-5 | Diamond Code: NOV140323 | Price: $12.99 /$15.99 CAN | Format: TP

TEEN TITANS GO!: TITANS TOGETHER

Based on the hit TV show! Join Robin, Starfire, Beast Boy, Cyborg and Raven as they display their unique brand of hijinks, mayhem and justice.

Writer: J. Torres | Artist: Mike Norton | ISBN: 978-1-4012-5367-7 | Diamond Code: JUL140263 | Price: $12.99 /$15.99 CAN | Format: TP

TEEN TITANS GO! VOL. 1

Spinning off of the Cartoon Network series, this all-ages comic book series features the Titans taking on giant pizza monsters and more!

Writer: Sholly Fisch | Artist: Lea Hernandez | ISBN: 978-1-4012-5242-7 | Diamond Code: DEC140400 | Price: $12.99 /$15.99 CAN | Format: TP

BIZARRO

Superman's mirror-opposite enemy is back in this hilarious new series.

Writer: Heath Corson | Artist: Gustavo Duarte | ISBN: 978-1-4012-5971-6 | Diamond Code: NOV150274 | Price: $14.99 /$17.99 CAN | Format: TP

DC COLLECTIBLES™

DC Collectibles produces an exclusive line of high-quality products, bringing to life stories and characters from DC Comics, Vertigo and MAD Magazine. Ranging from action figures to cold-cast porcelain statues to finely detailed prop replicas, these products are based on the world-famous DC Comics Super Heroes, the edgy stars of Vertigo, the timeless icons of MAD Magazine and some of the most popular licensed properties from TV, film and video games.

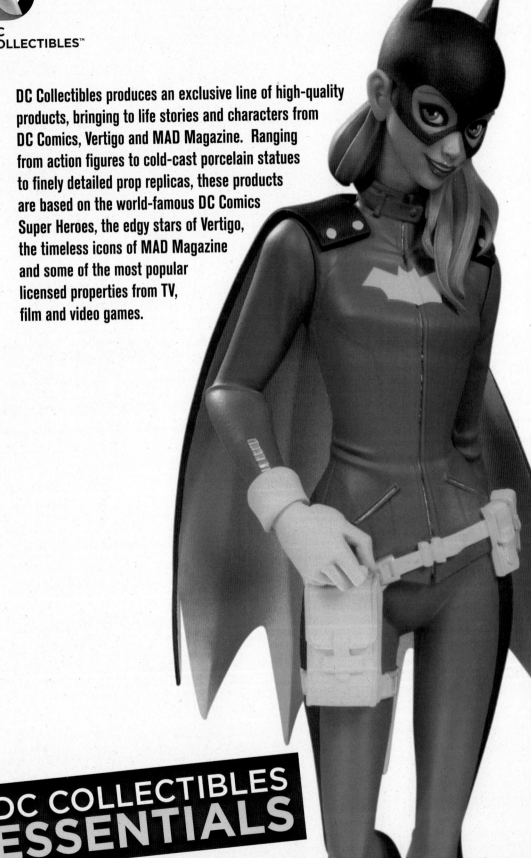

DC COLLECTIBLES ESSENTIALS

BATMAN: ARKHAM SERIES

FROM BATMAN: ARKHAM ASYLUM...

FROM BATMAN: ARKHAM CITY...

FROM BATMAN: ARKHAM ORIGINS...

**JOKER/HARLEY QUINN/BATMAN/
SCARECROW ACTION FIGURE 4-PACK**
Diamond Code: MAR140312
Price: $60.00

**HARLEY QUINN/BATMAN/NIGHTWING/
ROBIN ACTION FIGURE 4-PACK**
Diamond Code: APR140323
Price: $60.00

BATMAN VS. BANE ACTION FIGURE 2-PACK
Diamond Code: JUN130320
Price: $60.00

**BATMAN/DEATHSTROKE/JOKER/BLACK
MASK ACTION FIGURE 4-PACK**
Diamond Code: JUL140295
Price: $60.00

FROM BATMAN: ARKHAM KNIGHT...

HARLEY QUINN ACTION FIGURE
Diamond Code: SEP140357
Price: $25.00

ARKHAM KNIGHT ACTION FIGURE
Diamond Code: SEP140355
Price: $25.00

SCARECROW ACTION FIGURE
Diamond Code: SEP140358
Price: $25.00

JUSTICE LEAGUE

The world's greatest superheroes are here and ready to save the universe! Each iconic Justice League member has their superhero stance perfected. What's yours?

BATMAN ACTION FIGURE
Diamond Code: JUL128115
Price: $25.00

SUPERMAN ACTION FIGURE
Diamond Code: OCT120316
Price: $25.00

WONDER WOMAN ACTION FIGURE
Diamond Code: AUG120306
Price: $25.00

THE FLASH ACTION FIGURE
Diamond Code: MAY120340
Price: $25.00

GREEN LANTERN ACTION FIGURE
Diamond Code: MAY128303
Price: $25.00

AQUAMAN ACTION FIGURE
Diamond Code: JUN128338
Price: $25.00

CYBORG ACTION FIGURE
Diamond Code: AUG120305
Price: $25.00

DC COLLECTIBLES:
BATMAN: THE ANIMATED SERIES

Collect all the classic friends and foes from *Batman: The Animated Series!* These action figures, sculpted after the original animation design pages, are ready to face-off to be your favorite collectible.

BATMAN: THE ANIMATED SERIES

BATMAN: THE ANIMATED SERIES

BATMAN: THE ANIMATED SERIES

THE NEW BATMAN ADVENTURES

THE NEW BATMAN ADVENTURES

DC COLLECTIBLES:
BATMAN:
BLACK & WHITE STATUES

Protecting the city has never been so dramatic. Designs from legendary Bat-artists are all represented in these classic and incomparable Batman statues.

BATMAN BY GREG CAPULLO
Diamond Code: MAR150330
Price: $80.00

BATMAN (DICK GRAYSON) BY JOCK
Diamond Code: JAN150429
Price: $80.00

BATMAN BY DARWYN COOKE
Diamond Code: FEB150308
Price: $90.00

BATMAN BY MIKE MIGNOLA
Diamond Code: DEC140431
Price: $80.00

BATMAN BY DAVE MAZZUCCHELLI
Diamond Code: JUN150355
Price: $80.00

THE JOKER BY JIM LEE
Diamond Code: APR150357
Price: $80.00

BATMAN BY JIM LEE
Diamond Code: JUN150356
Price: $80.00

BATGIRL BY BABS TARR
Diamond Code: FEB150303
Price: $80.00

ISBN	DIAMOND CODE	TITLE	AUTHOR	ARTIST	US$	FORMAT
		BATMAN BACKLIST AND SUGGESTED READING ORDER		
9781401204457 OCT138014	BATMAN CHRONICLES VOL. 1	FINGER, BILL	KANE, BOB	$14.99/$17.99 CAN	TP
9781401260095 JUL150308	BATMAN: THE GOLDEN AGE OMNIBUS VOL. 1	VARIOUS	VARIOUS	$75.00/$85.00 CAN	HC
9781401263768	BATMAN: THE GOLDEN AGE OMNIBUS VOL. 2	FINGER, BILL	KANE, BOB	$75.00/$85.00 CAN	HC
9781401263331	BATMAN: THE GOLDEN AGE VOL. 1	FINGER, BILL	KANE, BOB	$19.99/$23.99 CAN	TP
9781401261122	BATMAN & SUPERMAN IN WORLD'S FINEST: THE GOLDEN AGE OMNIBUS VOL. 1	VARIOUS	VARIOUS	$75.00/$85.00 CAN	HC
9781401207526 OCT060163	BATMAN: YEAR ONE	MILLER, FRANK	MAZZUCCHELLI, DAVID	$14.99/$17.99 CAN	TP
9781401255183	BATMAN: THE NEW ADVENTURES	COLLINS, MAX ALLAN	COCKRUM, DAVE	$19.99/$23.99 CAN	TP
9781401216269 SEP080167	BATMAN: THE MAN WHO LAUGHS	BRUBAKER, ED	MAHNKE, DOUG	$14.99/$17.99 CAN	TP
9781563892738 APR058324	BATMAN: HAUNTED KNIGHT	LOEB, JEPH	SALE, TIM	$14.99/$17.99 CAN	TP
9781401251222 APR140278	ABSOLUTE BATMAN: HAUNTED KNIGHT	LOEB, JEPH	SALE, TIM	$99.99/$112.00 CAN	HC
9781401232597 JUL110251	BATMAN: THE LONG HALLOWEEN	LOEB, JEPH	SALE, TIM	$24.99/$28.99 CAN	TP
9781401248833 JUL140253	BATMAN NOIR: THE LONG HALLOWEEN	LOEB, JEPH	SALE, TIM	$49.99/$58.00CAN	HC
9781401244019 NOV130237	BATMAN: DARK VICTORY	LOEB, JEPH	SALE, TIM	$24.99/$28.99 CAN	TP
9781401201876 APR050327	BATMAN/SUPERMAN/WONDER WOMAN: TRINITY	WAGNER, MATT	WAGNER, MATT	$17.99/$20.99 CAN	TP
9781401256906 SEP150286	BATMAN/SUPERMAN/WONDER WOMAN: TRINITY DELUXE EDITION	WAGNER, MATT	WAGNER, MATT	$28.99/$35.00 CAN	HC
9781401255169 MAR150277	BATMAN: GOTHIC DELUXE EDITION	MORRISON, GRANT	JANSON, KLAUS	$24.99/$28.99 CAN	HC
9781401251246 JUN140278	BATMAN ARKHAM ASYLUM 25TH ANNIVERSARY	MORRISON, GRANT	MCKEAN, DAVE	$19.99/$23.99 CAN	TP
9781401251253 JUN140277	BATMAN ARKHAM ASYLUM 25TH ANNIVERSARY DELUXE EDITION	MORRISON, GRANT	MCKEAN, DAVE	$29.99/$35.00 CAN	HC
9781401247515 FEB140259	BATMAN: ARKHAM ASYLUM LIVING HELL DELUXE EDITION	SLOTT, DAN	SOOK, RYAN	$22.99/$26.99 CAN	HC
9781401216672 NOV070226	BATMAN: THE KILLING JOKE	MOORE, ALAN	BOLLAND, BRIAN	$17.99/$20.99CAN	HC
9781401263645	BATMAN NOIR: THE KILLING JOKE	MOORE, ALAN	BOLLAND, BRIAN	$24.99/$29.99 CAN	HC
9781401255510 SEP150292	BATMAN BY NEAL ADAMS OMNIBUS	O'NEIL, DENNY	ADAMS, NEAL	$99.99/$112.00 CAN	HC
9781401232740 JUN110267	BATMAN: A DEATH IN THE FAMILY	STARLIN, JIM	APARO, JIM	$24.99/$28.99 CAN	TP
9781401233839 JAN120305	BATMAN: VENOM	O'NEIL, DENNIS	GARCIA-LOPEZ, JOSE LUIS	$14.99/$17.99 CAN	TP
9781401258054	BATMAN: SHAMAN	O'NEIL, DENNIS	HANNIGAN, ED	$14.99/$17.99 CAN	TP
9781401247645 NOV130238	BATMAN BY DOUG MOENCH AND KELLEY JONES VOL. 1	MOENCH, DOUG	JONES, KELLEY	$39.99/$47.99 CAN	HC
9781401263195	SHADOW OF THE BAT VOL. 1	VARIOUS	VARIOUS	$19.99/$23.99 CAN	TP
9781401233792 JAN120303	BATMAN: KNIGHTFALL VOL. 1	VARIOUS	VARIOUS	$29.99/$35.00 CAN	TP
9781401235369 FEB120266	BATMAN: KNIGHTFALL VOL. 2	VARIOUS	VARIOUS	$29.99/$35.00 CAN	TP
9781401237219 JUN120242	BATMAN: KNIGHTFALL VOL. 3	VARIOUS	VARIOUS	$29.99/$35.00 CAN	TP
9781401260682 DEC150342	BATMAN: CONTAGION	DIXON, CHUCK	VARIOUS	$29.99/$35.00 CAN	TP
9781401255152 MAR150278	BATMAN: CATACLYSM (NEW EDITION)	DIXON, CHUCK	APARO, JIM	$29.99/$35.00 CAN	TP
9781401258276 JUL150303	BATMAN: ROAD TO NO MAN'S LAND VOL. 1	DIXON, CHUCK	HAMNER, CULLY	$29.99/$35.00 CAN	TP
9781401260637	BATMAN: ROAD TO NO MAN'S LAND VOL. 2	DIXON, CHUCK	VARIOUS	$34.99/$41.99 CAN	TP
9781401232283 AUG110242	BATMAN: NO MAN'S LAND VOL. 1	VARIOUS	VARIOUS	$29.99/$35.00 CAN	TP
9781401233808 APR148300	BATMAN: NO MAN'S LAND VOL. 2	VARIOUS	VARIOUS	$29.99/$41.99 CAN	TP
9781401234560 MAY120289	BATMAN: NO MAN'S LAND VOL. 3	VARIOUS	VARIOUS	$34.99/$41.99 CAN	TP
9781401235642 SEP120237	BATMAN: NO MAN'S LAND VOL. 4	VARIOUS	VARIOUS	$34.99/$41.99 CAN	TP
9781401251741 JUN140276	BATMAN: GORDON OF GOTHAM	O'NEIL, DENNIS	DIXON, CHUCK; JANSON, KLAUS	$19.99/$23.99 CAN	TP
9781401246822 APR140276	BATMAN: BRUCE WAYNE - FUGITIVE (NEW EDITION)	VARIOUS	VARIOUS	$29.99/$35.00 CAN	TP
9781401246839 FEB148212	BATMAN: BRUCE WAYNE - MURDERER? (NEW EDITION)	BRUBAKER, ED	MCDANIEL, SCOTT	$29.99/$35.00 CAN	TP
9781401260651 OCT150242	BATMAN BY ED BRUBAKER VOL. 1	BRUBAKER, ED	VARIOUS	$19.99/$23.99 CAN	TP
9781401258139 JUL150304	BATMAN: WAR GAMES BOOK ONE	GABRYCH, ANDERSEN	WOODS, PETE	$34.99/$41.99 CAN	TP
9781401260705	BATMAN: WAR GAMES BOOK TWO	BRUBAKER, ED; DIXON, CHUCK	VARIOUS	$34.99/$41.99 CAN	TP
9781401263676	BATMAN: NEW GOTHAM	RUCKA, GREG	VARIOUS	$19.99/$23.99 CAN	TP
9781401223175 MAY090178	BATMAN: HUSH	LOEB, JEPH	LEE, JIM	$24.99/$28.99 CAN	TP
9781401258030 MAY150233	BATMAN NOIR: HUSH	LOEB, JEPH	LEE, JIM	$39.99/$48.99 CAN	HC
9781401238902 JAN130307	BATMAN NOIR: EDUARDO RISSO: THE DELUXE EDITION	RISSO, EDUARDO	AZZARELLO, BRIAN	$24.99/$28.99 CAN	HC
9781401231453 MAY110241	BATMAN: UNDER THE RED HOOD	WINICK, JUDD	MAHNKE, DOUG	$29.99/$35.00 CAN	TP
9781401231644 MAR110343	BATMAN: RED HOOD: LOST DAYS	WINICK, JUDD	VARIOUS	$14.99/$17.99 CAN	TP

DC COMICS READING ORDER

	ISBN | DIAMOND CODE	TITLE	AUTHOR | ARTIST	US$ | FORMAT
51.	9781401244026 OCT130238	BATMAN: BATMAN AND SON	MORRISON, GRANT | KUBERT, ANDY; WILLIAMS III, J.H.; DANIEL, TONY S.	$19.99/$23.99 CAN | TP
52.	9781401242428 OCT130247	BATMAN UNWRAPPED BY ANDY KUBERT	MORRISON, GRANT | KUBERT, ANDY	$34.99/$41.99 CAN | HC
53.	9781401220327 FEB090202	BATMAN: THE RESURRECTION OF RA'S AL GHUL	VARIOUS | VARIOUS	$19.99/$23.99 CAN | TP
54.	9781401225766 MAR100237	BATMAN: R.I.P.	MORRISON, GRANT | DANIEL, TONY S.	$14.99/$17.99 CAN | TP
55.	9781401256883 MAY150235	BATMAN R.I.P. UNWRAPPED	MORRISON, GRANT | DANIEL, TONY S.	$34.99/$41.99 CAN | HC
56.	9781401221249 DEC090202	BATMAN: HEART OF HUSH	DINI, PAUL | NGUYEN, DUSTIN	$14.99/$17.99 CAN | TP
57.	9781401229061 AUG110246	BATMAN: STREETS OF GOTHAM VOL. 2: LEVIATHAN	DINI, PAUL | NGUYEN, DUSTIN	$17.99/$20.99 CAN | TP
58.	9781401245177 JAN140352	FINAL CRISIS (NEW EDITION)	MORRISON, GRANT | JONES, J.G.; MAHNKE, DOUG	$19.99/$23.99 CAN | TP
59.	9781401227241 APR100218	BATMAN: WHATEVER HAPPENED TO THE CAPED CRUSADER?	GAIMAN, NEIL | KUBERT, ANDY	$14.99/$17.99 CAN | TP
60.	9781401224172 AUG100199	BATMAN: BATTLE FOR THE COWL	DANIEL, TONY S. | DANIEL, TONY S.	$14.99/$17.99 CAN | TP
61.	9781401229870 DEC100246	BATMAN & ROBIN VOL. 1: BATMAN REBORN	MORRISON, GRANT | QUITELY, FRANK	$14.99/$17.99 CAN | TP
62.	9781401232719 AUG110241	BATMAN & ROBIN VOL. 2: BATMAN VS. ROBIN	MORRISON, GRANT | STEWART, CAMERON	$17.99/$20.99 CAN | TP
63.	9781401235086 FEB120258	BATMAN & ROBIN VOL. 3: BATMAN & ROBIN MUST DIE!	MORRISON, GRANT | FRAZER, IRVING	$17.99/$20.99 CAN | TP
64.	9781401233822 OCT110245	BATMAN: THE RETURN OF BRUCE WAYNE	MORRISON, GRANT | PAQUETTE, YANICK	$19.99/$23.99 CAN | TP
65.	9781401233471 FEB120259	BATMAN: BRUCE WAYNE - THE ROAD HOME	VARIOUS | VARIOUS	$17.99/$20.99 CAN | TP
66.	9781401229757 JUL110250	BATMAN: LIFE AFTER DEATH	DANIEL, TONY S. | DANIEL, TONY S.	$14.99/$17.99 CAN | TP
67.	9781401229900 NOV110198	BATMAN: TIME AND THE BATMAN	VARIOUS | VARIOUS	$14.99/$17.99 CAN | TP
68.	9781401238278 OCT120258	BATMAN INCORPORATED	MORRISON, GRANT | PAQUETTE, YANICK	$19.99/$23.99 CAN | TP
69.	9781401242633 AUG130293	BATMAN INCORPORATED VOL. 1: DEMON STAR	MORRISON, GRANT | BURNHAM, CHRIS	$16.99/$19.99 CAN | TP
70.	9781401246976 MAY140369	BATMAN INCORPORATED VOL. 2: GOTHAM'S MOST WANTED	MORRISON, GRANT | BURNHAM, CHRIS	$16.99/$19.99 CAN | TP
71.	9781401251215 MAY140382	ABSOLUTE BATMAN INCORPORATED	MORRISON, GRANT | BURNHAM, CHRIS	$125.00/$144.00 CAN | HC
72.	9781401230715 MAR110340	BATMAN: KNIGHT AND SQUIRE	CORNELL, PAUL | BROXTON, JIMMY	$14.99/$17.99 CAN | TP
73.	9781401234706 JUL120220	BATMAN: EYE OF THE BEHOLDER	DANIEL, TONY S. | DANIEL, TONY S.	$14.99/$17.99 CAN | TP
74.	9781401238285 OCT120261	BATMAN: THE DARK KNIGHT: GOLDEN DAWN	FINCH, DAVID | FINCH, DAVID	$14.99/$17.99 CAN | TP
75.	9781401248840 NOV140293	BATMAN: THE DARK KNIGHT UNWRAPPED BY DAVID FINCH	FINCH, DAVID | FINCH, DAVID	$34.99/$41.99 CAN | HC
76.	9781401233419 NOV110194	BATMAN: GATES OF GOTHAM	SNYDER, SCOTT | MCCARTHY, TREVOR	$14.99/$17.99 CAN | TP
77.	9781401232078 NOV120268	BATMAN: THE BLACK MIRROR	SNYDER, SCOTT | JOCK; FRANCAVILLA, FRANCESCO	$16.99/$19.99 CAN | TP
78.	9781401259686 MAY150233	BATMAN NOIR: BLACK MIRROR	SNYDER, SCOTT | JOCK; FRANCAVILLA, FRANCESCO	$34.99/$41.99 CAN | HC
79.	9781401233389 OCT138324	FLASHPOINT	JOHNS, GEOFF | KUBERT, ANDY	$16.99/$19.99 CAN | TP
80.	9781401234058 DEC110277	FLASHPOINT: WORLD OF FLASHPOINT FEATURING BATMAN	AZZARELLO, BRIAN | RISSO, EDUARDO	$17.99/$20.99 CAN | TP
81.	9781401235420 DEC120323	BATMAN VOL. 1: THE COURT OF OWLS	SNYDER, SCOTT | CAPULLO, GREG	$16.99/$19.99 CAN | TP
82.	9781401237783 JUL130235	BATMAN VOL. 2: THE CITY OF OWLS	SNYDER, SCOTT | CAPULLO, GREG; ALBUQUERQUE, RAFAEL	$16.99/$19.99 CAN | TP
83.	9781401242527 AUG130291	BATMAN: NIGHT OF THE OWLS	SNYDER, SCOTT | CAPULLO, GREG	$19.99/$23.99 CAN | TP
84.	9781401245078 APR140256	BATMAN UNWRAPPED: THE COURT OF OWLS	SNYDER, SCOTT | CAPULLO, GREG	$39.99/$47.99 CAN | HC
85.	9781401246020 FEB140248	BATMAN VOL. 3: DEATH OF THE FAMILY	SNYDER, SCOTT | CAPULLO, GREG; JOCK	US$/$19.99 CAN | TP
86.	9781401246464 JAN140340	THE JOKER: DEATH OF THE FAMILY	SNYDER, SCOTT | CAPULLO, GREG	$24.99/$28.99 CAN | TP
87.	9781401249274 MAY140361	BATMAN: DEATH OF THE FAMILY BOOK AND JOKER MASK SET	SNYDER, SCOTT | CAPULLO, GREG	$39.99/$47.99 CAN | TP
88.	9781401249335 FEB140248	BATMAN VOL. 4: ZERO YEAR-SECRET CITY	SNYDER, SCOTT | CAPULLO, GREG	$16.99/$19.99 CAN | TP
89.	9781401253356 JUL140237	BATMAN VOL. 5: ZERO YEAR-DARK CITY	SNYDER, SCOTT | CAPULLO, GREG	$16.99/$19.99 CAN | TP
90.	9781401253370 JAN150363	DC COMICS: ZERO YEAR	SNYDER, SCOTT | CAPULLO, GREG	$24.99/$28.99 CAN | TP
91.	9781401257538 JUN150290	BATMAN VOL. 6: GRAVEYARD SHIFT	SNYDER, SCOTT | CAPULLO, GREG; KUBERT, ANDY	$16.99/$19.99 CAN | TP
92.	9781401261160 DEC150331	BATMAN VOL. 7: ENDGAME	SNYDER, SCOTT | CAPULLO, GREG	$19.99/$23.99 CAN | TP
93.	9781401261658	THE JOKER: ENDGAME	SNYDER, SCOTT | CAPULLO, GREG	$24.99/$29.99 CAN | TP
94.	9781401259693 NOV150271	BATMAN VOL. 8: SUPERHEAVY	SNYDER, SCOTT | CAPULLO, GREG	$24.99/$29.99 CAN | HC
95.	9781401251734 SEP140302	BATMAN ETERNAL VOL. 1	SNYDER, SCOTT; SEELEY, TIM; TYNION IV, JAMES; FAWKES, RAY | FABOK, JASON	$39.99/$47.99 CAN | TP
96.	9781401252311 APR150286	BATMAN ETERNAL VOL. 2	SNYDER, SCOTT; SEELEY, TIM; TYNION IV, JAMES; FAWKES, RAY | FABOK, JASON	$39.99/$47.99 CAN | TP
97.	9781401257521 AUG150261	BATMAN ETERNAL VOL. 3	SNYDER, SCOTT; TYNION IV, JAMES | QUINONES, JOE	$39.99/$48.99 CAN | TP
98.	9781401259679 DEC150341	BATMAN AND ROBIN ETERNAL VOL. 1	SNYDER, SCOTT; TYNION IV, JAMES; SEELEY, TIM; ORLANDO, STEVE | DANIEL, TONY S.	$24.99/$29.99 CAN | TP
99.	9781401262488	BATMAN AND ROBIN ETERNAL VOL. 2	SNYDER, SCOTT; TYNION IV, JAMES; SEELEY, TIM; ORLANDO, STEVE | VARIOUS	$29.99/$35.00 CAN | TP
100.	9781401234676 JAN130296	BATMAN: DETECTIVE COMICS VOL. 1: FACES OF DEATH	DANIEL, TONY S. | DANIEL, TONY S.	$16.99/$19.99 CAN | TP
101.	9781401242657 AUG130290	BATMAN: DETECTIVE COMICS VOL. 2: SCARE TACTICS	DANIEL, TONY S. | DANIEL, TONY S.; BENES, ED	$16.99/$19.99 CAN | TP

DC COMICS READING ORDER

	ISBN	DIAMOND CODE	TITLE	AUTHOR	ARTIST	US$	FORMAT
102.	9781401246341	MAR140251	BATMAN: DETECTIVE COMICS VOL. 3: EMPEROR PENGUIN	LAYMAN, JOHN	FABOK, JASON	$16.99/$19.99 CAN	TP
103.	9781401249977	AUG140329	BATMAN: DETECTIVE COMICS VOL. 4: THE WRATH	LAYMAN, JOHN	FABOK, JASON	$17.99/$20.99 CAN	TP
104.	9781401254667	FEB150249	BATMAN: DETECTIVE COMICS VOL. 5: GOTHTOPIA	LAYMAN, JOHN	FABOK, JASON	$16.99/$19.99 CAN	TP
105.	9781401258023	OCT150247	BATMAN: DETECTIVE COMICS VOL. 6: ICARUS	MANAPUL, FRANCIS; BUCCELLATO, BRIAN	MANAPUL, FRANCIS	$16.99/$19.99 CAN	TP
106.	9781401257491	SEP150289	BATMAN: DETECTIVE COMICS VOL. 7: ANARKY	MANAPUL, FRANCIS; BUCCELLATO, BRIAN	MANAPUL, FRANCIS	$24.99/$29.99 CAN	HC
107.	9781401263553		BATMAN: DETECTIVE COMICS VOL. 8	TOMASI, PETER J.	TAKARA, MARCIO	$22.99/$27.99 CAN	HC
108.	9781401237110	APR130221	BATMAN - THE DARK KNIGHT VOL. 1: KNIGHT TERRORS	JENKINS, PAUL; FINCH, DAVID	FINCH, DAVID	$16.99/$19.99 CAN	TP
109.	9781401242824	OCT130236	BATMAN - THE DARK KNIGHT VOL. 2: CYCLE OF VIOLENCE	HURWITZ, GREGG	FINCH, DAVID	$14.99/$17.99 CAN	TP
110.	9781401246198	APR140257	BATMAN - THE DARK KNIGHT VOL. 3: MAD	HURWITZ, GREGG	VAN SCIVER, ETHAN	$16.99/$19.99 CAN	TP
111.	9781401249304	NOV140294	BATMAN - THE DARK KNIGHT VOL. 4: CLAY	HURWITZ, GREGG	MALEEV, ALEX; PONTICELLI, ALBERTO	$16.99/$19.99 CAN	TP
112.	9781401238384	MAR130270	BATMAN & ROBIN VOL. 1: BORN TO KILL	TOMASI, PETER J.	GLEASON, PATRICK	$16.99/$19.99 CAN	TP
113.	9781401242671	FEB130207	BATMAN & ROBIN VOL. 2: PEARL	TOMASI, PETER J.	GLEASON, PATRICK	$16.99/$19.99 CAN	TP
114.	9781401246174	MAR140250	BATMAN AND ROBIN VOL. 3: DEATH OF THE FAMILY	TOMASI, PETER J.	GLEASON, PATRICK	$14.99/$17.99 CAN	TP
115.	9781401250584	AUG140330	BATMAN AND ROBIN VOL. 4: REQUIEM FOR DAMIAN	TOMASI, PETER J.	GLEASON, PATRICK	$16.99/$19.99 CAN	TP
116.	9781401253332	MAR150266	BATMAN AND ROBIN VOL. 5: THE BIG BURN	TOMASI, PETER J.	GLEASON, PATRICK	$16.99/$19.99 CAN	TP
117.	9781401258009	AUG150262	BATMAN AND ROBIN VOL. 6: THE HUNT FOR ROBIN	TOMASI, PETER J.	GLEASON, PATRICK; KUBERT, ANDY	$16.99/$19.99 CAN	TP
118.	9781401261146		BATMAN AND ROBIN VOL. 7: ROBIN RISES	TOMASI, PETER J.	GLEASON, PATRICK; KUBERT, ANDY	$16.99/$19.99 CAN	TP
119.	9781401249342	AUG140333	BATMAN/SUPERMAN VOL. 1: CROSS WORLD	PAK, GREG	LEE, JAE; OLIVER, BEN	$14.99/$17.99 CAN	TP
120.	9781401254230	FEB150252	BATMAN/SUPERMAN VOL. 2: GAME OVER	PAK, GREG	LEE, JAE; BOOTH, BRETT	$16.99/$19.99 CAN	TP
121.	9781401257545	SEP150290	BATMAN/SUPERMAN VOL. 3: SECOND CHANCE	PAK, GREG	LEE, JAE	$14.99/$17.99 CAN	TP
122.	9781401257552	AUG150267	BATMAN/SUPERMAN VOL. 4: SIEGE	PAK, GREG	SYAF, ARDIAN	$24.99/$29.99 CAN	HC
123.	9781401215811	JUL080124	JOKER	AZZARELLO, BRIAN	BERMEJO, LEE	$19.99/$23.99 CAN	HC
124.	9781401245047	APR130219	ABSOLUTE JOKER/LUTHOR	AZZARELLO, BRIAN	BERMEJO, LEE	$99.99/$112.00 CAN	HC

BATMAN COMPILATION GRAPHIC NOVELS

	ISBN	DIAMOND CODE	TITLE	AUTHOR	ARTIST	US$	FORMAT
1.	9781401247584	APR140254	BATMAN: A CELEBRATION OF 75 YEARS	VARIOUS	VARIOUS	$39.99/$47.99 CAN	HC
2.	9781401247591	APR140255	THE JOKER: A CELEBRATION OF 75 YEARS	VARIOUS	VARIOUS	$39.99/$47.99 CAN	HC
3.	9781401255138	FEB150251	BATMAN ARKHAM: RIDDLER	FOX, GARDNER	MOLDOFF, SHELDON	$19.99/$23.99 CAN	TP
4.	9781401260620	NOV150277	BATMAN ARKHAM: SCARECROW	VARIOUS	VARIOUS	$19.99/$23.99 CAN	TP
5.	9781401258153	FEB150251	BATMAN ARKHAM: TWO-FACE	DINI, PAUL	BACHS, RAMON; RISSO, EDUARDO	$19.99/$23.99 CAN	TP
6.	9781401263454	SEP150285	BATMAN ARKHAM VOL. 4: KILLER CROC	VARIOUS	VARIOUS	$19.99/$23.99 CAN	TP
7.	9781401255176	APR150289	BATMAN: HARLEY QUINN	DINI, PAUL	GOOGE, NEIL	$19.99/$23.99 CAN	TP
8.	9781401256982	SEP150285	BATMAN VS. SUPERMAN: THE GREATEST BATTLES	VARIOUS	VARIOUS	$9.99/$11.99 CAN	TP
9.	9781401238292	MAR130280	TALES OF THE BATMAN: ARCHIE GOODWIN	GOODWIN, ARCHIE	VARIOUS	$39.99/$47.99 CAN	HC
10.	9781401247553	JAN140356	TALES OF THE BATMAN: CARMINE INFANTINO	INFANTINO, CARMINE	VARIOUS	$49.99/$58.00 CAN	HC
11.	9781401232948	AUG110254	TALES OF THE BATMAN: DON NEWTON	VARIOUS	NEWTON, DON	$39.99/$46.99 CAN	HC
12.	9781401231019	MAR110346	TALES OF THE BATMAN: GENE COLAN VOL. 1	VARIOUS	COLAN, GENE	$39.99/$46.99 CAN	HC
13.	9781401247621	MAR140263	TALES OF THE BATMAN: J.H. WILLIAMS III	VARIOUS	WILLIAMS III, J.H.	$49.99/$58.00 CAN	HC
14.	9781401251543	AUG140343	TALES OF THE BATMAN: LEN WEIN	WEIN, LEN	APARO, JIM	$49.99/$58.00 CAN	HC
15.	9781401236847	JUL130240	BATMAN: ODYSSEY	ADAMS, NEAL	ADAMS, NEAL	$19.99/$23.99 CAN	TP
16.	9781401242961	MAY130233	LEGENDS OF THE DARK KNIGHT: JIM APARO VOL. 2	APARO, JIM	HANEY, BOB	$49.99/$58.00 CAN	HC
17.	9781401263492		LEGENDS OF THE DARK KNIGHT: JIM APARO VOL. 3	APARO, JIM	APARO, JIM	$49.99/$58.00 CAN	HC

BATMAN: FROM PAGE TO SCREEN

	ISBN	DIAMOND CODE	TITLE	AUTHOR	ARTIST	US$	FORMAT
1.	9781401249311	JUL140252	BATMAN '66 VOL. 1	PARKER, JEFF	CASE, JONATHAN	$14.99/$17.99 CAN	TP
2.	9781401254612	JAN150377	BATMAN '66 VOL. 2	PARKER, JEFF	CASE, JONATHAN	$14.99/$17.99 CAN	TP
3.	9781401257507	SEP150287	BATMAN '66 VOL. 3	PARKER, JEFF	CASE, JONATHAN	$14.99/$17.99 CAN	TP
4.	9781401257996	AUG150260	BATMAN '66/GREEN HORNET	SMITH, KEVIN; GARMAN, RALPH	TEMPLETON, TY	$14.99/$17.99 CAN	TP
5.	9781401261047		BATMAN '66 VOL. 4	PARKER, JEFF	CASE, JONATHAN	$14.99/$17.99 CAN	TP
6.	9781401261054	JAN160320	BATMAN '66 VOL. 5	PARKER, JEFF	CASE, JONATHAN	$19.99/$23.99 CAN	HC
7.	9781401252779	SEP140283	BATMAN: THE JIRO KUWATA BATMANGA VOL. 1	KUWATA, JIRO	KUWATA, JIRO	$14.99/$17.99 CAN	TP
8.	9781401255527	APR150260	BATMAN: THE JIRO KUWATA BATMANGA VOL. 2	KUWATA, JIRO	KUWATA, JIRO	$12.99/$15.99 CAN	TP
9.	9781401257569	OCT150250	BATMAN: THE JIRO KUWATA BATMANGA VOL. 3	KUWATA, JIRO	KUWATA, JIRO	$14.99/$17.99 CAN	TP

ISBN | DIAMOND CODE		TITLE	AUTHOR | ARTIST	US$ | FORMAT
10.	9781401244958 OCT130248	BATMAN: THE TV STORIES	VARIOUS | VARIOUS	$14.99/$17.99 CAN | TP
11.	9781401252298 AUG140337	BATMAN ADVENTURES VOL. 1	PUCKETT, KELLEY | TEMPLETON, TY	$19.99/$23.99 CAN | TP
12.	9781401254636 FEB150269	BATMAN ADVENTURES VOL. 2	PUCKETT, KELLEY | PAROBECK, MIKE	$19.99/$23.99 CAN | TP
13.	9781401258726 JUL150309	BATMAN ADVENTURES VOL. 3	DINI, PAUL | PUCKETT, KELLEY	$16.99/$19.99 CAN | TP
14.	9781401260613 JUL150309	BATMAN ADVENTURES VOL. 4	PUCKETT, KELLEY | PAROBECK, MIKE	$19.99/$23.99 CAN | TP
15.	9781401255121 NOV140306	BATMAN ADVENTURES: MAD LOVE DELUXE EDITION	DINI, PAUL | TIMM, BRUCE	$24.99/$29.99 CAN | HC
16.	9781401249366 OCT140378	BEWARE THE BATMAN VOL. 1	COHEN, IVAN | VECCHIO, LUCIANO	$12.99/$15.99 CAN | TP
17.	9781401247539 JAN140349	BATMAN BEYOND: BATGIRL BEYOND	BEECHEN, ADAM | ARCHER, ADAM	$14.99/$17.99 CAN | TP
18.	9781401250607 AUG140338	BATMAN BEYOND 2.0: REWIRED	HIGGINS, KYLE; SIEGEL, ALEC | SILAS, THONY	$16.99/$19.99 CAN | TP
19.	9781401254643 DEC140388	BATMAN BEYOND 2.0 VOL. 2: JUSTICE LORDS BEYOND	HIGGINS, KYLE; SIEGEL, ALEC | GAGE, CHRISTOS; SILAS, THONY	$16.99/$19.99 CAN | TP
20.	9781401258016 JUN150298	BATMAN BEYOND 2.0 VOL. 3: MARK OF THE PHANTASM	HIGGINS, KYLE | SILAS, THONY; HESTER, PHIL	$16.99/$19.99 CAN | TP
21.	9781401261917 DEC150317	BATMAN BEYOND VOL. 1: BRAVE NEW WORLDS	JURGENS, DAN | CHANG, BERNARD	$14.99/$17.99 CAN | TP
22.	9781401234935 JUN120243	BATMAN: ARKHAM CITY	DINI, PAUL | D'ANDA, CARLOS	$16.99/$19.99 CAN | TP
23.	9781401240189 MAY130229	BATMAN: ARKHAM UNHINGED VOL. 1	DINI, PAUL; FRIDOLFS, DEREK | VARIOUS	$14.99/$17.99 CAN | TP
24.	9781401242831 OCT130249	BATMAN: ARKHAM UNHINGED VOL. 2	FRIDOLFS, DEREK | VARIOUS	$14.99/$17.99 CAN | TP
25.	9781401246808 MAY140377	BATMAN: ARKHAM UNHINGED VOL. 3	FRIDOLFS, DEREK | ALEXANDER, JASON SHAWN	$16.99/$19.99 CAN | TP
26.	9781401250423 NOV140307	BATMAN: ARKHAM UNHINGED VOL. 4	TRAVISS, KAREN | DUCE, CHRISTIAN	$14.99/$17.99 CAN | TP
27.	9781401254650 APR150288	BATMAN: ARKHAM ORIGINS	BEECHEN, ADAM | WAGNER, DOUG; DUCE, CHRISTIAN	$14.99/$17.99 CAN | TP
28.	9781401260668 NOV150269	BATMAN: ARKHAM KNIGHT GENESIS	TOMASI, PETER J. | BOGDANOVIC, VIKTOR	$19.99/$23.99 CAN | HC
29.	9781401258047 FEB150258	BATMAN: ARKHAM KNIGHT VOL. 1	TOMASI, PETER J. | BOGDANOVIC, VIKTOR	$19.99/$23.99 CAN | HC
30.	9781401263409	BATMAN: ARKHAM KNIGHT VOL. 2	TOMASI, PETER J. | BOGDANOVIC, VIKTOR	$14.99/$17.99 CAN | TP
31.	9781401263393	BATMAN: ARKHAM KNIGHT VOL. 3	TOMASI, PETER J. | BOGDANOVIC, VIKTOR	$19.99/$23.99 CAN | HC

BATMAN STANDALONE GRAPHIC NOVELS

	ISBN | DIAMOND CODE	TITLE	AUTHOR | ARTIST	US$ | FORMAT
1.	9781401220082 MAR090174	ALL-STAR BATMAN & ROBIN, THE BOY WONDER VOL. 1	MILLER, FRANK | LEE, JIM	$19.99/$23.99 CAN | TP
2.	9781401247638 JAN140348	ABSOLUTE ALL-STAR BATMAN AND ROBIN, THE BOY WONDER	MILLER, FRANK | LEE, JIM	$99.99/$112.00 CAN | HC
3.	9781401263119 NOV150279	BATMAN: THE DARK KNIGHT RETURNS	MILLER, FRANK | MILLER, FRANK	$14.99/$17.99 CAN | TP
4.	9781563899294 FEB058404	BATMAN: THE DARK KNIGHT STRIKES AGAIN	MILLER, FRANK | MILLER, FRANK	$19.99/$23.99 CAN | TP
5.	9781401255145 DEC140389	BATMAN NOIR: DARK KNIGHT RETURNS	MILLER, FRANK | MILLER, FRANK; JANSON, KLAUS	$34.99/$41.99 CAN | HC
6.	9781401256913 MAY150234	BATMAN: THE DARK KNIGHT SAGA DELUXE EDITION	MILLER, FRANK | MILLER, FRANK	$49.99/$58.00 CAN | HC
7.	9781401233815 DEC110282	BATMAN: BIRTH OF THE DEMON	BARR, MIKE W. | VARIOUS	$29.99/$35.00 CAN | TP
8.	9781401215897 JUN070171	BATMAN: BLACK & WHITE VOL. 1	VARIOUS | VARIOUS	$19.99/$23.99 CAN | TP
9.	9781563899171 JUN080234	BATMAN: BLACK & WHITE VOL. 2	VARIOUS | VARIOUS	$19.99/$23.99 CAN | TP
10.	9781401213541 JUN080235	BATMAN: BLACK & WHITE VOL. 3	VARIOUS | VARIOUS	$19.99/$23.99 CAN | TP
11.	9781401250621 OCT140367	BATMAN: BLACK & WHITE VOL. 4	DINI, PAUL | ADAMS, NEAL; HUGHES, ADAM	$19.99/$23.99 CAN | TP
12.	9781401251260 NOV140309	BATMAN: BLINK	MCDUFFIE, DWAYNE | SEMEIKS, VAL	$14.99/$17.99 CAN | TP
13.	9781401224196 JUN100204	BATMAN: CACOPHONY	SMITH, KEVIN | FLANAGAN, WALT	$14.99/$17.99 CAN | TP
14.	9781401228767 JUN110270	BATMAN: THE WIDENING GYRE	SMITH, KEVIN | FLANAGAN, WALT	$17.99/$20.99 CAN | TP
15.	9781401237899 FEB130217	BATMAN: DEATH BY DESIGN	KIDD, CHIP | TAYLOR, DAVE	$14.99/$17.99 CAN | TP
16.	9781401250645 NOV140298	DAMIAN: SON OF BATMAN	KUBERT, ANDY; MORRISON, GRANT | KUBERT, ANDY	$16.99/$19.99 CAN | TP
17.	9781401251277 NOV140310	BATMAN: DARK NIGHT, DARK CITY	MILLIGAN, PETER | DWYER, KIERON; APARO, JIM	$16.99/$19.99 CAN | TP
18.	9781401258061 SEP150288	BATMAN: THE DOOM THAT CAME TO GOTHAM	MIGNOLA, MIKE | NIXEY, TROY	$16.99/$19.99 CAN | TP
19.	9781401232092 JUL158202	BATMAN: EARTH ONE	JOHNS, GEOFF | FRANK, GARY	$14.99/$15.99 CAN | TP
20.	9781401262518	BATMAN: EARTH ONE VOL. 2	JOHNS, GEOFF | FRANK, GARY	$14.99/$17.99 CAN | TP
21.	9781401259709 DEC150314	BATMAN: EUROPA	AZZARELLO, BRIAN | LEE, JIM; CAMMUNCOLI, GUISEPPE	$22.99/$27.99 CAN | HC
22.	9781401211530 DEC120332	BATMAN: GOTHAM BY GASLIGHT	AUGUSTYN, BRIAN | MIGNOLA, MIKE	$12.99/$15.99 CAN | TP
23.	9781401242398 JUN130259	BATMAN: LEGENDS OF THE DARK KNIGHT VOL. 1	VARIOUS | VARIOUS	$14.99/$17.99 CAN | TP
24.	9781401246006 FEB140254	BATMAN: LEGENDS OF THE DARK KNIGHT VOL. 2	VARIOUS | VARIOUS	$14.99/$17.99 CAN | TP
25.	9781401248154 SEP140320	BATMAN: LEGENDS OF THE DARK KNIGHT VOL. 3	VARIOUS | VARIOUS	$16.99/$19.99 CAN | TP
26.	9781401254674 FEB150259	BATMAN: LEGENDS OF THE DARK KNIGHT VOL. 4	SOULE, CHARLES | DAVIS, SHANE; CALERO, DENNIS	$16.99/$19.99 CAN | TP
27.	9781401258146 AUG150264	BATMAN: LEGENDS OF THE DARK KNIGHT VOL. 5	MARZ, RON | WOODS, PETE	$16.99/$19.99 CAN | TP
28.	9781401247232 APR140285	BATMAN: LI'L GOTHAM VOL. 2	NGUYEN, DUSTIN | FRIDOLFS, DEREK	$12.99/$15.99 CAN | TP

DC COMICS READING ORDER

	ISBN │ DIAMOND CODE	TITLE	AUTHOR │ ARTIST	US$ │ FORMAT
29.	9781401232139 JUL110245	BATMAN: NOEL	BERMEJO, LEE │ BERMEJO, LEE	$22.99/$26.99 CAN │ HC
30.	9781401227876 OCT120262	BATMAN: THROUGH THE LOOKING GLASS	JONES, BRUCE │ KIETH, SAM	$14.99/$17.99 CAN │ TP
31.	9781401211929 JAN130309	BATMAN: YEAR ONE HUNDRED	POPE, PAUL │ POPE, PAUL	$19.99/$23.99 CAN │ TP
32.	9781401258078 JUN150299	BATMAN: YEAR 100 & OTHER TALES DELUXE EDITION	POPE, PAUL │ POPE, PAUL	$29.99/$35.00 CAN │ HC

BATMAN CROSSOVERS

	ISBN │ DIAMOND CODE	TITLE	AUTHOR │ ARTIST	US$ │ FORMAT
1.	9781401247225 FEB140258	BATMAN/DEATHBLOW: AFTER THE FIRE	AZZARELLO, BRIAN │ BERMEJO, LEE	$14.99/$17.99 CAN │ TP
2.	9781401236786 SEP130278	THE BATMAN/JUDGE DREDD COLLECTION	GRANT, ALAN │ WAGNER, JOHN	$19.99/$23.99 CAN │ TP
3.	9781401231842 FEB110210	PLANETARY/BATMAN	ELLIS, WARREN │ CASSADAY, JOHN	$22.99/$25.99 CAN │ HC
4.	9781401262785	BATMAN/TMNT VOL. 1	TYNION IV, JAMES │ WILLIAMS II, FREDDIE E.	$16.99/$19.99 CAN │ TP

SUPERMAN BACKLIST AND SUGGESTED READING ORDER

	ISBN │ DIAMOND CODE	TITLE	AUTHOR │ ARTIST	US$ │ FORMAT
1.	9781401262563	SUPERMAN: AMERICAN ALIEN	LANDIS, MAX │ MANAPUL, FRANCIS; JOCK; LEE, JAE; DRAGOTTA, NICK	$22.99/$27.99 CAN │ TP
2.	9781401207649 OCT138013	SUPERMAN CHRONICLES VOL. 1	SIEGEL, JERRY │ SHUSTER, JOE	$17.99/$20.99 CAN │ TP
3.	9781401261092 DEC150348	SUPERMAN: THE GOLDEN AGE VOL. 1	SIEGEL, JERRY; SHUSTER, JOE │ VARIOUS	$19.99/$23.99 CAN │ TP
4.	9781401263249	SUPERMAN: THE GOLDEN AGE OMNIBUS VOL. 2	VARIOUS │ VARIOUS	$75.00/$85.00 CAN │ HC
5.	9781401238377 DEC120338	SHOWCASE PRESENTS: SUPERMAN FAMILY VOL. 4	VARIOUS │ VARIOUS	$19.99/$23.99 CAN │ TP
6.	9781401240486 APR130229	SHOWCASE PRESENTS: DC COMICS PRESENTS - SUPERMAN TEAM-UPS VOL. 2	VARIOUS │ VARIOUS	$19.99/$23.99 CAN │ TP
7.	9781401251529 OCT140371	SUPERMAN: THE POWER WITHIN	STERN, ROGER │ SWAN, CURT	$16.99/$19.99 CAN │ TP
8.	9781401243067 JUL130247	SUPERMAN: DARK KNIGHT OVER METROPOLIS	VARIOUS │ VARIOUS	$14.99/$17.99 CAN │ TP
9.	9781401227319 APR100219	SUPERMAN: WHATEVER HAPPENED TO THE MAN OF TOMORROW?	MOORE, ALAN │ SWAN, CURT	$14.99/$17.99 CAN │ TP
10.	9780930289287 JUL058226	SUPERMAN: THE MAN OF STEEL VOL. 1	BYRNE, JOHN │ BYRNE, JOHN	$14.99/$17.99 CAN │ TP
11.	9781401200053 MAR068126	SUPERMAN: THE MAN OF STEEL VOL. 2	BYRNE, JOHN │ BYRNE, JOHN	$19.99/$23.99 CAN │ TP
12.	9781401202460 JUL088086	SUPERMAN: THE MAN OF STEEL VOL. 3	BYRNE, JOHN │ BYRNE, JOHN	$19.99/$23.99 CAN │ TP
13.	9781401216795 DEC070254	SUPERMAN: THE MAN OF STEEL VOL. 6	BYRNE, JOHN │ BYRNE, JOHN	$19.99/$23.99 CAN │ TP
14.	9781401238209 OCT120268	SUPERMAN: THE MAN OF STEEL VOL. 7	BYRNE, JOHN │ BYRNE, JOHN; ORDWAY, JERRY	$19.99/$23.99 CAN │ TP
15.	9781401243913 OCT130252	SUPERMAN: THE MAN OF STEEL VOL. 8	BYRNE, JOHN │ BYRNE, JOHN	$16.99/$19.99 CAN │ TP
16.	9781401250782 FEB068194	SUPERMAN FOR ALL SEASONS DELUXE EDITION	LOEB, JEPH │ SALE, TIM	$29.99/$35.00 CAN │ HC
17.	9781401263232	SUPERMAN: PANIC IN THE SKY (NEW EDITION)	JURGENS, DAN │ ORDWAY, JERRY	$19.99/$23.99 CAN │ TP
18.	9781401260972 DEC150344	SUPERMAN & THE JUSTICE LEAGUE AMERICA VOL. 1	JURGENS, DAN │ JURGENS, DAN	$17.99/$21.99 CAN │ TP
19.	9781401263843	SUPERMAN & THE JUSTICE LEAGUE AMERICA VOL. 2	JURGENS, DAN │ JURGENS, DAN	$16.99/$19.99 CAN │ TP
20.	9781401241827 OCT120269	SUPERMAN: THE DEATH OF SUPERMAN	JURGENS, DAN │ JURGENS, DAN; ORDWAY, JERRY; SIMONSON, LOUISE; BOGDANOVE, JON; GRUMMETT, TOM	$14.99/$17.99 CAN │ TP
21.	9781563891496 OCT058018	THE RETURN OF SUPERMAN	VARIOUS │ VARIOUS	$19.99/$23.99 CAN │ TP
22.	9781401258184 AUG150269	LUTHOR	AZZARELLO, BRIAN │ BERMEJO, LEE	$14.99/$17.99 CAN │ TP
23.	9781401262136 JAN160324	EMPEROR JOKER	VARIOUS │ VARIOUS	$19.99/$23.99 CAN │ TP
24.	9781401237806 NOV120270	SUPERMAN: FOR TOMORROW	AZZARELLO, BRIAN │ LEE, JIM	$24.99/$28.99 CAN │ TP
25.	9781401212056 MAR080188	SUPERMAN: CAMELOT FALLS VOL.1	BUSIEK, KURT │ PACHECO, CARLOS	$12.99/$15.99 CAN │ TP
26.	9781401218652 NOV080181	SUPERMAN: CAMELOT FALLS VOL.2	BUSIEK, KURT │ PACHECO, CARLOS	$12.99/$15.99 CAN │ TP
27.	9781401221324 JAN100308	SUPERMAN: COMING OF ATLAS	ROBINSON, JAMES │ GUEDES, RENATO	$14.99/$17.99 CAN │ TP
28.	9781401232993 SEP110188	SUPERMAN: SECRET ORIGIN	JOHNS, GEOFF │ FRANK, GARY	$19.99/$23.99 CAN │ TP
29.	9781401237790 OCT120270	SUPERMAN: LAST SON OF KRYPTON	JOHNS, GEOFF; DONNER, RICHARD │ KUBERT, ADAM; FRANK, GARY	$19.99/$23.99 CAN │ TP
30.	9781401220334 FEB090217	SUPERMAN: ESCAPE FROM BIZARRO WORLD	JOHNS, GEOFF │ POWELL, ERIC	$14.99/$17.99 CAN │ TP
31.	9781401219048 APR090217	SUPERMAN AND THE LEGION OF SUPER-HEROES	JOHNS, GEOFF │ FRANK, GARY	$14.99/$17.99 CAN │ TP
32.	9781401209544 JUN060169	SUPERMAN: UP, UP & AWAY	JOHNS, GEOFF │ WOODS, PETE	$14.99/$17.99 CAN │ TP
33.	9781401230760 FEB120265	SUPERMAN: GROUNDED VOL. 1	STRACZYNSKI, MICHAEL J. │ BARROWS, EDDY	$17.99/$20.99 CAN │ TP
34.	9781401235321 SEP120241	SUPERMAN: GROUNDED VOL. 2	STRACZYNSKI, J. MICHAEL │ BARROWS, EDDY	$14.99/$17.99 CAN │ TP
35.	9781401232535 AUG110260	SUPERMAN: RETURN OF DOOMSDAY	VARIOUS │ VARIOUS	$14.99/$17.99 CAN │ TP
36.	9781401236885 DEC120340	SUPERMAN: REIGN OF DOOMSDAY	CORNELL, PAUL │ ROCAFORT, KENNETH	$16.99/$19.99 CAN │ TP
37.	9781401235475 FEB130215	SUPERMAN - ACTION COMICS VOL. 1: SUPERMAN AND THE MEN OF STEEL	MORRISON, GRANT │ MORALES, RAGS	$16.99/$19.99 CAN │ TP
38.	9781401242541 SEP130275	SUPERMAN - ACTION COMICS VOL. 2: BULLETPROOF	MORRISON, GRANT │ MORALES, RAGS	$16.99/$19.99 CAN │ TP
39.	9781401246068 APR140268	SUPERMAN - ACTION COMICS VOL. 3: AT THE END OF DAYS	MORRISON, GRANT │ MORALES, RAGS; WALKER, BRAD	$16.99/$19.99 CAN │ TP
40.	9781401250775 SEP140312	SUPERMAN - ACTION COMICS VOL. 4: HYBRID	DIGGLE, ANDY │ DANIEL, TONY S.	$16.99/$19.99 CAN │ TP
41.	9781401254889 MAR150272	SUPERMAN - ACTION COMICS VOL. 5: WHAT LIES BENEATH	PAK, GREG │ KUDER, AARON	$14.99/$17.99 CAN │ TP

DC COMICS READING ORDER

	ISBN	DIAMOND CODE	TITLE	AUTHOR	ARTIST	US$	FORMAT
42.	9781401258658 SEP150306	SUPERMAN - ACTION COMICS VOL. 6: SUPERDOOM	PAK, GREG	KUDER, AARON	$16.99/$19.99 CAN	TP
43.	9781401262624	SUPERMAN - ACTION COMICS VOL. 7: UNDER THE SKIN	PAK, GREG	KUDER, AARON	$16.99/$19.99 CAN	TP
44.	9781401262631	SUPERMAN - ACTION COMICS VOL. 8	PAK, GREG	KUDER, AARON	$22.99/$27.99 CAN	HC
45.	9781401236861 MAR130274	SUPERMAN VOL. 1: WHAT PRICE TOMORROW?	PÉREZ, GEORGE	MERINO, JESUS; SCOTT, NICOLA	$14.99/$17.99 CAN	TP
46.	9781401240288 OCT130246	SUPERMAN VOL. 2: SECRETS & LIES	JURGENS, DAN	GIFFEN, KEITH; JURGENS, DAN	$16.99/$19.99 CAN	TP
47.	9781401246228 MAY140370	SUPERMAN VOL. 3: FURY AT WORLD'S END	LOBDELL, SCOTT	ROCAFORT, KENNETH	$14.99/$17.99 CAN	TP
48.	9781401246129 MAR140259	SUPERMAN: H'EL ON EARTH	LOBDELL, SCOTT	VARIOUS	$19.99/$23.99 CAN	TP
49.	9781401250942 NOV140301	SUPERMAN VOL. 4: PSI-WAR	LOBDELL, SCOTT	ROCAFORT, KENNETH; KUDER, AARON	$16.99/$19.99 CAN	TP
50.	9781401250959 OCT140360	SUPERMAN VOL. 5: UNDER FIRE	LOBDELL, SCOTT	LASHLEY, KEN; BOOTH, BRETT	$24.99/$28.99 CAN	HC
51.	9781401255442 MAY150247	SUPERMAN: KRYPTON RETURNS	LOBDELL, SCOTT	ROCAFORT, KENNETH	$16.99/$19.99 CAN	TP
52.	9781401257699 SEP150305	SUPERMAN: DOOMED	SOULE, CHARLES; PAK, GREG	KUDER, AARON	$29.99/$35.00 CAN	TP
53.	9781401258689 JAN160314	SUPERMAN: THE MEN OF TOMORROW	JOHNS, GEOFF	ROMITA, JOHN JR; JANSON, KLAUS	$16.99/$19.99 CAN	TP
54.	9781401259815 NOV150284	SUPERMAN VOL. 1: BEFORE TRUTH	YANG, GENE LUEN	ROMITA JR., JOHN	$22.99/$27.99 CAN	HC
55.	9781401250935 JUL150378	SUPERMAN UNCHAINED	SNYDER, SCOTT	LEE, JIM; NGUYEN, DUSTIN	$24.99/$29.99 CAN	TP
56.	9781401262716	CONVERGENCE	KING, JEFF; LOBDELL, SCOTT	PAGULAYAN, CARLO	$19.99/$23.99 CAN	TP
57.	9781401258351 JUL150298	CONVERGENCE: FLASHPOINT BOOK ONE	RUCKA, GREG	WEEKS, LEE; HAMNER, CULLY	$19.99/$23.99 CAN	TP
58.	9781401262495	SUPERMAN: LOIS & CLARK	JURGENS, DAN	WEEKS, LEE	$17.99/$21.99 CAN	TP

SUPERMAN/BATMAN

	ISBN	DIAMOND CODE	TITLE	AUTHOR	ARTIST	US$	FORMAT
1.	9781401201876 APR050327	BATMAN/SUPERMAN/WONDER WOMAN: TRINITY	WAGNER, MATT	WAGNER, MATT	$17.99/$20.99 CAN	TP
2.	9781401234775 MAY120298	WORLD'S FINEST	GIBBONS, DAVE	RUDE, STEVE	$17.99/$20.99 CAN	TP
3.	9781401248185 JAN140354	SUPERMAN/BATMAN VOL. 1	LOEB, JEPH	MCGUINNESS, ED; TURNER, MICHAEL	$19.99/$23.99 CAN	TP
4.	9781401250799 SEP140323	SUPERMAN/BATMAN VOL. 2	LOEB, JEPH	MCGUINNESS, ED; PACHECO, CARLOS	$19.99/$23.99 CAN	TP
5.	9781401240967 FEB130216	ABSOLUTE SUPERMAN/BATMAN VOL. 1	LOEB, JEPH	MCGUINNESS, ED; TURNER, MICHAEL	$99.99/$112.00 CAN	HC
6.	9781401248178 OCT130253	ABSOLUTE SUPERMAN/BATMAN VOL. 2	LOEB, JEPH	MCGUINNESS, ED; PACHECO, CARLOS	$99.99/$112.00 CAN	HC
7.	9781401217402 NOV100234	SUPERMAN/BATMAN: TORMENT	BURNETT, ALAN	NGUYEN, DUSTIN	$14.99/$17.99 CAN	TP
8.	9781401228088 MAY110252	SUPERMAN/BATMAN: NIGHT & DAY	GREEN, MICHAEL	KOLINS, SCOTT	$17.99/$20.99 CAN	TP
9.	9781401229146 SEP100256	SUPERMAN/BATMAN: BIG NOISE	CASEY, JOE	KOLINS, SCOTT	$14.99/$17.99 CAN	TP
10.	9781401230326 JAN110333	SUPERMAN/BATMAN: WORSHIP	LEVITZ, PAUL	GUEDES, RENATO	$17.99/$20.99 CAN	TP
11.	9781401234461 JUL120227	SUPERMAN/BATMAN: SORCERER KINGS	BUNN, CULLEN	CHRISCROSS	$14.99/$17.99 CAN	TP
12.	9781401222772 MAR090192	TRINITY VOL. 1	BUSIEK, KURT	BAGLEY, MARK	$29.99/$35.00 CAN	TP
13.	9781401223182 MAY090196	TRINITY VOL. 2	BUSIEK, KURT	BAGLEY, MARK	$29.99/$35.00 CAN	TP
14.	9781401223571 JUL090243	TRINITY VOL. 3	BUSIEK, KURT	BAGLEY, MARK	$29.99/$35.00 CAN	TP
15.	9781401249342 AUG140333	BATMAN/SUPERMAN VOL. 1: CROSS WORLD	PAK, GREG	LEE, JAE; OLIVER, BEN	$14.99/$17.99 CAN	TP
16.	9781401254230 FEB150252	BATMAN/SUPERMAN VOL. 2: GAME OVER	PAK, GREG	LEE, JAE; BOOTH, BRETT	$16.99/$19.99 CAN	TP
17.	9781401257545 SEP150290	BATMAN/SUPERMAN VOL. 3: SECOND CHANCE	PAK, GREG	LEE, JAE	$14.99/$17.99 CAN	TP
18.	9781401257552 AUG150167	BATMAN/SUPERMAN VOL. 4: SIEGE	PAK, GREG	SYAF, ARDIAN	$24.99/$29.99 CAN	HC
19.	9781401263690	BATMAN/SUPERMAN VOL. 5	PAK, GREG	SYAF, ARDIAN	$22.99/$27.99 CAN	HC
20.	9781401253462 DEC140383	SUPERMAN/WONDER WOMAN VOL. 1: POWER COUPLE	SOULE, CHARLES	DANIEL, TONY S.; SIQUEIRA, PAULO	$16.99/$19.99 CAN	TP
21.	9781401257675 AUG150280	SUPERMAN/WONDER WOMAN VOL. 2: WAR AND PEACE	SOULE, CHARLES	DANIEL, TONY S.; BENES, ED	$16.99/$19.99 CAN	TP
22.	9781401263218	SUPERMAN/WONDER WOMAN VOL. 3: CASUALTIES OF WAR	TOMASI, PETER J.	MAHNKE, DOUG	$16.99/$19.99 CAN	TP
23.	9781401263225	SUPERMAN/WONDER WOMAN VOL. 4	TOMASI, PETER J.	MAHNKE, DOUG	$22.99/$27.99 CAN	HC

SUPERMAN COMPILATION GRAPHIC NOVELS

	ISBN	DIAMOND CODE	TITLE	AUTHOR	ARTIST	US$	FORMAT
1.	9781401203399 NOV058069	SUPERMAN: THE GREATEST STORIES EVER TOLD	VARIOUS	VARIOUS	$19.99/$23.99 CAN	TP
2.	9781401247041 JUL130224	SUPERMAN: A CELEBRATION OF 75 YEARS	VARIOUS	VARIOUS	$39.99/$47.99 CAN	HC
3.	9781401247034 JUL130225	LOIS LANE: A CELEBRATION OF 75 YEARS	VARIOUS	VARIOUS	$39.99/$47.99 CAN	HC
4.	9781401262075 SEP150301	LEX LUTHOR: A CELEBRATION OF 75 YEARS	VARIOUS	VARIOUS	$39.99/$48.99 CAN	HC
5.	9781401256982 SEP150285	BATMAN VS. SUPERMAN: THE GREATEST BATTLES	VARIOUS	VARIOUS	$9.99/$11.99 CAN	TP
6.	9781401219406 JUL080169	SUPERMAN VS. BRAINIAC	VARIOUS	VARIOUS	$19.99/$23.99 CAN	TP
7.	9781401255435 JAN150382	SUPERMAN VS. DARKSEID	BYRNE, JOHN	MCKONE, MIKE	$19.99/$23.99 CAN	TP
8.	9781401242565 SEP130285	SUPERMAN VS. MONGUL	VARIOUS	VARIOUS	$14.99/$17.99 CAN	TP
9.	9781401238216 NOV120273	SUPERMAN VS. SHAZAM!	THOMAS, ROY	BUCKLER, RICH; KANE, GIL	$19.99/$23.99 CAN	TP

DC COMICS READING ORDER

	ISBN | DIAMOND CODE	TITLE	AUTHOR | ARTIST	US$ | FORMAT
10.	9781401238490 DEC120339	SUPERMAN VS. ZOD	VARIOUS | VARIOUS	$9.99/$9.99 CAN | TP
11.	9781401240516 APR130230	SUPERMAN: PHANTOM ZONE	GERBER, STEVE | COLAN, GENE	$14.99/$17.99 CAN | TP
12.	9781401238568 NOV120277	ADVENTURES OF SUPERMAN: JOSE LUIS GARCIA-LOPEZ	GARCIA-LOPEZ, JOSE LUIS | VARIOUS	$39.99/$47.99 CAN | HC

SUPERMAN: FROM PAGE TO SCREEN

	ISBN | DIAMOND CODE	TITLE	AUTHOR | ARTIST	US$ | FORMAT
1.	9781401258672 AUG150279	SUPERMAN ADVENTURES VOL. 1	MCCLOUD, SCOTT BURCHETT, RICK	$19.99/$23.99 CAN | TP
2.	9781401260941	SUPERMAN ADVENTURES VOL. 2	MCCLOUD, SCOTT VARIOUS	$19.99/$23.99 CAN | TP
3.	9781401253455 FEB150262	SMALLVILLE SEASON 11 VOL. 6: ALIEN	MILLER, BRYAN Q. STAGGS, CAT; LOBEL, BEN	$16.99/$19.99 CAN | TP
4.	9781401258634 JUL150316	SMALLVILLE SEASON 11 VOL. 7: LANTERN	MILLER, BRYAN Q. STAGGS, CAT; TAKARA, MARCIO	$16.99/$19.99 CAN | TP
5.	9781401261597	SMALLVILLE SEASON 11 VOL. 8: CHAOS	MILLER, BRYAN Q. | VARIOUS	$16.99/$19.99 CAN | TP

SUPERMAN STAND-ALONE GRAPHIC NOVELS

	ISBN | DIAMOND CODE	TITLE	AUTHOR | ARTIST	US$ | FORMAT
1.	9781401232054 JUL110247	ALL-STAR SUPERMAN	MORRISON, GRANT | QUITELY, FRANK	$29.99/$35.00 CAN | TP
2.	9781401246884 JAN140346	ADVENTURES OF SUPERMAN VOL. 1	VARIOUS | VARIOUS	$14.99/$17.99 CAN | TP
3.	9781401250362 JUL140255	ADVENTURES OF SUPERMAN VOL. 2	KRUL, J.T. | TO, MARCUS; LAPHAM, DAVID	$14.99/$17.99 CAN | TP
4.	9781401253301 DEC140387	ADVENTURES OF SUPERMAN VOL. 3	LANDIS, MAX | JOCK	$16.99/$17.99 CAN | TP
5.	9781401202521 JUL050214	SUPERMAN: BIRTHRIGHT	WAID, MARK | IMMONEN, STUART	$19.99/$23.99 CAN | TP
6.	9781401224691 FEB130226	SUPERMAN: EARTH ONE	STRACZYNSKI, J. MICHAEL | DAVIS, SHANE	$12.99/$15.99 CAN | TP
7.	9781401235598 DEC130312	SUPERMAN: EARTH ONE VOL. 2	STRACZYNSKI, J. MICHAEL | DAVIS, SHANE	$14.99/$17.99 CAN | TP
8.	9781401259099 AUG150278	SUPERMAN: EARTH ONE VOL. 3	STRACZYNSKI, J. MICHAEL | SYAF, ARDIAN	$14.99/$17.99 CAN | TP
9.	9781401247119 JAN140353	SUPERMAN: RED SON (NEW EDITION)	MILLAR, MARK | JOHNSON, DAVE	$17.99/$20.99 CAN | TP
10.	9781401204518 JAN130315	SUPERMAN: SECRET IDENTITY	BUSIEK, KURT | IMMONEN, STUART	$19.99/$23.99 CAN | TP
11.	9781401258696 SEP150308	SUPERMAN: SECRET IDENTITY DELUXE EDITION	BUSIEK, KURT | IMMONEN, STUART	$29.99/$35.00 CAN | HC
12.	9781401228415 APR100224	SUPERMAN VS. MUHAMMAD ALI DELUXE EDITION	O'NEIL, DENNIS | ADAMS, NEIL	$19.99/$23.99 CAN | HC

WONDER WOMAN BACKLIST AND SUGGESTED READING ORDER

	ISBN | DIAMOND CODE	TITLE	AUTHOR | ARTIST	US$ | FORMAT
1.	9781401212162 JAN070323	WONDER WOMAN: THE GREATEST STORIES EVER TOLD	VARIOUS | VARIOUS	$19.99/$23.99 CAN | TP
2.	9781401238650 JUL120228	WONDER WOMAN: THE AMAZON PRINCESS ARCHIVES VOL. 1	KANIGHER, ROBERT | ANDRU, ROSS	$75.00/$85.00 CAN | HC
3.	9781401255473 APR150306	WONDER WOMAN BY GEORGE PÉREZ OMNIBUS	PÉREZ, GEORGE | PÉREZ, GEORGE	$75.00/$85.00 CAN | HC
4.	9781401263447	WONDER WOMAN BY GEORGE PÉREZ OMNIBUS VOL. 2	PÉREZ, GEORGE | PÉREZ, GEORGE	$49.99/$58.00 CAN | HC
5.	9781401263751	WONDER WOMAN BY GEORGE PÉREZ VOL. 1	PÉREZ, GEORGE | PÉREZ, GEORGE	$19.99/$23.99 CAN | TP
6.	9781401261078 DEC150347	WONDER WOMAN: WAR OF THE GODS	PÉREZ, GEORGE | PÉREZ, GEORGE	$24.99/$28.99 CAN | TP
7.	9781401261061	WONDER WOMAN BY MIKE DEODATO	MESSNER-LOEBS, WILLIAM | DEODATO, MIKE	$19.99/$23.99 CAN | TP
8.	9781401263324	WONDER WOMAN BY GREG RUCKA VOL. 1	RUCKA, GREG | VARIOUS	$19.99/$23.99 CAN | TP
9.	9781401234102 DEC110279	FLASHPOINT: WORLD OF FLASHPOINT FEATURING WONDER WOMAN	VARIOUS | VARIOUS	$17.99/$20.99 CAN | TP
10.	9781401235628 OCT120256	WONDER WOMAN VOL. 1: BLOOD	AZZARELLO, BRIAN | CHIANG, CLIFF	$14.99/$17.99 CAN | TP
11.	9781401238100 JUN130271	WONDER WOMAN VOL. 2: GUTS	AZZARELLO, BRIAN | CHIANG, CLIFF	$14.99/$17.99 CAN | TP
12.	9781401246075 DEC130308	WONDER WOMAN VOL. 3: IRON	AZZARELLO, BRIAN | CHIANG, CLIFF; AKINS, TONY	$16.99/$19.99 CAN | TP
13.	9781401249540 JUL140247	WONDER WOMAN VOL. 4: WAR	AZZARELLO, BRIAN | CHIANG, CLIFF; AKINS, TONY	$14.99/$17.99 CAN | TP
14.	9781401253493 JAN150375	WONDER WOMAN VOL. 5: FLESH	AZZARELLO, BRIAN | CHIANG, CLIFF; SUDZUKA, GORAN	$16.99/$19.99 CAN | TP
15.	9781401257750 JUN150295	WONDER WOMAN VOL. 6: BONES	AZZARELLO, BRIAN | CHIANG, CLIFF; SUDZUKA, GORAN	$14.99/$17.99 CAN | TP
16.	9781401261634	WONDER WOMAN VOL. 7: WAR-TORN	FINCH, MEREDITH | FINCH, DAVID	$16.99/$19.99 CAN | TP
17.	9781401261641 JAN160336	WONDER WOMAN VOL. 8: TWIST OF FATE	FINCH, MEREDITH | FINCH, DAVID	$22.99/$27.99 CAN | HC

WONDER WOMAN STAND-ALONE GRAPHIC NOVELS

	ISBN | DIAMOND CODE	TITLE	AUTHOR | ARTIST	US$ | FORMAT
1.	9781401262068	WONDER WOMAN: A CELEBRATION OF 75 YEARS	VARIOUS | VARIOUS	$39.99/$48.99 CAN | HC
2.	9781401229788 DEC150215	WONDER WOMAN: EARTH ONE VOL. 1	MORRISON, GRANT | PAQUETTE, YANICK	$22.99/$27.99 CAN | HC
3.	9781401253448 DEC140392	SENSATION COMICS FEATURING WONDER WOMAN VOL. 1	SIMONE, GAIL | VAN SCIVER, ETHAN	$14.99/$17.99 CAN | TP
4.	9781401258627 JUL150320	SENSATION COMICS FEATURING WONDER WOMAN VOL. 2	TYNION IV, JAMES | STEVENSON, NOELLE	$14.99/$17.99 CAN | TP
5.	9781401261573	SENSATION COMICS FEATURING WONDER WOMAN VOL. 3	VARIOUS | VARIOUS	$14.99/$17.99 CAN | TP
6.	9781401263287	WONDER WOMAN '77 VOL. 1	VARIOUS | VARIOUS	$16.99/$19.99 CAN | TP

JUSTICE LEAGUE BACKLIST AND SUGGESTED READING ORDER

	ISBN | DIAMOND CODE	TITLE	AUTHOR | ARTIST	US$ | FORMAT
1.	9781401261115 NOV150283	JUSTICE LEAGUE OF AMERICA: THE SILVER AGE VOL. 1	VARIOUS | VARIOUS	$19.99/$23.99 CAN | TP
2.	9781401212674 OCT060211	JUSTICE LEAGUE OF AMERICA: HEREBY ELECTS	VARIOUS | VARIOUS	$14.99/$17.99 CAN | TP
3.	9781401248420 NOV130241	JUSTICE LEAGUE OF AMERICA OMNIBUS VOL. 1	VARIOUS | VARIOUS	$99.99/$112.00 CAN | HC

	ISBN | DIAMOND CODE	TITLE	AUTHOR | ARTIST	US$ | FORMAT
4.	9781401238353 OCT120271	SHOWCASE PRESENTS: JUSTICE LEAGUE OF AMERICA VOL. 6	WEIN, LEN | DILLON, DICK	$19.99/$23.99 CAN | TP
5.	9781563897504 AUG058162	CRISIS ON INFINITE EARTHS	WOLFMAN, MARV | PÉREZ, GEORGE	$29.99/$35.00 CAN | TP
6.	9781401258412 JUN150303	CRISIS ON INFINITE EARTHS 30TH ANNIVERSARY DELUXE EDITION	WOLFMAN, MARV | PEREZ, GEORGE	$49.99/$58.00 CAN | HC
7.	9781401217396 DEC080163	JUSTICE LEAGUE INTERNATIONAL VOL. 1	GIFFEN, KEITH | MAGUIRE, KEVIN	$17.99/$21.99 CAN | TP
8.	9781401225384 AUG090174	JUSTICE LEAGUE INTERNATIONAL VOL. 3	GIFFEN, KEITH | MAGUIRE, KEVIN	$19.99/$23.99 CAN | TP
9.	9781401221973 DEC090212	JUSTICE LEAGUE INTERNATIONAL VOL. 4	GIFFEN, KEITH | MAGUIRE, KEVIN	$17.99/$22.99 CAN | TP
10.	9781401230104 OCT100269	JUSTICE LEAGUE INTERNATIONAL VOL. 5	GIFFEN, KEITH | MAGUIRE, KEVIN	$19.99/$23.99 CAN | TP
11.	9781563891847 JUN068105	ZERO HOUR	JURGENS, DAN | JURGENS, DAN; ORDWAY, JERRY	$17.99/$21.99 CAN | TP
12.	9781401258238 JUL150313	JUSTICE LEAGUE: A LEAGUE OF ONE	MOELLER, CHRISTOPHER | MOELLER, CHRISTOPHER	$19.99/$23.99 CAN | TP
13.	9781401233143 JUN110276	JLA VOL. 1	MORRISON, GRANT | PORTER, HOWARD	$19.99/$23.99 CAN | TP
14.	9781401235185 APR120256	JLA VOL. 2	MORRISON, GRANT | PORTER, HOWARD	$24.99/$28.99 CAN | TP
15.	9781401238322 OCT120267	JLA VOL. 3	MORRISON, GRANT | PORTER, HOWARD	$24.99/$28.99 CAN | TP
16.	9781401251352 JUN140281	JLA: EARTH 2	MORRISON, GRANT | QUITELY, FRANK	$14.99/$17.99 CAN | TP
17.	9781401243852 NOV130242	JLA VOL. 4	MORRISON, GRANT; WAID, MARK | PORTER, HOWARD; PAJARILLO, MARK	$24.99/$28.99 CAN | TP
18.	9781401247508 MAR140266	JLA VOL. 5	WAID, MARK | HITCH, BRYAN	$24.99/$28.99 CAN | TP
19.	9781401251369 OCT140369	JLA VOL. 6	KELLY, JOE | MAHNKE, DOUG	$24.99/$28.99 CAN | TP
20.	9781401255282 FEB150260	JLA VOL. 7	KELLY, JOE | MAHNKE, DOUG	$24.99/$28.99 CAN | TP
21.	9781401263423	JLA VOL. 8	KELLY, JOE | MAHNKE, DOUG	$24.99/$29.99 CAN | TP
22.	9781401204587 AUG118125	IDENTITY CRISIS	MELTZER, BRAD | MORALES, RAGS	$17.99/$20.99 CAN | TP
23.	9781401252786 AUG140340	IDENTITY CRISIS 10TH ANNIVERSARY	MELTZER, BRAD | MORALES, RAGS	$29.99/$35.00 CAN | HC
24.	9781401210601 FEB118149	INFINITE CRISIS	JOHNS, GEOFF | JIMENEZ, PHIL	$17.99/$20.99 CAN | TP
25.	9781401263256	52 BOOK 1	MORRISON, GRANT; JOHNS, GEOFF; RUCKA, GREG; WAID, MARK | GIFFEN, KEITH	$29.99/$35.00 CAN | TP
26.	9781401235567 JUL120217	52 OMNIBUS	JOHNS, GEOFF; MORRISON, GRANT; WAID, MARK; RUCKA, GREG | VARIOUS	$150.00/$176.00 CAN | HC
27.	9781401215804 JUN080244	JUSTICE LEAGUE OF AMERICA: THE TORNADO'S PATH, VOL. 1	MELTZER, BRAD | BENES, ED	$17.99/$21.99 CAN | TP
28.	9781401218690 OCT080173	JUSTICE LEAGUE OF AMERICA: THE LIGHTNING SAGA, VOL. 2	MELTZER, BRAD | BENES, ED	$17.99/$21.99 CAN | TP
29.	9781401220105 OCT090247	JUSTICE LEAGUE OF AMERICA: SANCTUARY	MCDUFFIE, DWAYNE | BENES, ED	$14.99/$17.99 CAN | TP
30.	9781401222536 FEB100187	JUSTICE LEAGUE OF AMERICA: THE SECOND COMING	MCDUFFIE, DWAYNE | BENES, ED	$17.99/$20.99 CAN | TP
31.	9781401224233 JUL100203	JUSTICE LEAGUE OF AMERICA: WHEN WORLDS COLLIDE	MCDUFFIE, DWAYNE | BENES, ED	$14.99/$17.99 CAN | TP
32.	9781401245177 JAN140352	FINAL CRISIS	MORRISON, GRANT | JONES, J.G.; MAHNKE, DOUG; PACHECO, CARLOS	$19.99/$23.99 CAN | TP
33.	9781401225643 MAR110353	JUSTICE LEAGUE: CRY FOR JUSTICE	ROBINSON, JAMES | CASCIOLI, MAURO	$19.99/$23.99 CAN | TP
34.	9781401229535 APR110192	BLACKEST NIGHT	JOHNS, GEOFF | REIS, IVAN	$19.99/$23.99 CAN | TP
35.	9781401232603 JUN110277	JUSTICE LEAGUE OF AMERICA: TEAM HISTORY	ROBINSON, JAMES | BAGLEY, MARK	$17.99/$19.99 CAN | TP
36.	9781401231934 DEC110289	JUSTICE LEAGUE OF AMERICA: DARK THINGS	ROBINSON, JAMES | BAGLEY, MARK	$17.99/$19.99 CAN | TP
37.	9781401232436 MAY110247	JUSTICE LEAGUE OF AMERICA: OMEGA	ROBINSON, JAMES | BAGLEY, MARK	$24.99/$27.99 CAN | TP
38.	9781401234133 JUL120225	JUSTICE LEAGUE OF AMERICA: THE RISE OF ECLIPSO	ROBINSON, JAMES | BOOTH, BRETT	$16.99/$19.99 CAN | TP
39.	9781401230203 DEC100249	JUSTICE LEAGUE: GENERATION LOST VOL. 1	WINICK, JUDD | LOPRESTI, AARON	$39.99/$46.99 CAN | HC
40.	9781401233389 OCT138324	FLASHPOINT	JOHNS, GEOFF | KUBERT, ANDY	$16.99/$17.99 CAN | TP
41.	9781401237882 OCT120252	JUSTICE LEAGUE VOL. 1: ORIGIN	JOHNS, GEOFF | LEE, JIM	$16.99/$19.99 CAN | TP
42.	9781401237653 JUN130261	JUSTICE LEAGUE VOL. 2: THE VILLAIN'S JOURNEY	JOHNS, GEOFF | LEE, JIM	$16.99/$19.99 CAN | TP
43.	9781401246983 JAN140339	JUSTICE LEAGUE VOL. 3: THRONE OF ATLANTIS	JOHNS, GEOFF | REIS, IVAN; DANIEL, TONY S.	$16.99/$19.99 CAN | TP
44.	9781401250089 JUN140272	JUSTICE LEAGUE VOL. 4: THE GRID	JOHNS, GEOFF | REIS, IVAN	$16.99/$19.99 CAN | TP
45.	9781401249441 AUG140331	JUSTICE LEAGUE: TRINITY WAR	JOHNS, GEOFF; LEMIRE, JEFF | REIS, IVAN; MAHNKE, DOUG	$19.99/$23.99 CAN | TP
46.	9781401253387 FEB150254	FOREVER EVIL	JOHNS, GEOFF | FINCH, DAVID	$19.99/$23.99 CAN | TP
47.	9781401254193 DEC140382	JUSTICE LEAGUE VOL. 5: FOREVER HEROES	JOHNS, GEOFF | REIS, IVAN; MAHNKE, DOUG	$14.99/$17.99 CAN | TP
48.	9781401249397 JUN140268	FOREVER EVIL: A.R.G.U.S.	GATES, STERLING | TAN, PHILIP	$14.99/$17.99 CAN | TP
49.	9781401249403 JUN140267	FOREVER EVIL: ARKHAM WAR	TOMASI, PETER | EATON, SCOTT	$16.99/$19.99 CAN | TP
50.	9781401250065 JUN140269	FOREVER EVIL: BLIGHT	FAWKES, RAY; DEMATTEIS, J.M. | JANIN, MIKEL	$24.99/$28.99 CAN | TP
51.	9781401249410 JUN140270	FOREVER EVIL: ROGUES REBELLION	BUCCELLATO, BRIAN | HEPBURN, SCOTT; ZIRCHER, PATRICK	$16.99/$19.99 CAN | TP
52.	9781401258528 DEC150328	JUSTICE LEAGUE VOL. 6: INJUSTICE LEAGUE	JOHNS, GEOFF | MAHNKE, DOUG; FABOK, JASON	$19.99/$23.99 CAN | TP
53.	9781401262716	CONVERGENCE	KING, JEFF; LOBDELL, SCOTT | PAGULAYAN, CARLO	$19.99/$23.99 CAN | TP
54.	9781401258085 JUL150295	CONVERGENCE: CRISIS BOOK ONE	WOLFMAN, MARV; PARKER, JEFF | TRUMAN, TIM	$19.99/$23.99 CAN | TP

DC COMICS READING ORDER

	ISBN | DIAMOND CODE	TITLE	AUTHOR | ARTIST	US$ | FORMAT
55.	9781401258344 JUL150297	CONVERGENCE: CRISIS BOOK TWO	WEIN, LEN | JONES, KELLEY	$19.99/$23.99 CAN | TP
56.	9781401258351 JUL150298	CONVERGENCE: FLASHPOINT BOOK ONE	RUCKA, GREG | WEEKS, LEE; HAMNER, CULLY	$19.99/$23.99 CAN | TP
57.	9781401258368 JUL150300	CONVERGENCE: FLASHPOINT BOOK TWO	KWITNEY, ALISA | YEOWELL, STEVE; WINSLADE, PHIL	$19.99/$23.99 CAN | TP
58.	9781401258375 JUL150299	CONVERGENCE: INFINITE EARTHS BOOK ONE	LEVITZ, PAUL | ORDWAY, JERRY; CALDWELL, BEN	$19.99/$23.99 CAN | TP
59.	9781401258382 JUL150301	CONVERGENCE: INFINITE EARTHS BOOK TWO	JURGENS, DAN; PARKER, JEFF | SHANER, EVAN	$19.99/$23.99 CAN | TP
60.	9781401258399 JUL150294	CONVERGENCE: ZERO HOUR BOOK ONE	MARZ, RON | MORALES, RAGS	$19.99/$23.99 CAN | TP
61.	9781401258405 JUL150294	CONVERGENCE: ZERO HOUR BOOK TWO	GIFFEN, KEITH; BEDARD, TONY | RICHARDS, CLIFF	$19.99/$23.99 CAN | TP
62.	9781401259778 NOV150281	JUSTICE LEAGUE VOL. 7: DARKSEID WAR PART 1	JOHNS, GEOFF | FABOK, JASON	$24.99/$29.99 CAN | HC
63.	9781401263416	JUSTICE LEAGUE VOL. 8: DARKSEID WAR PART 2	JOHNS, GEOFF | FABOK, JASON	$22.99/$27.99 CAN | HC
64.	9781401261498 DEC150327	JUSTICE LEAGUE: DARKSEID WAR - POWER OF THE GODS	JOHNS, GEOFF | VARIOUS	$29.99/$35.00 CAN | HC

JUSTICE LEAGUE BACKLIST AND SUGGESTED READING ORDER

	ISBN | DIAMOND CODE	TITLE	AUTHOR | ARTIST	US$ | FORMAT
1.	9781401246891 APR140266	JUSTICE LEAGUE OF AMERICA VOL. 1: WORLD'S MOST DANGEROUS	JOHNS, GEOFF | FINCH, DAVID; MAHNKE, DOUG	$16.99/$19.99 CAN | TP
2.	9781401250478 DEC140381	JUSTICE LEAGUE OF AMERICA VOL. 2: SURVIVORS OF EVIL	KINDT, MATT | BARROWS, EDDY; MAHNKE, DOUG	$16.99/$19.99 CAN | TP
3.	9781401259761 OCT15026	JUSTICE LEAGUE OF AMERICA VOL. 1	HITCH, BRYAN | HITCH, BRYAN	$24.99/$29.99 CAN | HC
4.	9781401257651 SEP150300	JUSTICE LEAGUE UNITED VOL. 1: JUSTICE LEAGUE CANADA	LEMIRE, JEFF | MCKONE, MIKE	$16.99/$19.99 CAN | TP
5.	9781401257668 AUG150273	JUSTICE LEAGUE UNITED VOL. 2: THE INFINITUS SAGA	LEMIRE, JEFF | EDWARDS, NEIL	$24.99/$29.99 CAN | HC
6.	9781401263348	JUSTICE LEAGUE UNITED VOL. 3	PARKER, JEFF | FOREMAN, TRAVEL	$14.99/$17.99 CAN | TP
7.	9781401237936 OCT120255	JUSTICE LEAGUE INTERNATIONAL VOL. 2: BREAKDOWN	JURGENS, DAN | LOPRESTI, AARON	$16.99/$19.99 CAN | TP
8.	9781401237042 JUL120211	JUSTICE LEAGUE DARK VOL. 1: IN THE DARK	MILLIGAN, PETER | JANIN, MIKEL	$14.99/$19.99 CAN | TP
9.	9781401240240 APR130217	JUSTICE LEAGUE DARK VOL. 2: THE BOOKS OF MAGIC	LEMIRE, JEFF | JANIN, MIKEL	$16.99/$19.99 CAN | TP
10.	9781401242459 OCT130241	JUSTICE LEAGUE DARK VOL. 3: THE DEATH OF MAGIC	LEMIRE, JEFF | JANIN, MIKEL	$16.99/$19.99 CAN | TP
11.	9781401247256 MAY140365	JUSTICE LEAGUE DARK VOL. 4: THE REBIRTH OF EVIL	LEMIRE, JEFF | JANIN, MIKEL	$16.99/$19.99 CAN | TP
12.	9781401250072 NOV140299	JUSTICE LEAGUE DARK VOL. 5: PARADISE LOST	DEMATTEIS, J.M. | JANIN, MIKEL	$14.99/$19.99 CAN | TP
13.	9781401254810 MAY150242	JUSTICE LEAGUE DARK VOL. 6: LOST IN FOREVER	DEMATTEIS, J.M. | GUINALDO, ANDRES	$16.99/$19.99 CAN | TP
14.	9781401250461 JUL140244	JUSTICE LEAGUE 3000 VOL. 1: YESTERDAY LIVES	GIFFEN, KEITH; DEMATTEIS, J.M. | PORTER, HOWARD	$16.99/$19.99 CAN | TP
15.	9781401254148 JAN150372	JUSTICE LEAGUE 3000 VOL. 2: THE CAMELOT WAR	GIFFEN, KEITH; DEMATTEIS, J.M. | PORTER, HOWARD	$14.99/$19.99 CAN | TP
16.	9781401261481 DEC150334	JUSTICE LEAGUE 3001 VOL. 1: DÉJÀ VU ALL OVER AGAIN	GIFFEN, KEITH; DEMATTEIS, J.M. | PORTER, HOWARD	$16.99/$19.99 CAN | TP

JUSTICE LEAGUE: FROM PAGE TO SCREEN

	ISBN | DIAMOND CODE	TITLE	AUTHOR | ARTIST	US$ | FORMAT
1.	9781401247546 DEC130311	JUSTICE LEAGUE BEYOND: IN GODS WE TRUST	FRIDOLFS, DEREK; KRUL, J.T. | NGUYEN, DUSTIN	$17.99/$19.99 CAN | TP
2.	9781401250737 JUL140251	JUSTICE LEAGUE BEYOND: POWER STRUGGLE	GAGE, CHRISTOS | COELLO, IBAN	$16.99/$19.99 CAN | TP
3.	9781401261313 OCT15026	JLA: GODS AND MONSTERS	DEMATTEIS, J.M. | VARIOUS	$22.99/$27.99 CAN | HC
4.	9781401247577 FEB140262	SHOWCASE PRESENTS: SUPER FRIENDS VOL. 1	VARIOUS | VARIOUS	$19.99/$19.99 CAN | TP
5.	9781401248437 MAR140265	INJUSTICE: GODS AMONG US VOL. 1	TAYLOR, TOM | RAAPACK, JHEREMY	$16.99/$19.99 CAN | TP
6.	9781401250454 OCT140368	INJUSTICE: GODS AMONG US VOL. 2	TAYLOR, TOM | MILLER, MIKE S.; DERENICK, TOM	$16.99/$19.99 CAN | TP
7.	9781401260811 DEC150338	INJUSTICE YEAR ONE: THE COMPLETE EDITION	TAYLOR, TOM | VARIOUS	$24.99/$29.99 CAN | TP
8.	9781401253400 JAN150372	INJUSTICE: GODS AMONG US YEAR 2 VOL. 1	TAYLOR, TOM | REDONDO, BRUNO	$14.99/$19.99 CAN | TP
9.	9781401258504 JUL150315	INJUSTICE: GODS AMONG US YEAR TWO VOL. 2	TAYLOR, TOM | REDONDO, BRUNO	$16.99/$19.99 CAN | TP
10.	9781401263140 NOV150270	INJUSTICE: GODS AMONG US: YEAR THREE VOL. 1	TAYLOR, TOM | REDONDO, BRUNO	$22.99/$27.99 CAN | HC
11.	9781401261290	INJUSTICE: GODS AMONG US YEAR THREE VOL. 2	BUCCELLATO, BRIAN | REDONDO, BRUNO	$16.99/$19.99 CAN | TP
12.	9781401262679	INJUSTICE GODS AMONG US YEAR FOUR VOLUME 1	BUCCELLATO, BRIAN | REDONDO, BRUNO	$16.99/$19.99 CAN | TP
13.	9781401262686	INJUSTICE GODS AMONG US YEAR FOUR VOLUME 2	BUCCELLATO, BRIAN | REDONDO, BRUNO	$22.99/$27.99 CAN | HC

JUSTICE LEAGUE STAND-ALONE GRAPHIC NOVELS

	ISBN | DIAMOND CODE	TITLE	AUTHOR | ARTIST	US$ | FORMAT
1.	9781401248888 OCT140355	DC: THE NEW FRONTIER DELUXE EDITION	COOKE, DARWYN | COOKE, DARWYN	$49.99/$58.00 CAN | HC
2.	9781563894800 MAR045122	JUSTICE LEAGUE OF AMERICA: THE NAIL	DAVIS, ALAN | DAVIS, ALAN	$14.95/$19.99 CAN | TP
3.	9781401235260 MAR120254	JUSTICE	ROSS, ALEX | ROSS, ALEX	$29.99/$35.00 CAN | TP
4.	9781401220341 SEP138294	KINGDOM COME	WAID, MARK | ROSS, ALEX	$19.99/$19.99 CAN | TP
5.	9781401260828 JAN160321	KINGDOM COME 20TH ANNIVERSARY DELUXE EDITION	WAID, MARK | ROSS, ALEX	$39.99/$48.99 CAN | HC
6.	9781563895678 APR068118	KINGDOM	WAID, MARK | VARIOUS	$19.99/$19.99 CAN | TP

GREEN LANTERN BACKLIST AND SUGGESTED READING ORDER

	ISBN | DIAMOND CODE	TITLE	AUTHOR | ARTIST	US$ | FORMAT
1.	9781401209612 MAY060165	GREEN LANTERN: THE GREATEST STORIES EVER TOLD	VARIOUS | VARIOUS	$19.99/$23.99 CAN | TP
2.	9781401219864 JUL080158	GREEN LANTERN: IN BRIGHTEST DAY	BROOME, JOHN | KANE, GIL	$19.99/$23.99 CAN | TP

DC COMICS READING ORDER

	ISBN	DIAMOND CODE	TITLE	AUTHOR	ARTIST	US$	FORMAT
3.	9781401221638	OCT138011	GREEN LANTERN CHRONICLES VOL. 1	BROOME, JOHN	KANE, GIL	$17.99/$20.99 CAN	TP
4.	9781401233969	DEC110295	GREEN LANTERN CHRONICLES VOL. 4	BROOME, JOHN	KANE, GIL	$14.99/$17.99 CAN	TP
5.	9781401263485		GREEN LANTERN: THE SILVER AGE VOL. 1	VARIOUS	VARIOUS	$19.99/$23.99 CAN	TP
6.	9781401235178	MAY120290	GREEN LANTERN/GREEN ARROW	O'NEIL, DENNIS	ADAMS, NEAL	$29.99/$35.00 CAN	TP
7.	9781401263157		GREEN LANTERN/GREEN ARROW VOL. 2	O'NEIL, DENNIS	ADAMS, NEAL	$29.99/$35.00 CAN	TP
8.	9781401236892	AUG120252	GREEN LANTERN: SECTOR 2814 VOL. 1	WEIN, LEN	GIBBONS, DAVE	$16.99/$19.99 CAN	TP
9.	9781401240783	MAY130231	GREEN LANTERN: SECTOR 2814 VOL. 2	WEIN, LEN	GIBBONS, DAVE	$16.99/$19.99 CAN	TP
10.	9781401243272	OCT130250	GREEN LANTERN: SECTOR 2814 VOL. 3	ENGLEHART, STEVE	STATON, JOE; PATTERSON, BRUCE D.	$16.99/$19.99 CAN	TP
11.	9781401227555	FEB100185	GREEN LANTERN: REBIRTH	JOHNS, GEOFF	VAN SCIVER, ETHAN	$14.99/$17.99 CAN	TP
12.	9781401210588	FEB080244	GREEN LANTERN: NO FEAR	JOHNS, GEOFF	PACHECO, CARLOS	$12.99/$15.99 CAN	TP
13.	9781401209605	JUN098401	GREEN LANTERN: REVENGE OF THE GREEN LANTERNS	JOHNS, GEOFF	PACHECO, CARLOS	$14.99/$17.99 CAN	TP
14.	9781401215903	OCT080170	GREEN LANTERN: WANTED: HAL JORDAN	JOHNS, GEOFF	REIS, IVAN	$14.99/$35.00 CAN	TP
15.	9781401233013	JUN110275	GREEN LANTERN: THE SINESTRO CORPS WAR	JOHNS, GEOFF	REIS, IVAN	$29.99/$35.00 CAN	TP
16.	9781401230869	JAN110337	GREEN LANTERN: SECRET ORIGIN	JOHNS, GEOFF	REIS, IVAN	$14.99/$17.99 CAN	TP
17.	9781401223021	APR100214	GREEN LANTERN: RAGE OF THE RED LANTERNS	JOHNS, GEOFF	REIS, IVAN	$14.99/$17.99 CAN	TP
18.	9781401224202	AUG100204	GREEN LANTERN: AGENT ORANGE	JOHNS, GEOFF	TAN, PHILIP	$14.99/$17.99 CAN	TP
19.	9781401228064	APR110195	BLACKEST NIGHT: RISE OF THE BLACK LANTERNS	VARIOUS	VARIOUS	$19.99/$23.99 CAN	TP
20.	9781401228071	APR110196	BLACKEST NIGHT: TALES OF THE CORPS	VARIOUS	VARIOUS	$19.99/$23.99 CAN	TP
21.	9781401229535	APR110192	BLACKEST NIGHT	JOHNS, GEOFF	REIS, IVAN	$19.99/$23.99 CAN	TP
22.	9781401229528	APR110193	BLACKEST NIGHT: GREEN LANTERN	JOHNS, GEOFF	MAHNKE, DOUG	$19.99/$23.99 CAN	TP
23.	9781401228057	APR110194	BLACKEST NIGHT: GREEN LANTERN CORPS	TOMASI, PETER J.	GLEASON, PATRICK	$19.99/$23.99 CAN	TP
24.	9781401228040	APR110197	BLACKEST NIGHT: BLACK LANTERN CORPS VOL. 1	VARIOUS	VARIOUS	$19.99/$23.99 CAN	TP
25.	9781401228033	APR110198	BLACKEST NIGHT: BLACK LANTERN CORPS VOL. 2	VARIOUS	VARIOUS	$19.99/$23.99 CAN	TP
26.	9781401240738	JAN130306	ABSOLUTE BLACKEST NIGHT	JOHNS, GEOFF	REIS, IVAN	$125.00/$147.00 CAN	HC
27.	9781401256920	JUL150310	BLACKEST NIGHT UNWRAPPED	JOHNS, GEOFF	REIS, IVAN	$39.99/$48.99 CAN	HC
28.	9781401232764	SEP110177	BRIGHTEST DAY VOL. 1	JOHNS, GEOFF	REIS, IVAN	$19.99/$23.99 CAN	TP
29.	9781401230845	FEB120255	BRIGHTEST DAY VOL. 2	JOHNS, GEOFF	REIS, IVAN	$19.99/$23.99 CAN	TP
30.	9781401232177	JUN120244	BRIGHTEST DAY VOL. 3	JOHNS, GEOFF	REIS, IVAN	$16.99/$19.99 CAN	TP
31.	9781401231415	FEB120254	GREEN LANTERN: BRIGHTEST DAY	JOHNS, GEOFF	MAHNKE, DOUG	$19.99/$23.99 CAN	TP
32.	9781401245979	APR140272	BRIGHTEST DAY OMNIBUS	JOHNS, GEOFF; TOMASI, PETER J.	VARIOUS	$75.00/$85.00 CAN	HC
33.	9781401234522	JUN120246	GREEN LANTERN: WAR OF THE GREEN LANTERNS	VARIOUS	VARIOUS	$16.99/$19.99 CAN	TP
34.	9781401235383	OCT120265	WAR OF THE GREEN LANTERNS: AFTERMATH	TOMASI, PETER J.; BEDARD, TONY	VARIOUS	$16.99/$19.99 CAN	TP
35.	9781401234065	DEC110280	FLASHPOINT: THE WORLD OF FLASHPOINT FEATURING GREEN LANTERN	VARIOUS	VARIOUS	$17.99/$20.99 CAN	TP
36.	9781401234553	OCT120257	GREEN LANTERN VOL. 1: SINESTRO	JOHNS, GEOFF	MAHNKE, DOUG	$14.99/$17.99 CAN	TP
37.	9781401237677	JUL130229	GREEN LANTERN VOL. 2: THE REVENGE OF BLACK HAND	JOHNS, GEOFF	MAHNKE, DOUG; VAN SCIVER, ETHAN	$16.99/$19.99 CAN	TP
38.	9781401246846	JAN140338	GREEN LANTERN VOL. 3: THE END	JOHNS, GEOFF	MAHNKE, DOUG	$19.99/$23.99 CAN	TP
39.	9781401246136	DEC130302	GREEN LANTERN: RISE OF THE THIRD ARMY	JOHNS, GEOFF; TOMASI, PETER J.	VARIOUS	$24.99/$28.99 CAN	TP
40.	9781401246938	MAY140373	GREEN LANTERN: WRATH OF THE FIRST LANTERN	JOHNS, GEOFF; TOMASI, PETER J.	VARIOUS	$19.99/$23.99 CAN	TP
41.	9781401251345	SEP140319	GREEN LANTERN BY GEOFF JOHNS OMNIBUS VOL. 1	JOHNS, GEOFF	REIS, IVAN; VAN SCIVER, ETHAN	$125.00/$144.00 CAN	HC
42.	9781401255268	MAR150274	GREEN LANTERN BY GEOFF JOHNS OMNIBUS VOL. 2	JOHNS, GEOFF	REIS, IVAN; MAHNKE, DOUG	$99.99/$112.00 CAN	HC
43.	9781401258207	NOV150285	GREEN LANTERN BY GEOFF JOHNS OMNIBUS VOL. 3	JOHNS, GEOFF	MAHNKE, DOUG	$99.99/$112.00 CAN	HC
44.	9781401249427	JUL140243	GREEN LANTERN VOL. 4: DARK DAYS	VENDITTI, ROBERT	TAN, BILLY	$16.99/$19.99 CAN	TP
45.	9781401249434	SEP140306	GREEN LANTERN: LIGHTS OUT	VENDITTI, ROBERT; JORDAN, JUSTIN; JENSEN, VAN; SOULE, CHARLES	TAN, BILLY	$16.99/$19.99 CAN	TP
46.	9781401254162	FEB150255	GREEN LANTERN VOL. 5: TEST OF WILLS	VENDITTI, ROBERT	TAN, BILLY	$17.99/$20.99 CAN	TP
47.	9781401258467	JAN160317	GREEN LANTERN VOL. 6: THE LIFE EQUATION	VENDITTI, ROBERT	TAN, BILLY; PORTELA, FRANCIS	$16.99/$19.99 CAN	TP
48.	9781401261252	DEC150333	GREEN LANTERN VOL. 7: RENEGADE	VENDITTI, ROBERT	TAN, BILLY	$22.99/$27.99 CAN	HC
49.	9781401261276		GREEN LANTERN/NEW GODS: GODHEAD	VENDITTI, ROBERT; JENSEN, VAN	TAN, BILLY	$24.99/$29.99 CAN	TP
50.	9781401258191	MAY150241	GREEN LANTERN: A CELEBRATION OF 75 YEARS	JOHNS, GEOFF	KANE, GIL	$39.99/$48.99 CAN	HC

GREEN LANTERN CORPS

	ISBN	DIAMOND CODE	TITLE	AUTHOR	ARTIST	US$	FORMAT
1.	9781401221553	NOV080187	TALES OF GREEN LANTERN CORPS VOL. 1	VARIOUS	VARIOUS	$19.99/$23.99 CAN	TP
2.	9781401227029	OCT090254	TALES OF GREEN LANTERN CORPS VOL. 2	VARIOUS	VARIOUS	$19.99/$23.99 CAN	TP

DC COMICS READING ORDER

ISBN	DIAMOND CODE	TITLE	AUTHOR	ARTIST	US$	FORMAT
3.	9781401229344 SEP100259	TALES OF GREEN LANTERN CORPS VOL. 3	VARIOUS	VARIOUS	$19.99/$23.99 CAN	TP
4.	9781401222734 MAR090182	GREEN LANTERN CORPS: SINS OF THE STAR SAPPHIRE	TOMASI, PETER J.	GLEASON, PATRICK	$14.99/$17.99 CAN	TP
5.	9781401219758 AUG080181	GREEN LANTERN CORPS: RING QUEST	TOMASI, PETER J.	GLEASON, PATRICK	$14.99/$17.99 CAN	TP
6.	9781401231408 MAR120252	GREEN LANTERN CORPS: REVOLT OF THE ALPHA LANTERNS	BEDARD, TONY	SYAF, ARDIAN	$14.99/$17.99 CAN	TP
7.	9781401230807 APR120252	GREEN LANTERN: EMERALD WARRIORS VOL. 1	TOMASI, PETER J.	PASARIN, FERNANDO	$14.99/$17.99 CAN	TP
8.	9781401234416 JUL120222	GREEN LANTERN CORPS: THE WEAPONER	BEDARD, TONY	KIRKHAM, TYLER	$14.99/$17.99 CAN	TP
9.	9781401237028 APR130218	GREEN LANTERN CORPS VOL. 1: FEARSOME	TOMASI, PETER J.	PASARIN, FERNANDO	$14.99/$19.99 CAN	TP
10.	9781401242947 SEP130267	GREEN LANTERN CORPS VOL. 2: ALPHA WAR	TOMASI, PETER J.	PASARIN, FERNANDO	$16.99/$17.99 CAN	TP
11.	9781401247669 MAR140255	GREEN LANTERN CORPS VOL. 3: WILLPOWER	TOMASI, PETER J.	PASARIN, FERNANDO	$16.99/$19.99 CAN	TP
12.	9781401247454 APR140263	GREEN LANTERN CORPS VOL. 4: REBUILD	VENDITTI, ROBERT	JENSEN, VAN	$16.99/$19.99 CAN	TP
13.	9781401250874 OCT140361	GREEN LANTERN CORPS VOL. 5: UPRISING	VENDITTI, ROBERT	CHANG, BERNARD	$19.99/$23.99 CAN	TP
14.	9781401254759 APR150295	GREEN LANTERN CORPS VOL. 6: RECKONING	JENSEN, VAN	CHANG, BERNARD	$14.99/$17.99 CAN	TP
15.	9781401261269 JAN160316	GREEN LANTERN: LOST ARMY VOL. 1	BUNN, CULLEN	SAIZ, JESUS	$16.99/$19.99 CAN	TP
16.	9781401237080 APR130216	GREEN LANTERN: NEW GUARDIANS VOL. 1: THE RING BEARER	BEDARD, TONY	KIRKMAN, TYLER	$14.99/$17.99 CAN	TP
17.	9781401242930 OCT130239	GREEN LANTERN: NEW GUARDIANS VOL. 2: BEYOND HOPE	BEDARD, TONY	KIRKHAM, TYLER	$14.99/$17.99 CAN	TP
18.	9781401247102 APR140264	GREEN LANTERN: NEW GUARDIANS VOL. 3: LOVE & DEATH	BEDARD, TONY	KUDER, AARON	$16.99/$19.99 CAN	TP
19.	9781401247461 MAY140372	GREEN LANTERN: NEW GUARDIANS VOL. 4: GODS AND MONSTERS	JORDAN, JUSTIN	WALKER, BRAD	$16.99/$19.99 CAN	TP
20.	9781401250881 NOV140297	GREEN LANTERN: NEW GUARDIANS VOL. 5: GODKILLERS	JORDAN, JUSTIN	WALKER, BRAD	$16.99/$19.99 CAN	TP
21.	9781401254773 MAY150236	GREEN LANTERN: NEW GUARDIANS VOL. 6: STORMING THE GATES	JORDAN, JUSTIN	WALKER, BRAD	$14.99/$17.99 CAN	TP

RED LANTERNS

ISBN	DIAMOND CODE	TITLE	AUTHOR	ARTIST	US$	FORMAT
1.	9781401234911 MAR120243	RED LANTERNS VOL. 1: BLOOD AND RAGE	MILLIGAN, PETER	BENES, ED	$14.99/$17.99 CAN	TP
2.	9781401238476 DEC120329	RED LANTERNS VOL. 2: THE DEATH OF THE RED LANTERNS	MILLIGAN, PETER	SEPULVEDA, MIGUEL; BENES, ED	$16.99/$19.99 CAN	TP
3.	9781401244149 AUG130296	RED LANTERNS VOL. 3: THE SECOND PROPHECY	MILLIGAN, PETER	SEPULVEDA, MIGUEL	$19.99/$23.99 CAN	TP
4.	9781401247423 FEB140256	RED LANTERNS VOL. 4: BLOOD BROTHERS	SOULE, CHARLES	VITTI, ALESSANDRO	$16.99/$19.99 CAN	TP
5.	9781401250904 SEP140311	RED LANTERNS VOL. 5: ATROCITIES	SOULE, CHARLES; BEDARD, TONY	VITTI, ALESSANDRO	$19.99/$23.99 CAN	TP
6.	9781401254841 APR150297	RED LANTERNS VOL. 6: FORGED IN BLOOD	SOULE, CHARLES	CALIFORE, J.	$14.99/$17.99 CAN	TP

SINESTRO

ISBN	DIAMOND CODE	TITLE	AUTHOR	ARTIST	US$	FORMAT
1.	9781401250508 OCT140359	SINESTRO VOL. 1: THE DEMON WITHIN	BUNN, CULLEN	EAGLESHAM, DALE	$14.99/$17.99 CAN	TP
2.	9781401254865 APR150300	SINESTRO VOL. 2: SACRIFICE	BUNN, CULLEN	EAGLESHAM, DALE	$14.99/$17.99 CAN	TP
3.	9781401261580 NOV150286	SINESTRO VOL. 3: RISING	BUNN, CULLEN	WALKER, BRAD	$16.99/$19.99 CAN	TP

THE FLASH BACKLIST AND SUGGESTED READING ORDER

ISBN	DIAMOND CODE	TITLE	AUTHOR	ARTIST	US$	FORMAT
1.	9781401261108 OCT138012	FLASH: THE SILVER AGE VOL. 1	KANIGHER, ROBERT	VARIOUS	$19.99/$23.99 CAN	TP
2.	978-1401224714 JAN130310	THE FLASH CHRONICLES VOL. 1	VARIOUS	INFANTINO, CARMINE	$17.99/$20.99 CAN	TP
3.	9781401238315 JAN130310	THE FLASH CHRONICLES VOL. 4	BROOME, JOHN	INFANTINO, CARMINE	$14.99/$17.99 CAN	TP
4.	9781401255404 MAY140383	SHOWCASE PRESENTS: THE FLASH VOL. 5	KANIGHER, ROBERT	NOVICK, IRV	$19.99/$23.99 CAN	TP
5.	9781401251499 MAY140383	THE FLASH OMNIBUS VOL. 1	KANIGHER, ROBERT	BROOME, JOHN; INFANTINO, CARMINE	$99.99/$112.00 CAN	HC
6.	9781401261023 AUG150268	THE FLASH BY GRANT MORRISON & MARK MILLAR	MORRISON, GRANT; MILLAR, MARK	VARIOUS	$24.99/$29.99 CAN	HC
7.	9781401258733 AUG150268	THE FLASH BY GEOFF JOHNS BOOK ONE	JOHNS, GEOFF	KOLINS, SCOTT	$24.99/$48.99 CAN	HC
8.	9781401261016 APR100213	THE FLASH BY GEOFF JOHNS BOOK TWO	JOHNS, GEOFF	KOLINS, SCOTT	$29.99/$35.00 CAN	HC
9.	9781401223342 JAN110329	FINAL CRISIS: ROGUE'S REVENGE	JOHNS, GEOFF	KOLINS, SCOTT	$14.99/$17.99 CAN	TP
10.	9781401230012 OCT110249	THE FLASH: REBIRTH	JOHNS, GEOFF	VAN SCIVER, ETHAN	$14.99/$17.99 CAN	TP
11.	9781401231958 JUN120245	THE FLASH: THE DASTARDLY DEATH OF THE ROGUES	JOHNS, GEOFF	MANAPUL, FRANCIS	$14.99/$17.99 CAN	TP
12.	9781401234485 OCT138324	THE FLASH: ROAD TO FLASHPOINT	JOHNS, GEOFF	MANAPUL, FRANCIS	$14.99/$17.99 CAN	TP
13.	9781401233389 DEC110277	FLASHPOINT	JOHNS, GEOFF	KUBERT, ANDY	$16.99/$19.99 CAN	TP
14.	9781401234058 DEC110280	FLASHPOINT: WORLD OF FLASHPOINT FEATURING BATMAN	VARIOUS	VARIOUS	$17.99/$20.99 CAN	TP
15.	9781401234065 DEC110279	FLASHPOINT: WORLD OF FLASHPOINT FEATURING GREEN LANTERN	VARIOUS	VARIOUS	$17.99/$20.99 CAN	TP
16.	9781401234102 DEC110281	FLASHPOINT: WORLD OF FLASHPOINT FEATURING WONDER WOMAN	VARIOUS	VARIOUS	$17.99/$20.99 CAN	TP
17.	9781401234089 DEC110278	FLASHPOINT: WORLD OF FLASHPOINT FEATURING THE FLASH	VARIOUS	VARIOUS	$17.99/$20.99 CAN	TP
18.	9781401234348 MAY130224	FLASHPOINT: WORLD OF FLASHPOINT FEATURING SUPERMAN	VARIOUS	VARIOUS	$17.99/$20.99 CAN	TP
19.	9781401235543 NOV130229	THE FLASH VOL. 1: MOVE FORWARD	MANAPUL, FRANCIS; BUCCELLATO, BRIAN	MANAPUL, FRANCIS	$16.99/$19.99 CAN	TP
20.	9781401242732 MAY140367	THE FLASH VOL. 2: ROGUES REVOLUTION	MANAPUL, FRANCIS; BUCCELLATO, BRIAN	MANAPUL, FRANCIS	$16.99/$19.99 CAN	TP

DC COMICS READING ORDER

ISBN	DIAMOND CODE	TITLE	AUTHOR	ARTIST	US$	FORMAT
9781401247126	OCT140357	THE FLASH VOL. 3: GORILLA WARFARE	MANAPUL, FRANCIS; BUCCELLATO, BRIAN	MANAPUL, FRANCIS	$16.99/$19.99 CAN	TP
9781401249496	OCT140357	THE FLASH VOL. 4: REVERSE	MANAPUL, FRANCIS; BUCCELLATO, BRIAN	MANAPUL, FRANCIS	$16.99/$19.99 CAN	TP
9781401261030	JUN150293	THE FLASH BY FRANCIS MANAPUL AND BRIAN BUCCELLATO DELUXE EDITION	BUCCELLATO, BRIAN; MANAPUL, FRANCIS	MANAPUL, FRANCIS	$49.99/$58.00 CAN	HC
9781401257729	JUN150293	THE FLASH VOL. 5: HISTORY LESSONS	BUCCELLATO, BRIAN	ZIRCHER, PATRICK	$14.99/$17.99 CAN	TP
9781401258740	SEP150296	THE FLASH VOL. 6: OUT OF TIME	VENDITTI, ROBERT; JENSEN, VAN	BOOTH, BRETT	$16.99/$19.99 CAN	TP
9781401258757	SEP150296	THE FLASH VOL. 7: SAVAGE WORLD	VENDITTI, ROBERT; JENSEN, VAN	BOOTH, BRETT	$22.99/$27.99 CAN	HC
9781401263669		THE FLASH VOL. 8	VENDITTI, ROBERT; JENSEN, VAN	BOOTH, BRETT	$22.99/$27.99 CAN	HC

THE FLASH COMPILATION GRAPHIC NOVELS

ISBN	DIAMOND CODE	TITLE	AUTHOR	ARTIST	US$	FORMAT
9781401251789	SEP140317	THE FLASH: A CELEBRATION OF 75 YEARS	FOX, GARDNER; JOHNS, GEOFF	INFANTINO, CARMINE	$39.99/$47.99 CAN	HC
9781401224974	AUG090173	FLASH VS THE ROGUES	BROOME, JOHN	INFANTINO, CARMINE	$14.99/$17.99 CAN	TP

THE FLASH: FROM PAGE TO SCREEN

ISBN	DIAMOND CODE	TITLE	AUTHOR	ARTIST	US$	FORMAT
9781401257712	JUN150297	THE FLASH SEASON ZERO	KREISBERG, ANDREW	HESTER, PHIL; TO, MARCUS	$19.99/$23.99 CAN	TP
9781401263386		THE FLASH: SEASON ZERO VOL. 2	KREISBERG, ANDREW	VARIOUS	$19.99/$23.99 CAN	TP

AQUAMAN BACKLIST AND SUGGESTED READING ORDER

ISBN	DIAMOND CODE	TITLE	AUTHOR	ARTIST	US$	FORMAT
9781401255107	APR150284	AQUAMAN: SUB-DIEGO	PFEIFER, WILL	GLEASON, PATRICK	$16.99/$19.99 CAN	TP
9781401263829		AQUAMAN: SUB DIEGO VOL. 2	PFEIFER, WILL	GLEASON, PATRICK	$16.99/$19.99 CAN	TP
9781401237103	FEB130206	AQUAMAN VOL. 1: THE TRENCH	JOHNS, GEOFF	REIS, IVAN	$14.99/$17.99 CAN	TP
9781401242954	AUG130295	AQUAMAN VOL. 2: THE OTHERS	JOHNS, GEOFF	REIS, IVAN	$14.99/$17.99 CAN	TP
9781401246952	FEB140252	AQUAMAN VOL. 3: THRONE OF ATLANTIS	JOHNS, GEOFF	PELLETIER, PAUL	$16.99/$19.99 CAN	TP
9781401249953	AUG140327	AQUAMAN VOL. 4: DEATH OF A KING	JOHNS, GEOFF	PELLETIER, PAUL	$75.00/$85.00 CAN	HC
9781401250393	JAN140339	AQUAMAN VOL. 5: SEA OF STORMS	PARKER, JEFF	PELLETIER, PAUL	$24.99/$28.99 CAN	HC
9781401260965	JUL140235	AQUAMAN VOL. 6: MAELSTROM	PARKER, JEFF	PELLETIER, PAUL	$16.99/$19.99 CAN	TP
9781401262730	APR150263	AQUAMAN VOL. 7: EXILED	BUNN, CULLEN	MCCARTHY, TREVOR	$16.99/$19.99 CAN	TP
9781401262723	MAR150264	AQUAMAN VOL. 8	BUNN, CULLEN	MCCARTHY, TREVOR	$22.99/$27.99 CAN	HC
9781401250386	OCT140353	AQUAMAN AND THE OTHERS VOL. 1: LEGACY OF GOLD	JURGENS, DAN	MEDINA, LAN	$16.99/$17.99 CAN	TP
9781401253318	MAR150265	AQUAMAN AND THE OTHERS VOL. 2: ALIGNMENT: EARTH	JURGENS, DAN	MEDINA, LAN; MARTINEZ, ALLEN	$16.99/$19.99 CAN	TP

GREEN ARROW BACKLIST AND SUGGESTED READING ORDER

ISBN	DIAMOND CODE	TITLE	AUTHOR	ARTIST	US$	FORMAT
9781401217433	JAN090227	GREEN ARROW: YEAR ONE	DIGGLE, ANDY	JOCK	$14.99/$17.99 CAN	TP
9781401235178	MAY120290	GREEN LANTERN/GREEN ARROW	O'NEIL, DENNIS	ADAMS, NEAL	$29.99/$35.00 CAN	TP
9781401238629	JUN120250	GREEN ARROW: THE LONGBOW HUNTERS	GRELL, MIKE	GRELL, MIKE	$14.99/$17.99 CAN	TP
9781401243265	AUG130294	GREEN ARROW VOL. 1: HUNTERS MOON	GRELL, MIKE; GIORDANO, DICK	HANNIGAN, ED	$14.99/$17.99 CAN	TP
9781401251338	JUL140250	GREEN ARROW VOL. 2: HERE THERE BE DRAGONS	GRELL, MIKE	HANNIGAN, ED	$14.99/$17.99 CAN	TP
9781401255237	MAR150279	GREEN ARROW VOL. 3: THE TRIAL OF OLIVER QUEEN	GRELL, MIKE	JURGENS, DAN; HANNIGAN, ED	$16.99/$19.99 CAN	TP
9781401258221	SEP150297	GREEN ARROW VOL. 4: BLOOD OF THE DRAGON	GRELL, MIKE	JURGENS, DAN	$17.99/$19.99 CAN	TP
9781401260798		GREEN ARROW VOL. 5: BLACK ARROW	GRELL, MIKE	VARIOUS	$19.99/$23.99 CAN	TP
9781401255480	SEP140315	ABSOLUTE GREEN ARROW BY KEVIN SMITH	SMITH, KEVIN	HESTER, PHIL	$99.99/$112.00 CAN	HC
9781401255251	APR150294	GREEN ARROW: ARCHER'S QUEST DELUXE EDITION	MELTZER, BRAD	HESTER, PHIL; PARKS, ANDE	$24.99/$28.99 CAN	HC
9781401235284	NOV120266	GREEN ARROW: SALVATION	KRUL, J.T.	NEVES, DIOGENES; CIFUENTES, VICENTE	$16.99/$19.99 CAN	TP
9781401234867	FEB120249	GREEN ARROW VOL. 1: THE MIDAS TOUCH	KRUL, J.T.	PÉREZ, GEORGE	$14.99/$17.99 CAN	TP
9781401238421	OCT120254	GREEN ARROW VOL. 2: TRIPLE THREAT	NOCENTI, ANN	TOLIBAO, HARVEY	$14.99/$17.99 CAN	TP
9781401244057	JUN130266	GREEN ARROW VOL. 3: HARROW	NOCENTI, ANN	WILLIAMS II, FREDDIE	$14.99/$17.99 CAN	TP
9781401246907	DEC130306	GREEN ARROW VOL. 4: THE KILL MACHINE	LEMIRE, JEFF	SORRENTINO, ANDREA	$16.99/$19.99 CAN	TP
9781401246907	DEC130306	GREEN ARROW VOL. 4: THE KILL MACHINE	LEMIRE, JEFF	SORRENTINO, ANDREA	$16.99/$19.99 CAN	TP
9781401250447	JUL140242	GREEN ARROW VOL. 5: THE OUTSIDERS WAR	LEMIRE, JEFF	SORRENTINO, ANDREA	$16.99/$19.99 CAN	TP
9781401254742	JAN150370	GREEN ARROW VOL. 6: BROKEN	LEMIRE, JEFF	SORRENTINO, ANDREA	$14.99/$17.99 CAN	TP
9781401257613	AUG150271	GREEN ARROW BY JEFF LEMIRE & ANDREA SORRENTINO DELUXE EDITION	LEMIRE, JEFF	SORRENTINO, ANDREA	$49.99/$58.00 CAN	HC
9781401257620	AUG150270	GREEN ARROW VOL. 7: KINGDOM	KREISBERG, ANDREW; SOKOLOWSKI, BEN	SAMPERE, DANIEL	$14.99/$17.99 CAN	TP
9781401262556	AUG150271	GREEN ARROW VOL. 8	PERCY, BENJAMIN	ZIRCHER, PATRICK	$14.99/$17.99 CAN	TP
9781401263867	AUG150270	GREEN ARROW: A CELEBRATION OF 75 YEARS	VARIOUS	VARIOUS	$39.99/$48.99 CAN	HC

GREEN ARROW: FROM PAGE TO SCREEN

ISBN	DIAMOND CODE	TITLE	AUTHOR	ARTIST	US$	FORMAT
9781401242992	JUN130265	ARROW VOL. 1	GUGGENHEIM, MARC; KREISBERG, ANDREW	GRELL, MIKE	$16.99/$19.99 CAN	TP

DC COMICS READING ORDER

	ISBN | DIAMOND CODE	TITLE	AUTHOR | ARTIST	US$ | FORMAT
2.	9781401246037 JAN140347	ARROW VOL. 2	VARIOUS | VARIOUS	$16.99/$19.99 CAN | TP
3.	9781401257484 JUN150296	ARROW SEASON 2.5	GUGGENHEIM, MARC | BENNETT, JOE	$16.99/$19.99 CAN | TP
4.	9781401263294 JAN140347	ARROW SEASON 2.5 VOL. 2	GUGGENHEIM, MARC | BENNETT, JOE	$14.99/$17.99 CAN | TP

TEEN TITANS BACKLIST AND SUGGESTED READING ORDER

	ISBN | DIAMOND CODE	TITLE	AUTHOR | ARTIST	US$ | FORMAT
1.	9781401251772 JUL140249	TEEN TITANS: A CELEBRATION OF 50 YEARS	WOLFMAN, MARV; JOHNS, GEOFF | PÉREZ, GEORGE	$39.99/$47.99 CAN | HC
2.	9781401251437 JUN140283	THE NEW TEEN TITANS VOL. 1	WOLFMAN, MARV | PÉREZ, GEORGE	$19.99/$23.99 CAN | TP
3.	9781401255329 JAN150380	THE NEW TEEN TITANS VOL. 2	WOLFMAN, MARV | PÉREZ, GEORGE; TANGHAL, ROMEO	$19.99/$23.99 CAN | TP
4.	9781401258542 JUN150304	THE NEW TEEN TITANS VOL. 3	WOLFMAN, MARV | PÉREZ, GEORGE	$19.99/$23.99 CAN | TP
5.	9781401260859 JAN150380	THE NEW TEEN TITANS VOL. 4	WOLFMAN, MARV | PÉREZ, GEORGE	$19.99/$23.99 CAN | TP
6.	9781401263584 JUN150304	THE NEW TEEN TITANS VOL. 5	WOLFMAN, MARV | PÉREZ, GEORGE	$19.99/$23.99 CAN | TP
7.	9781401238452 JAN130313	THE NEW TEEN TITANS OMNIBUS VOL. 3	WOLFMAN, MARV | PÉREZ, GEORGE	$75.00/$85.00 CAN | HC
8.	9781401263560	TITANS: TOTAL CHAOS	WOLFMAN, MARV | VARIOUS	$19.99/$23.99 CAN | TP
9.	9781401203191 NOV120275	THE NEW TEEN TITANS: GAMES	WOLFMAN, MARV | PÉREZ, GEORGE	$16.99/$19.99 CAN | TP
10.	9781401241056 APR130220	THE SILVER AGE TEEN TITANS ARCHIVES VOL. 2	HANEY, BOB | CARDY, NICK	$75.00/$85.00 CAN | HC
11.	9781401203085 SEP148048	TEEN TITANS VOL. 1: A KID'S GAME	JOHNS, GEOFF | MCKONE, MIKE	$16.99/$19.99 CAN | TP
12.	9781401236939 SEP120242	TEEN TITANS BY GEOFF JOHNS OMNIBUS	JOHNS, GEOFF | VARIOUS	$150.00/$176.00 CAN | HC
13.	9781401236984 JUN120239	TEEN TITANS VOL. 1: IT'S OUR RIGHT TO FIGHT	LOBDELL, SCOTT | BOOTH, BRETT	$14.99/$17.99 CAN | TP
14.	9781401241032 MAR130272	TEEN TITANS VOL. 2: THE CULLING	LOBDELL, SCOTT | BOOTH, BRETT	$16.99/$19.99 CAN | TP
15.	9781401237998 OCT120250	THE CULLING: RISE OF THE RAVAGERS	DEFALCO, TOM; LOBDELL, SCOTT | VARIOUS	$16.99/$19.99 CAN | TP
16.	9781401243210 SEP130274	TEEN TITANS VOL. 3: DEATH OF THE FAMILY	LOBDELL, SCOTT | BOOTH, BRETT	$14.99/$17.99 CAN | TP
17.	9781401246242 APR140262	TEEN TITANS VOL. 4: LIGHT AND DARK	LOBDELL, SCOTT | BARROWS, EDDY	$14.99/$17.99 CAN | TP
18.	9781401250539 NOV140302	TEEN TITANS VOL. 5: THE TRIAL OF KID FLASH	LOBDELL, SCOTT | KIRKHAM, TYLER	$17.99/$20.99 CAN | TP
19.	9781401252373 MAY150249	TEEN TITANS VOL. 1: BLINDED BY THE LIGHT	PFEIFER, WILL | ROCAFORT, KENNETH	$16.99/$19.99 CAN | TP
20.	9781401261627 NOV140302	TEEN TITANS VOL. 2: ROGUE TARGETS	PFEIFER, WILL | ROCAFORT, KENNETH	$16.99/$19.99 CAN | TP
21.	9781401262501	TITANS HUNT VOL. 1	ABNETT, DAN | SIQUEIRA, PAOLO	$14.99/$17.99 CAN | TP

TEEN TITANS: FROM PAGE TO SCREEN

	ISBN | DIAMOND CODE	TITLE	AUTHOR | ARTIST	US$ | FORMAT
1.	9781401253677 JUL140263	TEEN TITANS GO!: TITANS TOGETHER	TORRES, J. | NORTON, MIKE	$12.99/$15.99 CAN | TP
2.	9781401252427 DEC140400	TEEN TITANS GO! VOL. 1	FISCH, SHOLLY | HERNANDEZ, LEA	$12.99/$15.99 CAN | TP
3.	9781401261962 SEP150298	TEEN TITANS GO!: TRUTH, JUSTICE, PIZZA	VARIOUS | VARIOUS	$12.99/$15.99 CAN | TP

TEEN TITANS STAND-ALONE GRAPHIC NOVELS

	ISBN | DIAMOND CODE	TITLE	AUTHOR | ARTIST	US$ | FORMAT
1.	9781401259082 JUL150302	TEEN TITANS: EARTH ONE VOL. 1	LEMIRE, JEFF | DODSON, RACHAEL; DODSON, TERRY	$14.99/$17.99 CAN | TP
2.	9781401259068	TEEN TITANS: EARTH ONE VOL. 2	LEMIRE, JEFF | MACDONALD, ANDY	$22.99/$27.99 CAN | HC

JUSTICE SOCIETY BACKLIST AND SUGGESTED READING ORDER

	ISBN | DIAMOND CODE	TITLE	AUTHOR | ARTIST	US$ | FORMAT
1.	9781401255312 JAN150381	JUSTICE SOCIETY OF AMERICA: A CELEBRATION OF 75 YEARS	THOMAS, ROY; JOHNS, GEOFF | ORDWAY, JERRY	$39.99/$47.99 CAN | HC
2.	9781401255091 APR150287	AMERICA VS. THE JUSTICE SOCIETY	THOMAS, ROY | ORDWAY, JERRY; BENDER, HOWARD	$14.99/$17.99 CAN | TP
3.	9781401215859 JUL080163	JUSTICE SOCIETY OF AMERICA: THE NEXT AGE, VOL. 1	JOHNS, GEOFF | EAGLESHAM, DALE	$14.99/$17.99 CAN | TP
4.	9781401217419 JAN090231	JUSTICE SOCIETY OF AMERICA: THY KINGDOM COME PART I	JOHNS, GEOFF | EAGLESHAM, DALE	$14.99/$17.99 CAN | TP
5.	9781401219468 AUG090175	JUSTICE SOCIETY OF AMERICA: THY KINGDOM COME PART II	JOHNS, GEOFF | EAGLESHAM, DALE	$19.99/$24.99 CAN | TP
6.	9781401221676 JAN100298	JUSTICE SOCIETY OF AMERICA: THY KINGDOM COME PART III	JOHNS, GEOFF | EAGLESHAM, DALE	$19.99/$24.99 CAN | TP
7.	9781401225315 JUN100206	JUSTICE SOCIETY OF AMERICA: BLACK ADAM & ISIS	JOHNS, GEOFF | ORDWAY	$14.99/$17.99 CAN | TP
8.	9781401247614 JAN140343	JSA OMNIBUS VOL. 1	JOHNS, GEOFF; GOYER, DAVID | SADOWSKI, STEPHEN; BAIR, MICHAEL; PACHECO, CARLOS	$125.00/$144.00 CAN | HC
9.	9781401251383 JUL140254	JSA OMNIBUS VOL. 2	JOHNS, GEOFF | KRAMER, DON; MORALES, RAGS	$150.00/$172.00 CAN | HC
10.	9781401255305 FEB150261	JSA OMNIBUS VOL. 3	JOHNS, GEOFF | ROSS, ALEX; PÉREZ, GEORGE	$125.00/$144.00 CAN | HC
11.	9781401227142 FEB100189	JUSTICE SOCIETY OF AMERICA: THE BAD SEED	WILLINGHAM, BILL | MERINO, JESUS	$14.99/$17.99 CAN | TP
12.	9781401229016 SEP100251	JUSTICE SOCIETY OF AMERICA: AXIS OF EVIL	WILLINGHAM, BILL | MERINO, JESUS	$14.99/$17.99 CAN | TP
13.	9781401232849 JUN110279	JUSTICE SOCIETY OF AMERICA: SUPERTOWN	GUGGENHEIM, MARC | KOLINS, SCOTT	$14.99/$17.99 CAN | TP
14.	9781401233686 NOV110205	JUSTICE SOCIETY OF AMERICA: MONUMENT PARK	GUGGENHEIM, MARC | DERENICK, TOM	$14.99/$17.99 CAN | TP
15.	9781401235000 MAR120247	MISTER TERRIFIC VOL. 1: MIND GAMES	WALLACE, ERIC | GUGLIOTTA, GIANLUCA	$16.99/$17.99 CAN | TP
16.	9781401242817 JUL130241	EARTH 2 VOL. 1: THE GATHERING	ROBINSON, JAMES | SCOTT, NICOLA	$14.99/$17.99 CAN | TP
17.	9781401246143 JAN140344	EARTH 2 VOL. 2: THE TOWER OF FATE	ROBINSON, JAMES | SCOTT, NICOLA; CINAR, YILDARAY	$16.99/$19.99 CAN | TP
18.	9781401249380 JUL140241	EARTH 2 VOL. 3: BATTLE CRY	ROBINSON, JAMES | SCOTT, NICOLA	$14.99/$17.99 CAN | TP

DC COMICS READING ORDER

ISBN	DIAMOND CODE	TITLE	AUTHOR	ARTIST	US$	FORMAT
9781401254179	JAN150378	EARTH 2 VOL. 4: THE DARK AGE	TAYLOR, TOM	SCOTT, NICOLA	$14.99/$17.99 CAN	TP
9781401257576	AUG150265	EARTH 2 VOL. 5: THE KRYPTONIAN	TAYLOR, TOM	SCOTT, NICOLA	$16.99/$19.99 CAN	TP
9781401257583	JUL150311	EARTH 2 VOL. 6: COLLISION	WILSON, DANIEL	BENNETT, MARGUERITE	$22.99/$27.99 CAN	HC
9781401256036	FEB150253	EARTH 2: WORLD'S END VOL. 1	WILSON, DANIEL H.; BENNETT, MARGUERITE; JOHNSON, MIKE	BARROWS, EDDY	$29.99/$35.00 CAN	TP
9781401258443	SEP150294	EARTH 2 WORLD'S END VOL. 2	WILSON, DANIEL	BENNETT, MARGUERITTE; BARROWS, EDDY	$24.99/$29.99 CAN	TP
9781401262716	SEP150294	CONVERGENCE	KING, JEFF; LOBDELL, SCOTT	PAGULAYAN, CARLO	$19.99/$23.99 CAN	TP
9781401261238	DEC150321	EARTH 2: SOCIETY VOL. 1: PLANETFALL	WILSON, DANIEL H.	JIMENEZ, JORGE	$16.99/$19.99 CAN	TP
9781401242510	JUL130243	JSA LIBERTY FILES: THE WHISTLING SKULL	MOORE, B. CLAY	HARRIS, TONY	$14.99/$17.99 CAN	TP

LEGION OF SUPER-HEROES BACKLIST AND SUGGESTED READING ORDER

ISBN	DIAMOND CODE	TITLE	AUTHOR	ARTIST	US$	FORMAT
9781401237301	JUL120224	LEGION: SECRET ORIGIN	LEVITZ, PAUL	BAUTISTA, CHRIS	$14.99/$17.99 CAN	TP
9781401242909	MAR140268	SHOWCASE PRESENTS: THE GREAT DISASTER FEATURING THE ATOMIC KNIGHTS	VARIOUS	VARIOUS	$19.99/$23.99 CAN	TP
9781401242978	SEP140326	SHOWCASE PRESENTS: THE LEGION OF SUPER-HEROES VOL. 5	BATES, CARY	COCKRUM, DAVE	$19.99/$23.99 CAN	TP
9781401244163	NOV130243	THE LEGION OF SUPER-HEROES: THE GREAT DARKNESS SAGA	LEVITZ, PAUL	GIFFEN, KEITH	$24.99/$28.99 CAN	TP
9781401251390	JUN140282	LEGION OF SUPER-HEROES: THE CURSE	LEVITZ, PAUL	GIFFEN, KEITH	$29.99/$35.00 CAN	TP
9781401219444	SEP080174	LEGION OF SUPER-HEROES: THE MORE THINGS CHANGE	LEVITZ, PAUL	GIFFEN, KEITH	$17.99/$21.99 CAN	TP
9781401223250	JUL100195	FINAL CRISIS: LEGION OF 3 WORLDS	JOHNS, GEOFF	PÉREZ, GEORGE	$14.99/$17.99 CAN	TP
9781401231682	FEB110203	SUPERBOY AND THE LEGION OF SUPER-HEROES: EARLY YEARS	LEVITZ, PAUL	PANSICA, EDUARDO	$14.99/$17.99 CAN	TP
9781401219048	APR090217	SUPERMAN AND THE LEGION OF SUPER-HEROES	JOHNS, GEOFF	FRANK, GARY	$14.99/$17.99 CAN	TP
9781401220181	JUL090236	LEGION OF SUPER-HEROES: ENEMY RISING	SHOOTER, JIM	LOPRESTI, AARON	$14.99/$17.99 CAN	TP
9781401223052	FEB100190	LEGION OF SUPER-HEROES: ENEMY MANIFEST	SHOOTER, JIM	MANAPUL, FRANCIS	$14.99/$17.99 CAN	TP
9781401230395	DEC100250	LEGION OF SUPER-HEROES VOL. 1: THE CHOICE	LEVITZ, PAUL	CINAR, YILDIRAY	$24.99/$27.99 CAN	TP
9781401233679	JAN120311	LEGION OF SUPER-HEROES: WHEN EVIL CALLS	LEVITZ, PAUL	CINAR, YILDIRAY	$29.99/$35.00 CAN	TP
9781401237035	JUN120238	LEGION LOST VOL. 1: RUN FROM TOMORROW	NICIEZA, FABIAN	WOODS, PETE	$14.99/$17.99 CAN	TP
9781401240257	MAY130223	LEGION LOST VOL. 2: THE CULLING	DEFALCO, TOM	WOODS, PETE; GUINALDO, ANDRES	$16.99/$19.99 CAN	TP
9781401235017	MAR120246	LEGION OF SUPER-HEROES VOL. 1: HOSTILE WORLD	LEVITZ, PAUL	PORTELA, FRANCIS	$14.99/$17.99 CAN	TP
9781401240974	FEB130213	LEGION OF SUPER-HEROES VOL. 2: THE DOMINATORS	LEVITZ, PAUL	PORTELA, FRANCIS; KOLINS, SCOTT	$16.99/$19.99 CAN	TP
9781401243326	NOV130232	LEGION OF SUPER-HEROES VOL. 3: THE FATAL FIVE	LEVITZ, PAUL	GIFFEN, KEITH; KOLINS, SCOTT	$16.99/$19.99 CAN	TP

DC COMICS SELECTED BACKLIST

ISBN	DIAMOND CODE	TITLE	AUTHOR	ARTIST	US$	FORMAT
9781401263263		ALL-STAR SECTION EIGHT	ENNIS, GARTH	MCCREA, JOHN	$16.99/$19.99 CAN	TP
9781401237097	JUL120213	ALL STAR WESTERN VOL. 1: GUNS AND GOTHAM	PALMIOTTI, JIMMY; GRAY, JUSTIN	MORITAT	$16.99/$19.99 CAN	TP
9781401238513	DEC120325	ALL STAR WESTERN VOL. 2: THE WAR OF LORDS AND OWLS	PALMIOTTI, JIMMY; GRAY, JUSTIN	MORITAT	$16.99/$19.99 CAN	TP
9781401243999	AUG130300	ALL STAR WESTERN VOL. 3: THE BLACK DIAMOND PROBABILITY	PALMIOTTI, JIMMY; GRAY, JUSTIN	MORITAT	$16.99/$19.99 CAN	TP
9781401246266	FEB140250	ALL STAR WESTERN VOL. 4: GOLD STANDARD	PALMIOTTI, JIMMY; GRAY, JUSTIN	MORITAT	$16.99/$19.99 CAN	TP
9781401249939	JUL140236	ALL STAR WESTERN VOL. 5: MAN OUT OF TIME	PALMIOTTI, JIMMY; GRAY, JUSTIN	MORITAT	$16.99/$19.99 CAN	TP
9781401254131	DEC140377	ALL STAR WESTERN VOL. 6: END OF THE TRAIL	PALMIOTTI, JIMMY; GRAY, JUSTIN	JOHNSON, STAZ	$14.99/$17.99 CAN	TP
9781401246877	APR140277	AME-COMI GIRLS VOL. 2: RISE OF THE BRAINIAC	PALMIOTTI, JIMMY; GRAY, JUSTIN	VARIOUS	$14.99/$17.99 CAN	TP
9781401250379	OCT140366	AME-COMI GIRLS VOL. 3: EARTH IN CRISIS	PALMIOTTI, JIMMY; GRAY, JUSTIN	ARCHER, ADAM	$14.99/$17.99 CAN	TP
9781401235079	FEB120247	ANIMAL MAN VOL. 1: THE HUNT	LEMIRE, JEFF	FOREMAN, TRAVEL	$14.99/$17.99 CAN	TP
9781401238001	OCT120251	ANIMAL MAN VOL. 2: ANIMAL VS. MAN	LEMIRE, JEFF	PUGH, STEVE; GREEN, TIMOTHY	$16.99/$19.99 CAN	TP
9781401242626	JUN130267	ANIMAL MAN VOL. 3: ROTWORLD: THE RED KINGDOM	LEMIRE, JEFF; SNYDER, SCOTT	PUGH, STEVE	$16.99/$19.99 CAN	TP
9781401246440	DEC130298	ANIMAL MAN VOL. 4: SPLINTER SPECIES	LEMIRE, JEFF	PUGH, STEVE	$14.99/$17.99 CAN	TP
9781401249946	AUG140326	ANIMAL MAN VOL. 5: EVOLVE OR DIE!	LEMIRE, JEFF	FOREMAN, TRAVEL	$14.99/$17.99 CAN	TP
9781401254582	APR150285	ARKHAM MANOR VOL. 1	DUGGAN, GERRY	CRYSTAL, SHAWN	$14.99/$17.99 CAN	TP
9781401260606	NOV150287	AZRAEL VOL. 1	O'NEIL, DENNIS	QUESADA, JOE	$16.99/$19.99 CAN	TP
9781401261009	MAR130279	BAT-MITE	JURGENS, DAN	HOWELL, CORIN	$16.99/$19.99 CAN	TP
9781401240332	MAR130279	BATGIRL/ROBIN YEAR ONE	DIXON, CHUCK	BEATTY, SCOTT; MARTIN, MARCOS	$24.99/$28.99 CAN	TP
9781401260729	OCT150244	BATGIRL VOL. 1: SILENT KNIGHT	PUCKETT, KELLEY	SCOTT, DAMION	$16.99/$19.99 CAN	TP
9781401263522		BATGIRL: CASSANDRA CAIN VOL. 2	PUCKETT, KELLEY	SCOTT, DAMION	$19.99/$23.99 CAN	TP
9781401238148	NOV120261	BATGIRL VOL. 1: THE DARKEST REFLECTION	SIMONE, GAIL	SYAF, ARDIAN; CIFUENTES, VICENTE	$14.99/$17.99 CAN	TP
9781401238179	JUL130236	BATGIRL VOL. 2: KNIGHTFALL DESCENDS	SIMONE, GAIL	SYAF, ARDIAN; BENES, ED	$16.99/$19.99 CAN	TP
9781401246280	FEB140247	BATGIRL VOL. 3: DEATH OF THE FAMILY	SIMONE, GAIL	BENES, ED; SAMPERE, DANIEL	$16.99/$19.99 CAN	TP

DC COMICS SELECTED BACKLIST

ISBN	DIAMOND CODE	TITLE	AUTHOR	ARTIST	US$	FORMAT
9781401250409	SEP140305	BATGIRL VOL. 4: WANTED	SIMONE, GAIL	PASARIN, FERNANDO	$16.99/$19.99 CAN	TP
9781401255114	FEB150250	BATGIRL VOL. 5: DEADLINE	SIMONE, GAIL	PASARIN, FERNANDO	$17.99/$20.99 CAN	TP
9781401257989	DEC148636	BATGIRL VOL. 1: THE BATGIRL OF BURNSIDE	STEWART, CAMERON; FLETCHER, BRENDEN	TARR, BABS	$14.99/$17.99 CAN	TP
9781401259662	NOV150268	BATGIRL VOL. 2: FAMILY BUSINESS	STEWART, CAMERON; FLETCHER, BRENDEN	TARR, BABS	$16.99/$19.99 CAN	TP
9781401262693		BATGIRL VOL. 3	STEWART, CAMERON; FLETCHER, BRENDEN	TARR, BABS	$16.99/$19.99 CAN	TP
9781401234768	APR120246	BATWING VOL. 1: THE LOST KINGDOM	WINICK, JUDD	OLIVER, BEN	$14.99/$17.99 CAN	TP
9781401237912	DEC120327	BATWING VOL. 2: IN THE SHADOW OF THE ANCIENTS	WINICK, JUDD	TO, MARCUS	$14.99/$17.99 CAN	TP
9781401244033	OCT130237	BATWING VOL. 3: ENEMY OF THE STATE	WINICK, JUDD	NICIEZA, FABIAN	TO, MARCUS	$14.99/$17.99 CAN	TP
9781401246310	APR140260	BATWING VOL. 4: WELCOME TO THE FAMILY	PALMIOTTI, JIMMY; GRAY, JUSTIN	PANSICA, EDUARDO	$16.99/$19.99 CAN	TP
9781401250812	NOV140295	BATWING VOL. 5: INTO THE DARK	PALMIOTTI, JIMMY; GRAY, JUSTIN	PANSICA, EDUARDO	$16.99/$19.99 CAN	TP
9781401231460	MAR110341	BATWOMAN: ELEGY	RUCKA, GREG	WILLIAMS III, J.H.	$17.99/$20.99 CAN	TP
9781401237844	OCT120253	BATWOMAN VOL. 1: HYDROLOGY	WILLIAMS III, J.H.; BLACKMAN, W. HADEN	WILLIAMS III, J.H.	$14.99/$17.99 CAN	TP
9781401237929	JUN130269	BATWOMAN VOL. 2: TO DROWN THE WORLD	WILLIAMS III, J.H.; BLACKMAN, W. HADEN	REEDER, AMY; MCCARTHY, TREVOR	$14.99/$17.99 CAN	TP
9781401246105	DEC130300	BATWOMAN VOL. 3: WORLD'S FINEST	WILLIAMS III, J.H.; BLACKMAN, W. HADEN	WILLIAMS III, J.H.	$14.99/$17.99 CAN	TP
9781401249991	JUN140271	BATWOMAN VOL. 4: THIS BLOOD IS THICK	WILLIAMS III, J.H.; BLACKMAN, W. HADEN	MCCARTHY, TREVOR	$14.99/$17.99 CAN	TP
9781401250829	AUG140335	BATWOMAN VOL. 5: WEBS	ANDREYKO, MARC	HAUN, JEREMY; MCCARTHY, TREVOR	$19.99/$23.99 CAN	TP
9781401254681	APR150291	BATWOMAN VOL. 6: THE UNKNOWNS	ANDREYKO, MARC	HAUN, JEREMY	$16.99/$17.99 CAN	TP
9781401258160	JUL150312	BIRDS OF PREY VOL. 1	DIXON, CHUCK	HALEY, MATT	$19.99/$23.99 CAN	TP
9781401260958	NOV150276	BIRDS OF PREY VOL. 2	DIXON, CHUCK	LAND, GREG	$19.99/$23.99 CAN	TP
9781401236991	JUN120236	BIRDS OF PREY VOL. 1: TROUBLE IN MIND	SWIERCZYNSKI, DUANE	SAIZ, JESUS	$14.99/$17.99 CAN	TP
9781401238131	JAN130297	BIRDS OF PREY VOL. 2: YOUR KISS MIGHT KILL	SWIERCZYNSKI, DUANE	FOREMAN, TRAVEL; SAIZ, JESUS	$14.99/$17.99 CAN	TP
9781401244040	SEP130270	BIRDS OF PREY VOL. 3: A CLASH OF DAGGERS	SWIERCZYNSKI, DUANE	MOLENAAR, ROMANO	$14.99/$17.99 CAN	TP
9781401246358	APR140259	BIRDS OF PREY VOL. 4: THE CRUELEST CUT	MARX, CHRISTY	MOLENAAR, ROMANO; CIFUENTES, VICENTE	$16.99/$19.99 CAN	TP
9781401250836	OCT140354	BIRDS OF PREY VOL. 5: SOUL CRISIS	MARX, CHRISTY	ROCHA, ROBSON	$17.99/$20.99 CAN	TP
9781401259716	NOV150274	BIZARRO	CORSON, HEATH	DUARTE, GUSTAVO	$14.99/$17.99 CAN	TP
9781401255497	MAR150259	BLACK CANARY AND ZATANNA: BLOODSPELL	DINI, PAUL	QUINONES, JOE	$14.99/$17.99 CAN	TP
9781401261177	DEC150319	BLACK CANARY VOL. 1: KICKING AND SCREAMING	FLETCHER, BRENDEN	WU, ANNIE	$14.99/$17.99 CAN	TP
9781401260712	JAN160326	BLACK LIGHTNING VOL. 1	ISABELLA, TONY	O'NEIL, DENNIS	$19.99/$23.99 CAN	TP
9781401237141	AUG120247	BLACKHAWKS VOL. 1: THE GREAT LEAP FORWARD	COSTA, MIKE	NOLAN, GRAHAM	$16.99/$19.99 CAN	TP
9781401251475	OCT140370	SHOWCASE PRESENTS: BLUE BEETLE	WEIN, LEN	CULLINS, PARIS; ANDRU, ROSS	$19.99/$23.99 CAN	TP
9781401237134	AUG120246	BLUE BEETLE VOL. 1: METAMORPHOSIS	BEDARD, TONY	GUARA, IG	$14.99/$17.99 CAN	TP
9781401238506	JAN130299	BLUE BEETLE VOL. 2: BLUE DIAMOND	BEDARD, TONY	GUARA, IG	$19.99/$23.99 CAN	TP
9781401255398		SHOWCASE PRESENTS: BLUE DEVIL VOL. 1	COHN, GARY	MISHKIN, DAN; CULLINS, PARIS	$19.99/$23.99 CAN	TP
9781401220143	SEP090164	BOOSTER GOLD: BLUE AND GOLD	JOHNS, GEOFF	JURGENS, DAN	$14.99/$17.99 CAN	TP
9781401230241	JAN110325	BOOSTER GOLD: PAST IMPERFECT	GIFFEN, KEITH	OLLIFFE, PATRICK	US$/$19.99 CAN	TP
9781401226435	JAN100297	BOOSTER GOLD : DAY OF DEATH	GIFFEN, KEITH	OLLIFFE, PATRICK	$14.99/$17.99 CAN	TP
9781401258177	JUN150302	BOY COMMANDOS BY JOE SIMON AND JACK KIRBY VOL. 2	KIRBY, JACK	KIRBY, JACK	$49.99/$58.00 CAN	HC
9781401240363	APR130228	CAMELOT 3000	BARR, MIKE W.	BOLLAND, BRIAN	$19.99/$23.99 CAN	TP
9781401237158	AUG120250	CAPTAIN ATOM VOL. 1: EVOLUTION	KRUL, J.T.	WILLIAMS II, FREDDIE	$14.99/$17.99 CAN	TP
9781401240998	MAY130222	CAPTAIN ATOM VOL. 2: GENESIS	KRUL, J.T.	WILLIAMS II, FREDDIE	$14.99/$23.99 CAN	TP
9781401247560	MAY140380	SHOWCASE PRESENTS: CAPTAIN CARROT AND HIS AMAZING ZOO CREW	VARIOUS	VARIOUS	$19.99/$23.99 CAN	TP
9781401207175	MAY098043	CATWOMAN: WHEN IN ROME	LOEB, JEPH	SALE, TIM	$14.99/$17.99 CAN	TP
9781401233846	OCT110246	CATWOMAN VOL. 1	BRUBAKER, ED	COOKE, DARWYN	$29.99/$35.00 CAN	TP
9781401240370	MAR130271	CATWOMAN VOL. 2: NO EASY WAY DOWN	BRUBAKER, ED	STEWART, CAMERON	$24.99/$17.99 CAN	TP
9781401245924	DEC130309	CATWOMAN VOL. 3: UNDER PRESSURE	BRUBAKER, ED; PALMIOTTI, JIMMY	GULACY, PAUL	$24.99/$28.99 CAN	TP
9781401260736		CATWOMAN VOL. 5	PFEIFER, WILL	LOPEZ, DAVID	$24.99/$29.99 CAN	TP
9781401234645	FEB120248	CATWOMAN VOL. 1: THE GAME	WINICK, JUDD	MARCH, GUILLEM	$14.99/$17.99 CAN	TP
9781401238391	NOV120260	CATWOMAN VOL. 2: DOLLHOUSE	WINICK, JUDD	MARCH, GUILLEM	$14.99/$17.99 CAN	TP
9781401242725	JUL130237	CATWOMAN VOL. 3: DEATH OF THE FAMILY	NOCENTI, ANN	SANDOVAL, RAFA	$16.99/$28.99 CAN	TP
9781401246273	FEB140253	CATWOMAN VOL. 4: GOTHAM UNDERGROUND	NOCENTI, ANN	SANDOVAL, RAFA; TARROGANA, JORDI	$17.99/$20.99 CAN	TP
9781401250638	AUG140332	CATWOMAN VOL. 5: RACE OF THIEVES	NOCENTI, ANN	OLIFFE, PATRICK	$17.99/$20.99 CAN	TP

ISBN	DIAMOND CODE	TITLE	AUTHOR	ARTIST	US$	FORMAT
9781401254698	APR150299	CATWOMAN VOL. 6: KEEPER OF THE CASTLE	VALENTINE, GENEVIEVE | BROWN, GARRY	$16.99/$17.99 CAN | TP
9781401261184	NOV150275	CATWOMAN VOL. 7: INHERITANCE	VALENTINE, GENEVIEVE | MESSINA, DAVE	$14.99/$17.99 CAN | TP
9781401260064	JUL150306	CATWOMAN: A CELEBRATION OF 75 YEARS	VARIOUS | VARIOUS	$39.99/$48.99 CAN | HC
9781401263539		CHECKMATE BY GREG RUCKA VOL. 1	RUCKA, GREG | SAIZ, JESUS	$19.99/$23.99 CAN | TP
9781401246389	APR140271	CINDER & ASHE	CONWAY, GERRY | GARCIA-LOPEZ, JOSE LUIS	$14.99/$17.99 CAN | TP
9781401243234	NOV130227	CONSTANTINE VOL. 1: THE SPARK AND THE FLAME	LEMIRE, JEFF; FAWKES, RAY | GUEDES , RENATO	$9.99/$17.99 CAN | TP
9781401247478	MAY140366	CONSTANTINE VOL. 2: BLIGHT	FAWKES, RAY | GUEDES, RENATO	$14.99/$17.99 CAN | TP
9781401250850	NOV140296	CONSTANTINE VOL. 3: THE VOICE IN THE FIRE	FAWKES, RAY | ACO	$14.99/$17.99 CAN | TP
9781401254704	MAY150240	CONSTANTINE VOL. 4: THE APOCALYPSE ROAD	FAWKES, RAY | SALAZAR, EDGAR	$14.99/$17.99 CAN | TP
9781401259723	NOV150263	CONSTANTINE: THE HELLBLAZER VOL. 1: GOING DOWN	DOYLE, MING; TYNION IV, JAMES | ROSSMO, RILEY	$14.99/$17.99 CAN | TP
9781401263713		CONSTANTINE: THE HELLBLAZER VOL. 2	DOYLE, MING; TYNION IV, JAMES	$14.99/$17.99 CAN | TP
9781401243821	SEP130281	CREATURE COMMANDOS	VARIOUS | VARIOUS	$19.99/$17.99 CAN | TP
9781563898952	OCT098268	CRISIS ON MULTPLE EARTHS VOL. 1	FOX, GARDNER | SEKOWSKY, MIKE	$14.99/$17.99 CAN | TP
9781401200039	APR058270	CRISIS ON MULTPLE EARTHS VOL. 2	FOX, GARDNER | SEKOWSKY, MIKE	$14.99/$17.99 CAN | TP
9781401202316	MAY040298	CRISIS ON MULTPLE EARTHS VOL. 3	FRIEDRICH, MIKE | SEKOWSKY, MIKE	$14.99/$17.99 CAN | TP
9781401209575	FEB060261	CRISIS ON MULTPLE EARTHS VOL. 4	VARIOUS | DILLIN, DICK	$14.99/$17.99 CAN | TP
9781401238223	MAR130278	CRISIS ON MULTIPLE EARTHS VOL. 6	CONWAY, GERRY | PÉREZ, GEORGE	$19.99/$23.99 CAN | TP
9781401261191	DEC150318	CYBORG VOL. 1: UNPLUGGED	WALKER, DAVID | REIS, IVAN; PRADO, JOE	$14.99/$17.99 CAN | TP
9781401237950	DEC120330	DAY OF JUDGMENT	JOHNS, GEOFF | SMITH, MATT	$14.99/$23.99 CAN | TP
9781401242435	JUN130262	DC COMICS ONE MILLION OMNIBUS	MORRISON, GRANT | VARIOUS	$99.99/$112.00 CAN | HC
9781401261320	DEC150323	DC COMICS: BOMBSHELLS VOL. 1	BENNETT, MARGUERITE | SAUVAGE, MARGUERITE	$16.99/$19.99 CAN | TP
9781401262471		DC SUPER HERO GIRLS	FONTANA, SHEA	$16.99/$19.99 CAN | TP
9781401262600		DC UNIVERSE BY NEIL GAIMAN	GAIMAN, NEIL | VARIOUS	$24.99/$29.99 CAN | HC
9781401238841	AUG120249	DC COMICS: THE NEW 52 ZERO OMNIBUS	VARIOUS | VARIOUS	$150.00/$112.00 CAN | HC
9781401244965	AUG130289	DC COMICS: THE NEW 52 VILLAINS OMNIBUS	VARIOUS | VARIOUS	$150.00/$176.00 CAN | HC
9781401219178	JUN080241	DC UNIVERSE ILLUSTRATED BY NEAL ADAMS VOL. 1	VARIOUS | ADAMS, NEAL	$39.99/$45.99 CAN | HC
9781401237165	AUG120251	DC UNIVERSE PRESENTS VOL. 1 FEATURING DEADMAN & CHALLENGERS OF THE UNKNOWN	JENKINS, PAUL | CHANG, BERNARD	$16.99/$19.99 CAN | TP
9781401240769	MAY130227	DC UNIVERSE PRESENTS VOL. 2: VANDAL SAVAGE	VARIOUS | VARIOUS	$14.99/$17.99 CAN | TP
9781401242770	NOV130230	DC UNIVERSE PRESENTS VOL. 3: BLACK LIGHTNING AND BLUE DEVIL	ANDREYKO, MARC | ROCHA, ROBSON	$14.99/$17.99 CAN | TP
9781401226466	NOV090173	DC UNIVERSE: ORIGINS	VARIOUS | VARIOUS	$14.99/$17.99 CAN | TP
9781401234041	JAN130303	DC UNIVERSE SECRET ORIGINS	VARIOUS | VARIOUS	$24.99/$17.99 CAN | TP
9781401233402	DEC120333	DC UNIVERSE BY ALAN MOORE	MOORE, ALAN | VARIOUS	$24.99/$28.99 CAN | TP
9781401231347	FEB120262	DC UNIVERSE: LEGACIES	WEIN, LEN | VARIOUS	$24.99/$27.99 CAN | TP
9781401231163	FEB110198	DEADMAN BOOK ONE	VARIOUS | ADAMS, NEAL	$19.99/$23.99 CAN | TP
9781401233884	NOV110199	DEADMAN BOOK TWO	VARIOUS | ADAMS, NEAL	$14.99/$17.99 CAN | TP
9781401237288	SEP120236	DEADMAN BOOK THREE	LEVITZ, PAUL | VARIOUS	$16.99/$19.99 CAN | TP
9781401243241	SEP130282	DEADMAN BOOK FOUR	WEIN, LEN | APARO, JIM; GARCIA-LOPEZ, JOSE LUIS	$14.99/$17.99 CAN | TP
9781401246112	JAN140351	DEADMAN BOOK FIVE	HELFER, ANDREW | GARCIA-LOPEZ, JOSE LUIS	$16.99/$19.99 CAN | TP
9781401242985	JUL130244	DEADSHOT: BEGINNINGS	OSTRANDER, JOHN | YALE, KIM; MCDONNELL, LUKE	$14.99/$17.99 CAN | TP
9781401255190	JAN150376	DEADSHOT: BULLETPROOF	GAGE, CHRISTOS N. | CUMMINGS, STEVE	$14.99/$17.99 CAN | TP
9781401263805		SUICIDE SQUAD: DEADSHOT	BUCCELLATO, BRIAN | BOGDANOVIC, VIKTOR	$14.99/$17.99 CAN | TP
9781401251307	OCT140356	DEATHBLOW	CHOI, BRANDON | LEE, JIM; SALE, TIM	$19.99/$23.99 CAN | TP
9781401254285	JAN150379	DEATHSTROKE, THE TERMINATOR VOL. 1: ASSASSINS	WOLFMAN, MARV | ERWIN, STEVE; BLYBERG, WILL	$19.99/$23.99 CAN | TP
9781401258429	SEP150293	DEATHSTROKE, THE TERMINATOR VOL. 2: SYMPATHY FOR THE DEVIL	WOLFMAN, MARV; GOLDEN, MICHAEL | NICHOLS, ART	$14.99/$17.99 CAN | TP
9781401260767		DEATHSTROKE, THE TERMINATOR VOL. 3	WOLFMAN, MARV | ERWIN, STEVE	$19.99/$23.99 CAN | TP
9781401234812	MAY120282	DEATHSTROKE VOL. 1: LEGACY	HIGGINS, KYLE | BENNETT, JOE	$16.99/$19.99 CAN | TP
9781401240387	NOV130231	DEATHSTROKE VOL. 2: LOBO HUNT	LIEFELD, ROB | LIEFELD, ROB	$19.99/$23.99 CAN | TP
9781401254711	MAR150267	DEATHSTROKE VOL. 1: GODS OF WAR	DANIEL, TONY S. | DANIEL, TONY S.	$14.99/$17.99 CAN | TP
9781401259983	JUN150300	DEATHSTROKE VOL. 1 BOOK & MASK SET	DANIEL, TONY S. | DANIEL, TONY S.	$29.99/$35.00 CAN | TP
9781401261207	NOV150272	DEATHSTROKE VOL. 2: GOD KILLER	DANIEL, TONY S. | DANIEL, TONY S.	$14.99/$17.99 CAN | TP
9781401242503	OCT130251	THE DEMON: FROM THE DARKNESS	WAGNER, MATT | VARIOUS	$14.99/$17.99 CAN | TP

DC COMICS SELECTED BACKLIST

ISBN	DIAMOND CODE	TITLE	AUTHOR	ARTIST	US$	FORMAT
9781401258214	SEP150295	THE DEMON VOL. 1: HELL'S HITMAN	ENNIS, GARTH	MCREA, JOHN	$19.99/$23.99 CAN	TP
9781401260996		THE DEMON VOL. 2: THE LONGEST DAY	ENNIS, GARTH	DOBBYN, NIGEL	$19.99/$23.99 CAN	TP
9781401240394	FEB130208	DEMON KNIGHTS VOL. 2: THE AVALON TRAP	CORNELL, PAUL	NEVES, DIOGENES	$14.99/$17.99 CAN	TP
9781401242695	OCT130242	DEMON KNIGHTS VOL. 3: THE GATHERING STORM	CORNELL, PAUL; VENDITTI, ROBERT	CHANG, BERNARD	$19.99/$23.99 CAN	TP
9781401244972	APR130243	DIABLO: SWORD OF JUSTICE	WILLIAMS, AARON	LACROIX, JOSEPH	$14.99/$17.99 CAN	TP
9781401237752	JAN130295	DIAL H VOL. 1: INTO YOU	MIEVILLE, CHINA	SANTOLOUCO, MATEUS	$14.99/$17.99 CAN	TP
9781401243838	NOV130228	DIAL H VOL. 2: EXCHANGE	MIEVILLE, CHINA	PONTICELLI, ALBERTO; GREEN, DAN	$16.99/$19.99 CAN	TP
9781401255206	JAN150371	DIAL H DELUXE EDITION	MIEVILLE, CHINA	SANTOLOUCO, MATEUS; PONTICELLI, ALBERTO	$34.99/$41.99 CAN	HC
9781401248901	SEP140318	DIVINE RIGHT: THE ADVENTURES OF MAX FARADAY	LEE, JIM	LEE, JIM	$24.99/$28.99 CAN	TP
9781401261214	DEC150320	DOCTOR FATE VOL. 1: THE BLOOD PRICE	LEVITZ, PAUL	LIEW, SONNY	$14.99/$17.99 CAN	TP
9781401243258	SEP130283	DOCTOR MID-NITE	WAGNER, MATT	SNYDER, JOHN K.	$14.99/$17.99 CAN	TP
9781401261221	NOV150282	DOOMED	LOBDELL, SCOTT	FERNANDEZ, JAVI	$14.99/$17.99 CAN	TP
9781401245177	JAN140352	FINAL CRISIS	MORRISON, GRANT	JONES, J.G.	$19.99/$19.99 CAN	TP
9781401223250	JUL100195	FINAL CRISIS: LEGION OF 3 WORLDS	JOHNS, GEOFF	PÉREZ, GEORGE	$14.99/$17.99 CAN	TP
9781401223236	MAY100186	FINAL CRISIS: REVELATIONS	RUCKA, GREG	TAN, PHILIP	$14.99/$17.99 CAN	TP
9781401231835	APR110202	FIRESTORM: THE NUCLEAR MAN	CONWAY, GERRY	MILGROM, AL	$17.99/$19.99 CAN	TP
9781401237004	JUN120237	THE FURY OF FIRESTORM: THE NUCLEAR MEN VOL. 1: GOD PARTICLE	VAN SCIVER, ETHAN	CINAR, YILDIRAY	$14.99/$17.99 CAN	TP
9781401240325	MAR130275	THE FURY OF FIRESTORM: THE NUCLEAR MEN VOL. 2: THE FIRESTORM PROTOCOLS	HARRIS, JOE	VAN SCIVER, ETHAN; CINAR, YILDIRAY	$14.99/$17.99 CAN	TP
9781401242923	SEP130272	THE FURY OF FIRESTORM: THE NUCLEAR MEN VOL. 3: TAKEOVER	JURGENS, DAN	JURGENS, DAN	$16.99/$19.99 CAN	TP
9781401234713	MAR120244	FRANKENSTEIN, AGENT OF S.H.A.D.E. VOL. 1: WAR OF THE MONSTERS	LEMIRE, JEFF	PONTICELLI, ALBERTO	$14.99/$17.99 CAN	TP
9781401238186	JAN130298	FRANKENSTEIN AGENT OF S.H.A.D.E. VOL. 2: SECRETS OF THE DEAD	KINDT, MATT; LEMIRE, JEFF	PONTICELLI, ALBERTO	$16.99/$19.99 CAN	TP
9781401251291	AUG140325	FUTURES END: FIVE YEARS LATER OMNIBUS	VARIOUS	VARIOUS	$99.99/$112.00 CAN	HC
9781401238537	DEC120328	G.I. COMBAT VOL. 1: THE WAR THAT TIME FORGOT	KRUL, J.T.	PANOSIAN, DAN	$19.99/$23.99 CAN	TP
9781401254872	star-spangled	G.I. ZOMBIE: A STAR-SPANGLED WAR STORY	PALMIOTTI, JIMMY; GRAY, JUSTIN	HAMPTON, SCOTT	$16.99/$19.99 CAN	TP
9781401236960	SEP130280	GEARS OF WAR BOOK THREE	TRAVISS, KAREN	MHAN, POP	$19.99/$23.99 CAN	TP
9781401252526	JUL148008	GODZILLA: AWAKENING (LEGENDARY COMICS)	BORENSTEIN, MAX; BORENSTEIN, GREG	BATTLE, ERIC	$12.99/$15.99 CAN	TP
9781401254728	MAR150269	GOTHAM ACADEMY VOL. 1: WELCOME TO GOTHAM ACADEMY	CLOONAN, BECKY; FLETCHER, BRENDEN	KERSCHL, KARL	$14.99/$17.99 CAN	TP
9781401256814	DEC150332	GOTHAM ACADEMY VOL. 2: CALAMITY	CLOONAN, BECKY; FLETCHER, BRENDEN	KERSCHL, KARL	$14.99/$17.99 CAN	TP
9781401220372	DEC100248	GOTHAM CENTRAL BOOK 1: IN THE LINE OF DUTY	RUCKA, GREG; BRUBAKER, ED	LARK, MICHAEL	$19.99/$23.99 CAN	TP
9781401225438	APR110203	GOTHAM CENTRAL BOOK 2: JOKERS AND MADMEN	RUCKA, GREG; BRUBAKER, ED	LARK, MICHAEL	$19.99/$23.99 CAN	TP
9781401232320	JUL110257	GOTHAM CENTRAL BOOK 3: ON THE FREAK BEAT	RUCKA, GREG; BRUBAKER, ED	LARK, MICHAEL	$19.99/$23.99 CAN	TP
9781401231941	JAN120307	GOTHAM CENTRAL BOOK 4: CORRIGAN	RUCKA, GREG; BRUBAKER, ED	KANO	$19.99/$23.99 CAN	TP
9781401261924	DEC150343	GOTHAM CENTRAL OMNIBUS	BRUBAKER, ED; RUCKA, GREG	LARK, MICHAEL; KANO	$99.99/$112.00 CAN	HC
9781401254735	MAY150238	GOTHAM BY MIDNIGHT VOL. 1: WE DO NOT SLEEP	FAWKES, RAY	SORRENTINO, ANDREA	$14.99/$17.99 CAN	TP
9781401261245	JAN160328	GOTHAM BY MIDNIGHT VOL. 2: REST IN PEACE	FAWKES, RAY	FERREYRA, JUAN	$16.99/$19.99 CAN	TP
9781401251758	JUL140248	GOTHAM CITY SIRENS BOOK ONE	DINI, PAUL	MARCH, GUILLEM	$24.99/$28.99 CAN	TP
9781401254124	JAN150373	GOTHAM CITY SIRENS BOOK TWO	CALLOWAY, PETER	GUINALDO, ANDRES	$24.99/$28.99 CAN	TP
9781401258092	JUN150305	GRAPHIC INK: THE DC COMICS ART OF DARWYN COOKE	COOKE, DARWYN	COOKE, DARWYN	$39.99/$48.99 CAN	HC
9781401248406	FEB140264	GRAPHIC INK: THE DC COMICS ART OF FRANK QUITELY	QUITELY, FRANK	QUITELY, FRANK	$39.99/$47.99 CAN	HC
9781401263607		GRAPHIC INK: THE DC COMICS ART OF GARY FRANK	VARIOUS	FRANK, GARY	$39.99/$48.99 CAN	HC
9781401255220	AUG150263	GRAPHIC INK: THE DC COMICS ART OF IVAN REIS	REIS, IVAN	REIS, IVAN	$39.99/$47.99 CAN	HC
9781401259730	JAN160314	GRAPHIC INK: THE DC COMICS ART OF JIM LEE	LEE, JIM		$39.99/$48.99 CAN	HC
9781401234973	APR120248	GRIFTER VOL. 1: MOST WANTED	EDMONDSON, NATHAN	CAFU	$16.99/$17.99 CAN	TP
9781401240981	FEB130209	GRIFTER VOL. 2: NEWFOUND POWER	LIEFELD, ROB; TIERI, FRANK	CLARK, SCOTT	$16.99/$19.99 CAN	TP
9781401237943	OCT120266	HARD TIME: SIXTEEN	GERBER, STEVE	HURTT, BRIAN	$14.99/$17.99 CAN	TP
9781401245559	APR140244	HARLAN ELLISON'S 7 AGAINST CHAOS	ELLISON, HARLAN	CHADWICK, PAUL	$16.99/$19.99 CAN	TP
9781401216573	SEP080168	HARLEY QUINN: PRELUDES & KNOCK-KNOCK JOKES	KESEL, KARL	DODSON, TERRY	$19.99/$23.99 CAN	TP
9781401240417	MAR130276	HARLEY QUINN: NIGHT AND DAY	KESEL, KARL	DODSON, TERRY; WOODS, PETE	$16.99/$19.99 CAN	TP
9781401245955	DEC130313	HARLEY QUINN: WELCOME TO METROPOLIS	KESEL, KARL	DODSON, TERRY; BADEAUX, BRANDON	$19.99/$23.99 CAN	TP
9781401250683	JUN140280	HARLEY QUINN: VENGEANCE UNLIMITED	LIEBERMAN, A.J.	HUDDLESTON, MIKE; NIXEY, TROY	$19.99/$23.99 CAN	TP
9781401254155	JAN150369	HARLEY QUINN VOL. 1: HOT IN THE CITY	PALMIOTTI, JIMMY; CONNER, AMANDA; HARDIN, CHAD		$16.99/$19.99 CAN	TP

ISBN	DIAMOND CODE	TITLE	AUTHOR	ARTIST	US$	FORMAT
9781401257637 SEP150302	HARLEY QUINN VOL. 2: POWER OUTAGE	CONNER, AMANDA; PALMIOTTI, JIMMY;HARDIN, CHAD	$16.99/$19.99 CAN	TP
9781401262525	HARLEY QUINN VOL. 3: KISS KISS BANG STAB	PALMIOTTI, JIMMY; CONNER, AMANDA;HARDIN, CHAD	$16.99/$19.99 CAN	TP
9781401262532	HARLEY QUINN VOL. 4	PALMIOTTI, JIMMY; CONNER, AMANDA;HARDIN, CHAD	$22.99/$27.99 CAN	HC
9781401259747 DEC150324	HARLEY QUINN AND POWER GIRL	PALMIOTTI, JIMMY; CONNER, AMANDA;ROUX, STEPHANE	$14.99/$17.99 CAN	TP
9781401255176 APR150289	BATMAN: HARLEY QUINN	DINI, PAUL	GOOGE, NEIL	$19.99/$23.99 CAN	TP
9781401260804 OCT150255	HARLEY AND IVY: THE DELUXE EDITION	DINI, PAUL; WINICK, JUDD	TIMM, BRUCE; CHIODO, JOE	$24.99/$29.99 CAN	HC
9781401234980 MAY120281	HAWK AND DOVE VOL. 1: FIRST STRIKES	GATES, STERLING	LIEFELD, ROB	$16.99/$19.99 CAN	TP
9781401243296 NOV130240	HAWKWORLD (NEW EDITION)	TRUMAN,TIMOTHY TRUMAN, TIMOTHY; ALCATENA, ENRIQUE	$14.99/$17.99 CAN	TP
9781401232221 SEP110186	HAWKMAN OMNIBUS VOL. 1	JOHNS, GEOFF	MORALES, RAGS	$75.00/$85.00 CAN	HC
9781401237066 JUL120215	THE SAVAGE HAWKMAN VOL. 1: DARKNESS RISING	DANIEL,TONY S.	TAN, PHILIP	$16.99/$19.99 CAN	TP
9781401240844 SEP130277	THE SAVAGE HAWKMAN VOL. 2: WANTED	LIEFELD, ROB; POULTON, MARK	BENNETT, JOE	$19.99/$23.99 CAN	TP
9781401240226 APR130245	HE-MAN AND THE MASTERS OF THE UNIVERSE VOL. 1	ROBINSON, JAMES; GIFFEN, KEITH	TAN, PHILIP	$14.99/$17.99 CAN	TP
9781401243128 NOV130244	HE-MAN AND THE MASTERS OF THE UNIVERSE VOL. 2: ORIGINS OF ETERNIA	GIFFEN, KEITH; FIALKOV, JOSHUA HALE	IRVING, FRAZER; GIFFEN, KEITH	$14.99/$17.99 CAN	TP
9781401247195 MAY140378	HE-MAN AND THE MASTERS OF THE UNIVERSE VOL. 3	GIFFEN, KEITH	MHAN, POP	$14.99/$17.99 CAN	TP
9781401250690 NOV140311	HE-MAN AND THE MASTERS OF THE UNIVERSE VOL. 4: WHAT LIES WITHIN	ABNETT, DAN	O'HARE, MICHAEL; KAYANAN, RAFAEL	$14.99/$19.99 CAN	TP
9781401253394 MAR150280	HE-MAN AND THE MASTERS OF THE UNIVERSE VOL. 5: THE BLOOD OF GRAYSKULL	ABNETT, DAN	MHAN, POP	$14.99/$17.99 CAN	TP
9781401258481 JUL150314	HE-MAN: THE ETERNITY WAR VOL. 1	ABNETT, DAN	MAHN, POP	$14.99/$17.99 CAN	TP
9781401261283 JAN160329	HE-MAN: THE ETERNITY WAR VOL. 2	ABNETT, DAN	MHAN, POP	$14.99/$17.99 CAN	TP
9781401247201 MAY140379	DC UNIVERSE VS. MASTERS OF THE UNIVERSE	GIFFEN, KEITH	SOY, DEXTER	$14.99/$17.99 CAN	TP
9781563897986 FEB090206	HISTORY OF THE DC UNIVERSE	WOLFMAN, MARV	VARIOUS	$12.99/$15.99 CAN	TP
9781401237332 JUL120223	HUNTRESS: CROSSBOW AT THE CROSSROADS	LEVITZ, PAUL	TO, MARCUS	$14.99/$17.99 CAN	TP
9781401233716 NOV110204	I, VAMPIRE	DEMATTEIS, MARK J.	SUTTON, THOMAS	$29.99/$15.99 CAN	TP
9781401236878 JUL120212	I, VAMPIRE VOL. 1: TAINTED LOVE	FIALKOV, JOSHUA HALE	SORRENTINO, ANDREA	$14.99/$17.99 CAN	TP
9781401237837 DEC120326	I, VAMPIRE VOL. 2: RISE OF THE VAMPIRES	FIALKOV, JOSHUA HALE	SORRENTINO, ANDREA	$16.99/$19.99 CAN	TP
9781401242787 JUL130238	I, VAMPIRE VOL. 3: WAVE OF MUTILATION	FIALKOV, JOSHUA HALE	SORRENTINO, ANDREA	$16.99/$19.99 CAN	TP
9781401263508	ICON VOL. 1	VARIOUS	VARIOUS	$19.99/$23.99 CAN	TP
9781401254797 MAY150239	INFINITE CRISIS: FIGHT FOR THE MULTIVERSE	ABNETT, DAN	RANEY,TOM	$14.99/$17.99 CAN	TP
9781401258498 SEP150299	INFINITE CRISIS: FIGHT FOR THE MULTIVERSE VOL. 2	ABNETT, DAN	DUCE, CHRISTIAN; FRANCISCO, EDUARDO	$16.99/$19.99 CAN	TP
9781401210601 FEB118149	INFINITE CRISIS	JOHNS, GEOFF	JIMENEZ, PHIL	$17.99/$20.99 CAN	TP
9781401209223 JUL060154	INFINITE CRISIS COMPANION	RUCKA, GREG	VARIOUS	$14.99/$17.99 CAN	TP
9781401231057 FEB110201	INFINITY INC.: THE GENERATIONS SAGA VOL. 1	THOMAS, ROY	ORDWAY, JERRY	$39.99/$46.99 CAN	HC
9781401240790 FEB130220	IN THE DAYS OF THE MOB	KIRBY, JACK	KIRBY, JACK	$39.99/$47.99 CAN	HC
9781401238339 DEC120331	THE JACK KIRBY OMNIBUS VOL. 2	KIRBY, JACK	KIRBY, JACK	$39.99/$47.99 CAN	HC
9781401243302 AUG110306	JOE KUBERT PRESENTS	KUBERT, JOE; GLANZMAN, SAM	KUBERT, JOE	$19.99/$23.99 CAN	TP
9781401242589 AUG130307	THE JOKER: THE CLOWN PRINCE OF CRIME	VARIOUS	VARIOUS	$16.99/$19.99 CAN	TP
9781401241063 DEC130315	SHOWCASE PRESENTS: JONAH HEX VOL. 2	VARIOUS	VARIOUS	$19.99/$23.99 CAN	TP
9781401210953 JUN060192	JONAH HEX: FACE FULL OF VIOLENCE	GRAY, JUSTIN & PALMIOTTI, JIMMY	ROSS, LUKE	$12.99/$15.99 CAN	TP
9781401227579 FEB120186	JONAH HEX: WELCOME TO PARADISE	ALBANO, JOHN	VARIOUS	$17.99/$20.99 CAN	TP
9781401212490 JAN070305	JONAH HEX: GUNS OF VENGEANCE	GRAY, JUSTIN & PALMIOTTI, JIMMY	ROSS, LUKE	$12.99/$15.99 CAN	TP
9781401228996 JUL100196	JONAH HEX: COUNTING CORPSES	GRAY, JUSTIN & PALMIOTTI, JIMMY	VARIOUS	$14.99/$17.99 CAN	TP
9781401230098 JAN110330	JONAH HEX: TALL TALES	GRAY, JUSTIN & PALMIOTTI, JIMMY	VARIOUS	$14.99/$17.99 CAN	TP
9781401232498 AUG110248	JONAH HEX: BURY ME IN HELL	GRAY, JUSTIN & PALMIOTTI, JIMMY	VARIOUS	$17.99/$19.99 CAN	TP
9781401225513 FEB110207	JONAH HEX: NO WAY BACK	GRAY, JUSTIN & PALMIOTTI, JIMMY	DEZUNIGA,TONY	$14.99/$17.99 CAN	TP
9781401243975 AUG130308	THE JUDAS COIN	SIMONSON, WALT	SIMONSON, WALT	$14.99/$17.99 CAN	TP
9781401238858 AUG130309	JUST IMAGINE STAN LEE CREATING THE DC UNIVERSE OMNIBUS	LEE, STAN	VARIOUS	$75.00/$85.00 CAN	HC
9781401243319 APR140269	JUSTICE LEAGUE OF AMERICA'S VIBE VOL. 1: BREACH	JOHNS, GEOFF; KREISBERG, ANDREW	WOODS, PETE	$16.99/$19.99 CAN	TP
9781401236724 AUG120257	KAMANDI, THE LAST BOY ON EARTH OMNIBUS VOL. 2	KIRBY, JACK	KIRBY, JACK	$49.99/$58.00 CAN	HC
9781401244118 MAY140368	KATANA VOL. 1: SOULTAKER	NOCENTI, ANN	SANCHEZ, ALEX	$19.99/$23.99 CAN	TP
9781401245214 MAR140254	LARFLEEZE VOL. 1: REVOLT OF THE ORANGE LANTERNS	GIFFEN, KEITH; DEMATTEIS, J.M.	KOLINS, SCOTT	$16.99/$19.99 CAN	TP
9781401250102 SEP140307	LARFLEEZE VOL. 2: THE FACE OF GREED	GIFFEN, KEITH; DEMATTEIS, J.M.	KOLINS, SCOTT	$14.99/$17.99 CAN	TP
9781401263164	LEGENDS 30TH ANNIVERSARY EDITION	OSTRANDER, JOHN	BYRNE, JOHN	$19.99/$23.99 CAN	TP

DC COMICS SELECTED BACKLIST

ISBN	DIAMOND CODE	TITLE	AUTHOR	ARTIST	US$	FORMAT
9781401254834	MAY150244	LOBO VOL. 1: TARGETS	BUNN, CULLEN	BROWN, REILLY	$14.99/$17.99 CAN	TP
9781401261504	JAN160318	LOBO VOL. 2: BEWARE HIS MIGHT	BUNN, CULLEN	RICHARDS, CLIFF	$14.99/$17.99 CAN	TP
9781401263591		BEST OF LOONEY TUNES VOL. 1	VARIOUS	VARIOUS	$12.99/$15.99 CAN	TP
9781401251406	SEP140322	MARSHAL LAW	MILLS, PAT	O'NEILL, KEVIN	$29.99/$35.00 CAN	TP
9781401243869	NOV130245	MARTIAN MANHUNTER: SON OF MARS	OSTRANDER, JOHN	MANDRAKE, TOM	$19.99/$23.99 CAN	TP
9781401251413	JUN140275	MARTIAN MANHUNTER: RINGS OF SATURN	OSTRANDER, JOHN	MANDRAKE, TOM	$19.99/$23.99 CAN	TP
9781401261511	NOV150264	MARTIAN MANHUNTER VOL. 1: THE EPIPHANY	WILLIAMS, ROB	BARROWS, EDDY	$16.99/$19.99 CAN	TP
9781401243883	NOV130246	SHOWCASE PRESENTS: MEN OF WAR	VARIOUS	VARIOUS	$19.99/$23.99 CAN	TP
9781401234997	APR120249	MEN OF WAR VOL. 1: UNEASY COMPANY	BRANDON, IVAN	DERENICK, TOM	$19.99/$23.99 CAN	TP
9781401238674	AUG120258	THE METAL MEN ARCHIVES VOL. 2	KANIGHER, ROBERT	ANDRU, ROSS	$75.00/$85.00 CAN	HC
9781401263188		METAMORPHO VOL. 1	VARIOUS	VARIOUS	$16.99/$19.99 CAN	TP
9781401259785	NOV150265	MIDNIGHTER VOL. 1: OUT	ORLANDO, STEVE	ACO	$14.99/$17.99 CAN	TP
9781401257088	JAN150383	MORTAL KOMBAT X VOL. 1: BLOOD TIES	KITTELSEN, SHAWN	SOY, DEXTER	$14.99/$17.99 CAN	TP
9781401258535	JUL150317	MORTAL KOMBAT X VOL. 2: BLOOD GODS	KITTELSEN, SHAWN	SOY, DEXTER	$14.99/$17.99 CAN	TP
9781401260842	JAN160332	MORTAL KOMBAT X VOL. 3: BLOOD ISLAND	KITTELSEN, SHAWN	SOY, DEXTER	$16.99/$19.99 CAN	TP
9781401246402	FEB140255	THE MOVEMENT VOL. 1: CLASS WARFARE	SIMONE, GAIL	WILLIAMS II, FREDDIE	$14.99/$17.99 CAN	TP
9781401249526	SEP140308	THE MOVEMENT VOL. 2: FIGHTING FOR THE FUTURE	SIMONE, GAIL	WILLIAMS II, FREDDIE	$14.99/$17.99 CAN	TP
9781401256821	JUN150291	THE MULTIVERSITY DELUXE EDITION	MORRISON, GRANT	QUITELY, FRANK; REIS, IVAN; LEE, JIM	$49.99/$58.00 CAN	HC
9781401245030	JUN130270	NECESSARY EVIL: SUPER-VILLAINS OF DC COMICS	VARIOUS	VARIOUS	$16.99/$19.99 CAN	TP
9781401252441	SEP140303	THE NEW 52: FUTURES END VOL. 1	LEMIRE, JEFF; AZZARELLO, BRIAN; JURGENS, DAN; GIFFEN, KEITH	ZIRCHER, PATRICK	$39.99/$47.99 CAN	TP
9781401256029	APR150296	THE NEW 52: FUTURES END VOL. 2	LEMIRE, JEFF; AZZARELLO, BRIAN; JURGENS, DAN; GIFFEN, KEITH	ZIRCHER, PATRICK	$29.99/$35.00 CAN	TP
9781401258788	JUN150294	THE NEW 52: FUTURES END VOL. 3	LEMIRE, JEFF; AZZARELLO, BRIAN	ZIRCHER, PATRICK	$29.99/$35.00 CAN	TP
9781401260866		NEWSBOY LEGION BY SIMON AND KIRBY VOL. 2	SIMON, JOE	KIRBY, JACK	$24.99/$29.99 CAN	HC
9781401240448	MAY130230	NIGHTWING: OLD FRIENDS, NEW ENEMIES	WOLFMAN, MARV VARIOUS		$14.99/$17.99 CAN	TP
9781401251444	SEP140321	NIGHTWING VOL. 1: BLUDHAVEN	O'NEIL, DENNIS	LAND, GREG; MCDANIEL, SCOTT	$19.99/$23.99 CAN	TP
9781401255336	MAR150281	NIGHTWING VOL. 2: ROUGH JUSTICE	DIXON, CHUCK	MCDANIEL, SCOTT; STORY, KARL	$19.99/$23.99 CAN	TP
9781401258559	SEP150303	NIGHTWING VOL. 3: FALSE STARTS	DIXON, CHUCK	MCDANIEL, SCOTT; STORY, KARL	$19.99/$23.99 CAN	TP
9781401260873	JAN160333	NIGHTWING VOL. 4: LOVE & BULLETS	DIXON, CHUCK	MCDANIEL, SCOTT	$24.99/$29.99 CAN	TP
9781401237059	JUL120214	NIGHTWING VOL. 1: TRAPS AND TRAPEZES	HIGGINS, KYLE	BARROWS, EDDY	$14.99/$17.99 CAN	TP
9781401240271	APR130225	NIGHTWING VOL. 2: NIGHT OF THE OWLS	HIGGINS, KYLE	BARROWS, EDDY	$14.99/$17.99 CAN	TP
9781401244132	SEP130273	NIGHTWING VOL. 3: DEATH OF THE FAMILY	HIGGINS, KYLE	BARROWS, EDDY	$16.99/$19.99 CAN	TP
9781401246303	APR140258	NIGHTWING VOL. 4: SECOND CITY	HIGGINS, KYLE	BOOTH, BRETT	$14.99/$17.99 CAN	TP
9781401250119	SEP140309	NIGHTWING VOL. 5: SETTING SON	HIGGINS, KYLE	CONRAD, WILL	$16.99/$19.99 CAN	TP
9781401257590	OCT150253	GRAYSON VOL. 1: AGENTS OF SPYRAL	KING, TOM; SEELEY, TIM	JANIN, MIKEL	$14.99/$17.99 CAN	TP
9781401257606	OCT150234	GRAYSON VOL. 2: WE ALL DIE AT DAWN	KING, TOM; SEELEY, TIM	JANIN, MIKEL	$16.99/$19.99 CAN	TP
9781401262761		GRAYSON VOL. 3	KING, TOM; SEELEY, TIM	JANIN, MIKEL	$16.99/$19.99 CAN	TP
9781401240424	MAY130232	JACK KIRBY'S O.M.A.C.	KIRBY, JACK	KIRBY, JACK	$16.99/$19.99 CAN	TP
9781401234829	MAY120283	O.M.A.C. VOL. 1: OMACTIVATE!	DIDIO, DAN	GIFFEN, KEITH	$19.99/$23.99 CAN	TP
9781401261535		OMEGA MEN: THE COMPLETE SERIES	KING, TOM	BAGENDA, BARNABY	$16.99/$19.99 CAN	TP
9781401255350	NOV140312	ORION BY WALTER SIMONSON OMNIBUS	SIMONSON, WALTER	SIMONSON, WALTER	$75.00/$85.00 CAN	HC
9781401237325	JUN120249	PENGUIN: PAIN AND PREJUDICE	HURWITZ, GREGG	KUDRANSKI, SZYMON	$14.99/$17.99 CAN	TP
9781563896484	FEB068129	PLANETARY VOL.1: ALL OVER THE WORLD AND OTHER STORIES	ELLIS, WARREN	CASSADAY, JOHN	$14.99/$17.99 CAN	TP
9781563897641	JAN068213	PLANETARY VOL. 2: THE FOURTH MAN	ELLIS, WARREN	CASSADAY, JOHN	$14.99/$17.99 CAN	TP
9781401202941	JAN050354	PLANETARY VOL. 3: LEAVING THE 20TH CENTURY	ELLIS, WARREN	CASSADAY, JOHN	$14.99/$17.99 CAN	TP
9781401223458	SEP100285	PLANETARY VOL. 4: SPACETIME ARCHAEOLOGY	ELLIS, WARREN	CASSADAY, JOHN	$17.99/$20.99 CAN	TP
9781401242381	SEP130279	THE PLANETARY OMNIBUS	ELLIS, WARREN	CASSADAY, JOHN	$75.00/$85.00 CAN	HC
9781401243074	NOV130247	POWER GIRL: POWER TRIP	PALMIOTTI, JIMMY; JOHNS, GEOFF	CONNER, AMANDA	$29.99/$35.00 CAN	TP
9781401263171		PREZ: THE FIRST TEEN PRESIDENT (BACKLIST)	BRUBAKER, ED	SIMON, JOE	$19.99/$23.99 CAN	TP
9781401259792	NOV150266	PREZ VOL. 1: CORNDOG IN CHIEF	RUSSELL, MARK	CALDWELL, BEN	$14.99/$17.99 CAN	TP
9781401252274	NOV150248	QUARANTINE ZONE	WILSON, DANIEL H.	PASARIN, FERNANDO	$22.99/$27.99 CAN	HC
9781401255466		THE QUESTION: FALLING IN PLACE	VEITCH, RICK	EDWARDS, TOMMY LEE	$14.99/$17.99 CAN	TP

ISBN	DIAMOND CODE	TITLE	AUTHOR	ARTIST	US$	FORMAT
9781401243135	NOV130233	THE RAVAGERS VOL. 2: HEAVENLY DESTRUCTION	NELSON, MICHAEL ALAN | GUARA, IG	$14.99/$17.99 CAN | TP
9781401237127	AUG120248	RED HOOD AND THE OUTLAWS VOL. 1: REDEMPTION	LOBDELL, SCOTT | ROCAFORT, KENNETH	$14.99/$17.99 CAN | TP
9781401240905	MAR130273	RED HOOD AND THE OUTLAWS VOL. 2: THE STARFIRE	LOBDELL, SCOTT | ROCAFORT, KENNETH	$14.99/$17.99 CAN | TP
9781401244125	AUG130301	RED HOOD AND THE OUTLAWS VOL. 3: DEATH OF THE FAMILY	LOBDELL, SCOTT | GREEN, TIMOTHY	$16.99/$19.99 CAN | TP
9781401246365	MAR140256	RED HOOD AND THE OUTLAWS VOL. 4: LEAGUE OF ASSASSINS	TYNION IV, JAMES | GOPEZ, JULIUS; BARRIONUEVO, AL	$16.99/$19.99 CAN | TP
9781401250485	SEP140310	RED HOOD AND THE OUTLAWS VOL. 5: THE BIG PICTURE	TYNION IV, JAMES | GOPEZ, JULIUS	$14.99/$17.99 CAN | TP
9781401253424	MAR150271	RED HOOD AND THE OUTLAWS VOL. 6: LOST AND FOUND	LOBDELL, SCOTT | SANDOVAL, RAFA	$14.99/$17.99 CAN | TP
9781401258566	OCT150260	RED HOOD AND THE OUTLAWS VOL. 7: LAST CALL	LOBDELL, SCOTT | SILVA, R.B.	$14.99/$17.99 CAN | TP
9781401261542	DEC150322	RED HOOD/ARSENAL VOL. 1: OPEN FOR BUSINESS	LOBDELL, SCOTT | MEDRI, DENIS	$14.99/$17.99 CAN | TP
9781401233631	OCT110247	RESURRECTION MAN VOL. 1	ABNETT, DAN; LANNING, ANDY | GUICE, BUTCH	$29.99/$35.00 CAN | TP
9781401235291	MAY120284	RESURRECTION MAN VOL. 1: DEAD AGAIN	ABNETT, DAN; LANNING, ANDY | DAGNINO, FERNANDO	$14.99/$17.99 CAN | TP
9781401238667	MAR130281	RESURRECTION MAN VOL. 2: A MATTER OF DEATH AND LIFE	ABNETT, DAN; LANNING, ANDY | GUICE, JACKSON	$14.99/$17.99 CAN | TP
9781401258573	AUG150276	ROBIN VOL. 1: REBORN	DIXON, CHUCK | LYLE, ROM	$19.99/$23.99 CAN | TP
9781401260897	DEC150339	ROBIN VOL. 2: TRIUMPHANT	DIXON, CHUCK | GRUMMETT, TOM	$24.99/$28.99 CAN | TP
9781401263621		ROBIN VOL. 3	DIXON, CHUCK | VARIOUS	$19.99/$23.99 CAN | TP
9781401261559	NOV150267	ROBIN: SON OF BATMAN VOL. 1: YEAR OF BLOOD	GLEASON, PATRICK | GLEASON, PATRICK	$22.99/$27.99 CAN | HC
9781401262082		ROBIN WAR	VARIOUS | VARIOUS	$19.99/$23.99 CAN | HC
9781401255367	DEC140391	ROBIN THE BOY WONDER: A CELEBRATION OF 75 YEARS	FINGER, BILL | KANE, BOB	$39.99/$47.99 CAN | HC
9781401248956	JUN140284	RONIN DELUXE EDITION	MILLER, FRANK | MILER, FRANK	$29.99/$35.00 CAN | HC
9781401222994	APR090212	SANDMAN BY KIRBY AND SIMON	KIRBY, JACK | KIRBY, JACK	$39.99/$49.99 CAN | HC
9781401249465	NOV140323	SCOOBY-DOO TEAM-UP	FISCH, SHOLLY | BRIZUELA, DARIO	$12.99/$15.99 CAN | TP
9781401249267	NOV140313	SCRIBBLENAUTS UNMASKED: A DC COMICS ADVENTURE	ELDER, JOSH | ARCHER, ADAM	$14.99/$17.99 CAN | TP
9781401250492	NOV140303	SECRET ORIGINS VOL. 1	LEMIRE, JEFF | SORRENTINO, ANDREA	$14.99/$17.99 CAN | TP
9781401253431	MAY150243	SECRET ORIGINS VOL. 2	AZZARELLO, BRIAN | CHIANG, CLIFF	$14.99/$17.99 CAN | TP
9781401250751	NOV140314	SECRET SIX VOL. 1: VILLAINS UNITED	SIMONE, GAIL | EAGLESHAM, DALE; WALKER, BRAD	$19.99/$23.99 CAN | TP
9781401255374	MAR150283	SECRET SIX VOL. 2: MONEY FOR MURDER	SIMONE, GAIL | SCOTT, NICOLA	$19.99/$23.99 CAN | TP
9781401258610	JUL150321	SECRET SIX VOL. 3: CAT'S CRADLE	SIMONE, GAIL | CALAFIORE, JIM	$19.99/$23.99 CAN | TP
9781401260903	JAN160334	SECRET SIX VOL. 4: CAUTION TO THE WIND	SIMONE, GAIL | CALAFIORE, JIM	$19.99/$23.99 CAN | TP
9781401254858	NOV130288	SECRET SIX VOL. 1: FRIENDS IN LOW PLACES	SIMONE, GAIL | LASHLEY, KEN; EAGLESHAM, DALE	$14.99/$17.99 CAN | TP
9781401242893	JUN130272	THE SECRET SOCIETY OF SUPER-VILLAINS VOL. 1	VARIOUS | VARIOUS	$19.99/$23.99 CAN | TP
9781401212483	JAN070311	SGT. ROCK: THE PROPHECY	KUBERT, JOE | KUBERT, JOE	$17.99/$21.99 CAN | TP
9781401238117	NOV120267	SHOWCASE PRESENTS: SGT. ROCK VOL. 4	KANIGHER, ROBERT | KUBERT, JOE	$19.99/$23.99 CAN | TP
9781401237820	NOV120272	THE SHADE	ROBINSON, JAMES | VARIOUS	$19.99/$23.99 CAN | TP
9781401255381	NOV140315	SHAZAM!: A CELEBRATION OF 75 YEARS	PARKER, BILL | BECK, C.C.	$39.99/$47.99 CAN | HC
9781401209742	DEC080160	SHAZAM! AND THE MONSTER SOCIETY OF EVIL	SMITH, JEFF | SMITH, JEFF	$19.99/$23.99 CAN | TP
9781401216740	DEC070251	SHAZAM!: GREATEST STORIES EVER TOLD, VOL. 1	VARIOUS | VARIOUS	$24.99/$28.99 CAN | TP
9781401246990	FEB140251	SHAZAM! VOL. 1	JOHNS, GEOFF | FRANK, GARY	$16.99/$19.99 CAN | TP
9781401238896	FEB130218	SOLO: THE DELUXE EDITION	VARIOUS | VARIOUS	$49.99/$58.00 CAN | HC
9781401234188	SEP110190	SPIRIT WORLD	KIRBY, JACK | KIRBY, JACK	$39.99/$46.99 CAN | HC
9781401247188	FEB140263	THE SPECTRE VOL. 1: CRIMES AND JUDGMENTS	OSTRANDER, JOHN | MANDRAKE, TOM	$19.99/$23.99 CAN | TP
9781401251505	SEP140324	THE SPECTRE VOL. 2: WRATH OF GOD	OSTRANDER, JOHN | MANDRAKE, TOM	$19.99/$23.99 CAN | TP
9781401261603	DEC150325	STARFIRE VOL. 1: WELCOME HOME	PALMIOTTI, JIMMY; CONNER, AMANDA | LUPACCHINO, EMANUELA	$14.99/$17.99 CAN | TP
9781401263362		STARMAN OMNIBUS VOL. 3	ROBINSON, JAMES | HARRIS, TONY	$29.99/$35.00 CAN | TP
9781401263836		STATIC SHOCK VOL. 1	MCDUFFIE, DWAYNE | VARIOUS	$19.99/$23.99 CAN | TP
9781401231118	APR110208	THE STEVE DITKO OMNIBUS VOL. 1	VARIOUS | DITKO, STEVE	$59.99/$68.00 CAN | HC
9781401232351	AUG110256	THE STEVE DITKO OMNIBUS VOL. 2	VARIOUS | DITKO, STEVE	$59.99/$68.00 CAN | HC
9781401234218	MAR130282	STORMWATCH VOL. 1	ELLIS, WARREN | LEE, JIM; RANEY, TOM	$19.99/$23.99 CAN | TP
9781401237271	MAR140267	STORMWATCH VOL. 2	ELLIS, WARREN | VARIOUS	$19.99/$23.99 CAN | TP
9781401247072	FEB140257	THE AUTHORITY VOL. 1	ELLIS, WARREN | HITCH, BRYAN	$19.99/$23.99 CAN | TP
9781401250805	SEP140316	THE AUTHORITY VOL. 2	MILLAR, MARK | QUITELY, FRANK	$24.99/$28.99 CAN | TP
9781401234836	FEB120251	STORMWATCH VOL. 1: DARK SIDE	CORNELL, PAUL | SEPULVEDA, MIGUEL	$14.99/$17.99 CAN | TP

DC COMICS SELECTED BACKLIST

ISBN	DIAMOND CODE	TITLE	AUTHOR	ARTIST	US$	FORMAT
9781401238483	NOV120263	STORMWATCH VOL. 2: ENEMIES OF EARTH	MILLIGAN, PETER	CALERO, IGNACIO; SEPULVEDA, MIGUEL	$14.99/$17.99 CAN	TP
9781401243159	JUN130273	STORMWATCH VOL. 3: BETRAYAL	MILLIGAN, PETER	CONRAD, WILL	$16.99/$19.99 CAN	TP
9781401248413	MAR140260	STORMWATCH VOL. 4: RESET	STARLIN, JIM	GUICHET, YVET	$19.99/$23.99 CAN	TP
9781401238469	SEP130284	SHOWCASE PRESENTS: STRANGE ADVENTURES VOL. 2	VARIOUS	VARIOUS	$19.99/$23.99 CAN	TP
9781401263430		SUICIDE SQUAD: THE SILVER AGE	ANDRU, ROSS	VARIOUS	$24.99/$29.99 CAN	TP
9781401258313	JUN150292	SUICIDE SQUAD VOL. 1: TRIAL BY FIRE	OSTRANDER, JOHN	MCDONNELL, LUKE	$19.99/$23.99 CAN	TP
9781401258337	SEP150307	SUICIDE SQUAD VOL. 2: THE NIGHTSHADE ODYSSEY	OSTRANDER, JOHN	MCDONNELL, LUKE	$19.99/$23.99 CAN	TP
9781401260910	JAN160335	SUICIDE SQUAD VOL. 3: ROGUES	OSTRANDER, JOHN	VARIOUS	$19.99/$23.99 CAN	TP
9781401262617		SUICIDE SQUAD VOL. 4	OSTRANDER, JOHN	VARIOUS	$19.99/$23.99 CAN	TP
9781401235444	APR120250	SUICIDE SQUAD VOL. 1: KICKED IN THE TEETH	GLASS, ADAM	DALLOCCHIO, FREDERICO	$14.99/$17.99 CAN	TP
9781401238445	NOV120264	SUICIDE SQUAD VOL. 2: BASILISK RISING	GLASS, ADAM	DAGNINO, FERNANDO	$16.99/$19.99 CAN	TP
9781401243166	JUL130239	SUICIDE SQUAD VOL. 3: DEATH IS FOR SUCKERS	GLASS, ADAM	VARIOUS	$14.99/$17.99 CAN	TP
9781401247010	JAN140341	SUICIDE SQUAD VOL. 4: DISCIPLINE AND PUNISH	KOT, ALES	ZIRCHER, PATRICK	$14.99/$17.99 CAN	TP
9781401250126	JUL140245	SUICIDE SQUAD VOL. 5: WALLED IN	KINDT, MATT	ZIRCHER, PATRICK	$16.99/$19.99 CAN	TP
9781401252380	APR150302	NEW SUICIDE SQUAD VOL. 1: PURE INSANITY	RYAN, SEAN	ROBERTS, JEREMY	$16.99/$19.99 CAN	TP
9781401261528	NOV150280	NEW SUICIDE SQUAD VOL. 2: MONSTERS	RYAN, SEAN	BRIONES, PHILIPPE	$16.99/$19.99 CAN	TP
9781401262648		NEW SUICIDE SQUAD VOL. 3	RYAN, SEAN	BRIONES, PHILIPPE	$14.99/$17.99 CAN	TP
9781401232511	SEP110189	SUPERBOY VOL. 1: SMALLVILLE ATTACKS	LEMIRE, JEFF	GALLO, PIER	$24.99/$28.99 CAN	TP
9781401234850	MAY120285	SUPERBOY VOL. 1: INCUBATION	LOBDELL, SCOTT	SILVA, R.B.	$14.99/$17.99 CAN	TP
9781401240493	FEB130214	SUPERBOY VOL. 2: EXTRACTION	LOBDELL, SCOTT; DEFALCO, TOM	SILVA, R.B.	$14.99/$17.99 CAN	TP
9781401243173	OCT130244	SUPERBOY VOL. 3: LOST	DEFALCO, TOM	SILVA, R.B.	$16.99/$19.99 CAN	TP
9781401246853	APR140274	SUPERBOY VOL. 4: BLOOD AND STEEL	JORDAN, JUSTIN	SILVA, RB	$16.99/$19.99 CAN	TP
9781401250928	OCT140363	SUPERBOY VOL. 5: PARADOX	WOLFMAN, MARV	KUDER, AARON; JIMENEZ, JORGE	$17.99/$20.99 CAN	TP
9781401262464	JAN160337	SUPERGIRL: THE SILVER AGE VOL. 1 OMNIBUS	VARIOUS	VARIOUS	$75.00/$85.00 CAN	HC
9781401263461		DARING ADVENTURES OF SUPERGIRL VOL. 1	VARIOUS	VARIOUS	$19.99/$23.99 CAN	TP
9781401260927		SUPERGIRL BY PETER DAVID & GARY FRANK	DAVID, PETER	FRANK, GARY	$19.99/$23.99 CAN	TP
9781401260934	OCT150252	SUPERGIRL VOL. 1: THE GIRL OF STEEL	LOEB, JEPH	TURNER, MICHAEL	$16.99/$19.99 CAN	TP
9781401236809	JUL120216	SUPERGIRL VOL. 1: LAST DAUGHTER OF KRYPTON	GREEN, MICHAEL; JOHNSON, MIKE	ASRAR, MAHMUD	$14.99/$17.99 CAN	TP
9781401240875	APR130223	SUPERGIRL VOL. 2: GIRL IN THE WORLD	GREEN, MICHAEL; JOHNSON, MIKE	ASRAR, MAHMUD	$14.99/$17.99 CAN	TP
9781401243180	NOV130235	SUPERGIRL VOL. 3: SANCTUARY	JOHNSON, MIKE	ASRAR, MAHMUD	$16.99/$19.99 CAN	TP
9781401247003	APR140273	SUPERGIRL VOL. 4: OUT OF THE PAST	NELSON, MICHAEL ALAN	ASRAR, MAHMUD	$14.99/$17.99 CAN	TP
9781401250515	OCT140364	SUPERGIRL VOL. 5: RED DAUGHTER OF KRYPTON	NELSON, MICHAEL ALAN	NEVES, DIOGENES	$17.99/$20.99 CAN	TP
9781401255411	APR150301	SUPERGIRL VOL. 6: CRUCIBLE	BEDARD, TONY	LUPACCHINO, EMANUELA	$16.99/$19.99 CAN	TP
9781401262655		SUPERGIRL: DIGITAL FIRST VOL. 1	VARIOUS	VARIOUS	$14.99/$17.99 CAN	TP
9781401263201		SUPERGIRL: COSMIC ADVENTURES OF THE 8TH GRADE (NEW EDITION)	WALKER, LANDRY	VARIOUS	$12.99/$15.99 CAN	TP
9781401263812		ROOTS OF THE SWAMP THING VOL. 2	VARIOUS	VARIOUS	$39.99/$48.99 CAN	HC
9781401234621	MAY120280	SWAMP THING VOL. 1: RAISE THEM BONES	SNYDER, SCOTT	PAQUETTE, YANICK	$14.99/$17.99 CAN	TP
9781401238438	JAN130301	SWAMP THING VOL. 2: FAMILY TREE	SNYDER, SCOTT	PAQUETTE, YANICK	$14.99/$17.99 CAN	TP
9781401242640	AUG130299	SWAMP THING VOL. 3: ROTWORLD: THE GREEN KINGDOM	SNYDER, SCOTT; LEMIRE, JEFF	PAQUETTE, YANICK	$16.99/$19.99 CAN	TP
9781401258702	MAY150248	SWAMP THING BY SCOTT SNYDER DELUXE EDITION	SNYDER, SCOTT	PAQUETTE, YANICK	$49.99/$58.00 CAN	HC
9781401246396	MAR140257	SWAMP THING VOL. 4: SEEDER	SOULE, CHARLES	KANO	$14.99/$17.99 CAN	TP
9781401250522	SEP140313	SWAMP THING VOL. 5: THE KILLING FIELD	SOULE, CHARLES	SAIZ, JESUS	$14.99/$17.99 CAN	TP
9781401254902	MAR150275	SWAMP THING VOL. 6: THE SUREEN	SOULE, CHARLES	SAIZ, JESUS	$16.99/$19.99 CAN	TP
9781401257705	OCT150262	SWAMP THING VOL. 7: SEASON'S END	SOULE, CHARLES	SAIZ, JESUS; PINA, JAVI	$16.99/$19.99 CAN	TP
9781401241001	MAY130228	SWORD OF SORCERY VOL. 1: AMETHYST	MARX, CHRISTY	LOPRESTI, AARON	$24.99/$28.99 CAN	TP
9781401238872	MAY130217	TALON VOL. 1: SCOURGE OF THE OWLS	TYNION IV, JAMES; SNYDER, SCOTT	MARCH, GUILLEM	$16.99/$19.99 CAN	TP
9781401246259	APR140261	TALON VOL. 2: THE FALL OF THE OWLS	TYNION IV, JAMES	SEPULVEDA, MIGUEL	$19.99/$23.99 CAN	TP
9781401240929	APR130224	TEAM 7 VOL. 1: FIGHT FIRE WITH FIRE	JORDAN, JUSTIN	MERINO, JESUS	$16.99/$19.99 CAN	TP
9781401228095	MAY110253	TEAM-UPS OF THE BRAVE AND BOLD	STRACZYNSKI, J. MICHAEL	SAIZ, JESUS	$17.99/$19.99 CAN	TP
9781401263744		TELOS VOL. 1	KING, JEFF	PAGULAYAN, CARLO	$14.99/$17.99 CAN	TP
9781401243333	NOV130236	THRESHOLD VOL. 1: THE HUNTED	GIFFEN, KEITH	RANEY, TOM; KOLINS, SCOTT	$19.99/$23.99 CAN	TP

DC COMICS SELECTED BACKLIST

ISBN	DIAMOND CODE	TITLE	AUTHOR	ARTIST	US$	FORMAT
9781401254926	DEC140398	TINY TITANS: RETURN TO THE TREEHOUSE	BALTAZAR, ART	FRANCO	$12.99/$15.99 CAN	TP
9781401249533	JUN140285	TOE TAGS FEATURING GEORGE A. ROMERO	ROMERO, GEORGE A.	CASTILLO, TOMMY	$14.99/$17.99 CAN	TP
9781401250140	SEP140325	TWILIGHT	CHAYKIN, HOWARD	GARCIA-LOPEZ, JOSE LUIS	$14.99/$17.99 CAN	TP
9781401245245	DEC130305	TRINITY OF SIN - PANDORA VOL. 1: THE CURSE	FAWKES, RAY	SAMPERE, DANIEL; CIFUENTES, VICENTE	$14.99/$17.99 CAN	TP
9781401250133	JUL140246	TRINITY OF SIN - PANDORA VOL. 2: CHOICES	FAWKES, RAY	PORTELLA, FRANCIS	$16.99/$19.99 CAN	TP
9781401240882	FEB130210	TRINITY OF SIN - PHANTOM STRANGER VOL. 1: A STRANGER AMONG US	DIDIO, DAN	ANDERSON, BRENT	$14.99/$17.99 CAN	TP
9781401247140	DEC130304	TRINITY OF SIN - THE PHANTOM STRANGER VOL. 2: BREACH OF FAITH	DEMATTEIS, J.M.	HA, GENE	$14.99/$17.99 CAN	TP
9781401250966	OCT140365	TRINITY OF SIN - THE PHANTOM STRANGER VOL. 3: THE CRACK IN CREATION	DEMATTEIS, J.M.	BLANCO, FERNANDO	$19.99/$23.99 CAN	TP
9781401254940	APR150304	TRINITY OF SIN VOL. 1: THE WAGES OF SIN	DEMATTEIS, J.M.	GUICHET, YVEL	$14.99/$17.99 CAN	TP
9781401240813	AUG140341	SHOWCASE PRESENTS UNKNOWN SOLDIER VOL. 2	MICHELINIE, DAVID	TALAOC, GERRY	$19.99/$23.99 CAN	TP
9781401248994	AUG140344	THE VAMPIRE DIARIES	DORAN, COLLEEN	SHASTEEN, ANTHONY	$24.99/$28.99 CAN	TP
9781401263706		BEST OF VIXEN	VARIOUS	VARIOUS	$16.99/$19.99 CAN	TP
9781401235611	JUN120240	VOODOO VOL. 1: WHAT LIES BENEATH	MARZ, RON	BASRI, SAMI	$14.99/$17.99 CAN	TP
9781401238155	NOV120265	VOODOO VOL. 2: THE KILLER IN ME	WILLIAMSON, JOSH	BASRI, SAMI	$14.99/$17.99 CAN	TP
9781401245122	MAR140269	BEFORE WATCHMEN: MINUTEMEN/SILK SPECTRE	COOKE, DARWYN; CONNER, AMANDA	COOKE, DARWYN; CONNER, AMANDA	$19.99/$23.99 CAN	TP
9781401245139	MAR140270	BEFORE WATCHMEN: COMEDIAN/RORSCHACH	AZZARELLO, BRIAN	BERMEJO, LEE; JONES, J.G.	$19.99/$23.99 CAN	TP
9781401245146	MAR140271	BEFORE WATCHMEN: NITE OWL/DR. MANHATTAN	STRACZYNSKI, J. MICHAEL	HUGHES, ADAM; KUBERT, ANDY; KUBERT, JOE	$19.99/$23.99 CAN	TP
9781401245153	MAR140272	BEFORE WATCHMEN: OZYMANDIAS/CRIMSON CORSAIR	WEIN, LEN; HIGGINS, JOHN	LEE, JAE; HIGGINS, JOHN	$19.99/$23.99 CAN	TP
9781401245252	FEB140265	WATCHMEN	MOORE, ALAN	GIBBONS, DAVE	$19.99/$23.99 CAN	TP
9781401248192	FEB140266	WATCHMEN: INTERNATIONAL EDITION	MOORE, ALAN	GIBBONS, DAVE	$19.99/$23.99 CAN	TP
9781401238964	FEB130225	WATCHMEN: THE DELUXE EDITION	MOORE, ALAN	GIBBONS, DAVE	$39.99/$47.99 CAN	HC
9781401259822	DEC150326	WE ARE ROBIN VOL. 1: THE VIGILANTE BUSINESS	BERMEJO, LEE	HAYNES, ROB; RANDOLPH, KHARY	$14.99/$17.99 CAN	TP
9781401227470	DEC090221	WEDNESDAY COMICS	VARIOUS	VARIOUS	$49.99/$59.99 CAN	HC
9781401238346	JAN130302	WORLDS' FINEST VOL. 1: THE LOST DAUGHTERS OF EARTH 2	LEVITZ, PAUL	PÉREZ, GEORGE; MCGUIRE, KEVIN	$14.99/$17.99 CAN	TP
9781401242763	AUG130302	WORLDS' FINEST VOL. 2: HUNT AND BE HUNTED	LEVITZ, PAUL	PÉREZ, GEORGE; MCGUIRE, KEVIN	$14.99/$17.99 CAN	TP
9781401246167	MAR140261	WORLDS' FINEST VOL. 3: CONTROL ISSUES	LEVITZ, PAUL	MCGUIRE, KEVIN	$14.99/$17.99 CAN	TP
9781401250980	SEP140314	WORLDS' FINEST VOL. 4: FIRST CONTACT	LEVITZ, PAUL; PAK, GREG	SILVA, R.B.	$16.99/$19.99 CAN	TP
9781401254209	MAR150276	WORLDS' FINEST VOL. 5: HOMEWARD BOUND	LEVITZ, PAUL	SILVA, R.B.	$14.99/$17.99 CAN	TP
9781401257767	SEP150304	WORLDS' FINEST VOL. 6: SECRET HISTORY	LEVITZ, PAUL	DOUGHERTY, JED	$14.99/$17.99 CAN	TP
9781401261085	DEC150349	WORLD'S FUNNEST	VARIOUS	VARIOUS	$19.99/$23.99 CAN	TP
9781401230302	MAY140381	WORLD OF WARCRAFT: BLOODSWORN	WAGNER, DOUG	RAAPACK, JHEREMY	$16.99/$19.99 CAN	TP
9781401230289	FEB140261	WORLD OF WARCRAFT: DARK RIDERS	COSTA, MICHAEL	GOOGE, NEIL	$16.99/$19.99 CAN	TP
9781401243968	JUN130284	WORLD OF WARCRAFT: PEARL OF PANDARIA	NEILSON, MICKY	GALLOWAY, SEAN	$16.99/$19.99 CAN	TP

VERTIGO SELECTED BACKLIST

ISBN	DIAMOND CODE	TITLE	AUTHOR	ARTIST	US$	FORMAT
9781401221331	JAN100348	100%	POPE, PAUL	POPE, PAUL	$29.99/$37.99 CAN	TP
9781401250560	JUL140274	100 BULLETS BOOK ONE	AZZARELLO, BRIAN	RISSO, EDUARDO	$24.99/$28.99 CAN	TP
9781401254315	JAN150409	100 BULLETS BOOK TWO	AZZARELLO, BRIAN	RISSO, EDUARDO	$24.99/$28.99 CAN	TP
9781401257958	JAN150323	100 BULLETS BOOK THREE	AZZARELLO, BRIAN	RISSO, EDUARDO	$24.99/$29.99 CAN	TP
9781401257941	OCT150272	100 BULLETS BOOK FOUR	AZZARELLO, BRIAN	RISSO, EDUARDO	$24.99/$29.99 CAN	TP
9781401261337	DEC150363	100 BULLETS BOOK FIVE	AZZARELLO, BRIAN	RISSO, EDUARDO	$24.99/$29.99 CAN	TP
9781401245061	JAN140371	100 BULLETS: BROTHER LONO	AZZARELLO, BRIAN	RISSO, EDUARDO	$16.99/$19.99 CAN	TP
9781401230890	MAY110282	99 DAYS	CASALI, MATTEO	DONALDSON, KRISTIAN	$19.99/$22.99 CAN	TP
9781401221478	AUG120291	A FLIGHT OF ANGELS	VARIOUS	GUAY, REBECCA	$17.99/$20.99 CAN	TP
9781401210816	JUN100261	A SICKNESS IN THE FAMILY	MINA, DENISE	FUSO, ANTONIO	$19.99/$23.99 CAN	TP
9781401221539	DEC080208	AIR VOL. 1: LETTERS FROM LOST COUNTRIES	WILSON, G. WILLOW	PERKER, M.K.	$9.99/$12.99 CAN	TP
9781401224837	AUG090226	AIR VOL. 2: FLYING MACHINE	WILSON, G. WILLOW	PERKER, M.K.	$12.99/$15.99 CAN	TP
9781401227067	FEB100248	AIR VOL. 3: PURELAND	WILSON, G. WILLOW	PERKER, M.K.	$14.99/$17.99 CAN	TP
9781401229832	NOV090267	AIR VOL. 4: A HISTORY OF THE FUTURE	WILSON, G. WILLOW	PERKER, M.K.	$14.99/$16.99 CAN	TP
9781401210571	JUN090256	THE ALCOHOLIC	AMES, JONATHAN	HASPIEL, DEAN	$14.99/$18.99 CAN	TP
9781401212353	JAN070366	AMERICAN SPLENDOR VOL. 1: ANOTHER DAY	PEKAR, HARVEY	HASPIEL, DEAN	$14.99/$17.99 CAN	TP
9781401221737	OCT080214	AMERICAN SPLENDOR VOL. 2: ANOTHER DOLLAR	PEKAR, HARVEY	LAPHAM, DAVID	$14.99/$16.99 CAN	TP

VERTIGO SELECTED BACKLIST

ISBN	DIAMOND CODE	TITLE	AUTHOR	ARTIST	US$	FORMAT
9781401229740	JUL110284	AMERICAN VAMPIRE VOL. 1	SNYDER, SCOTT; KING, STEPHEN | ALBUQUERQUE, RAFAEL	$19.99/$23.99 CAN | TP
9781401230708	FEB120289	AMERICAN VAMPIRE VOL. 2	SNYDER, SCOTT | ALBUQUERQUE, RAFAEL	$17.99/$20.99 CAN | TP
9781401233341	JUN120280	AMERICAN VAMPIRE VOL. 3	SNYDER, SCOTT | ALBUQUERQUE, RAFAEL	$16.99/$19.99 CAN | TP
9781401237196	JUN130293	AMERICAN VAMPIRE VOL. 4	SNYDER, SCOTT | ALBUQUERQUE, RAFAEL; BERNETT, JORDI	$16.99/$19.99 CAN | TP
9781401237714	DEC130346	AMERICAN VAMPIRE VOL. 5	SNYDER, SCOTT | ALBUQUERQUE, RAFAEL; NGUYEN, DUSTIN	$16.99/$19.99 CAN | TP
9781401249298	AUG140356	AMERICAN VAMPIRE VOL. 6	SNYDER, SCOTT | ALBUQUERQUE, RAFAEL	$14.99/$17.99 CAN | TP
9781401254322	AUG150288	AMERICAN VAMPIRE VOL. 7	SNYDER, SCOTT | ALBUQUERQUE, RAFAEL	$14.99/$17.99 CAN | TP
9781401254339	OCT150274	AMERICAN VAMPIRE VOL. 8	SNYDER, SCOTT | ALBUQUERQUE, RAFAEL	$22.99/$26.99 CAN | HC
9781401259655		AMERICAN VAMPIRE VOL. 9	SNYDER, SCOTT | ALBURQUERQUE, RAFAEL	$22.99/$27.99 CAN | HC
9781563890055	OCT068037	ANIMAL MAN VOL. 1	MORRISON, GRANT | TRUOG, CHAS	$19.99/$17.99 CAN | TP
9781563898907	JAN058098	ANIMAL MAN VOL. 2: ORIGIN OF THE SPECIES	MORRISON, GRANT | PUGH, STEVE	$19.99/$19.99 CAN | TP
9781563899683	JAN068276	ANIMAL MAN VOL. 3: DEUS EX MACHINA	MORRISON, GRANT | TRUOG, CHAS	$19.99/$19.99 CAN | TP
9781401238018	NOV120297	ANIMAL MAN VOL. 4: BORN TO BE WILD	MILLIGAN, PETER | VEITCH, TOM; DILLON, STEVE	$19.99/$23.99 CAN | TP
9781401242848	OCT130282	ANIMAL MAN VOL. 5: THE MEANING OF FLESH	VEITCH, TOM | DILLON, STEVE	$24.99/$17.99 CAN | TP
9781401246792	APR140292	ANIMAL MAN VOL. 6: FLESH AND BLOOD	DELANO, JAMIE | PUGH, STEVE	$24.99/$28.99 CAN | TP
9781401251239	OCT140386	ANIMAL MAN VOL. 7: RED PLAGUE	DELANO, JAMIE | PUGH, STEVE	$29.99/$35.00 CAN | TP
9781401238995	MAR130299	THE ANIMAL MAN OMNIBUS	MORRISON, GRANT | TRUOG, CHAS	$75.00/$85.00 CAN | HC
9781401226305	JAN110424	AREA 10	GAGE, CHRISTOS | SAMNEE, CHRIS	$12.99/$14.99 CAN | TP
9781401256876		ART OPS VOL. 1	SIMON, SHAUN | ALLRED, MICHAEL	$14.99/$17.99 CAN | TP
9781401232627	APR110229	ASTRO CITY: LIFE IN THE BIG CITY	BUSIEK, KURT | ANDERSON, BRENT	$17.99/$20.99 CAN | TP
9781401258306	MAY150260	ASTRO CITY: CONFESSION	BUSIEK, KURT | ANDERSON, BRENT	$24.99/$29.99 CAN | HC
9781401229917	JAN140374	ASTRO CITY: SHINING STARS	BUSIEK, KURT | ANDERSON, BRENT	$16.99/$19.99 CAN | TP
9781401249960	JUN140296	ASTRO CITY: THROUGH OPEN DOORS	BUSIEK, KURT | ANDERSON, BRENT	$16.99/$19.99 CAN | TP
9781401254605	DEC140407	ASTRO CITY: VICTORY	BUSIEK, KURT | ANDERSON, BRENT	$16.99/$19.99 CAN | TP
9781401258245	JUL150337	ASTRO CITY: PRIVATE LIVES	BUSIEK, KURT | ANDERSON, BRENT	$16.99/$19.99 CAN | TP
9781401261344	JUL150336	ASTRO CITY : LOVER'S QUARREL	BUSIEK, KURT | ANDERSON, BRENT	$16.99/$19.99 CAN | TP
9781401263874		ASTRO CITY VOL. 13	BUSIEK, KURT | ANDERSON, BRENT	$22.99/$27.99 CAN | HC
9781401232450	JUL110285	BAD DOING AND BIG IDEAS: A BILL WILLINGHAM DELUXE EDITION	WILLINGHAM, BILL | VARIOUS	$49.99/$57.00 CAN | HC
9781401240202	APR130260	BEWARE THE CREEPER	HALL, JASON | CHIANG, CLIFF	$14.99/$17.99 CAN | TP
9781401240356	APR130261	BLACK ORCHID	GAIMAN, NEIL | MCKEAN, DAVE	$16.99/$19.99 CAN | TP
9781401252755	FEB150278	BODIES	SPENCER, SI | LOTAY, TULA; WINSLADE, PHIL	$16.99/$19.99 CAN | TP
9781401246860	JAN140372	THE BOOKS OF MAGIC	GAIMAN, NEIL | ZELAZNY, ROGER; BOLTON, JOHN; HAMPTON, SCOTT; VESS, CHARLES	$16.99/$19.99 CAN | TP
9781401226312	DEC100291	THE BRONX KILL	MILLIGAN, PETER | ROMBERGER, JAMES	$12.99/$14.99 CAN | TP
9781401217341	JUN080290	CAIRO	WILSON, G. WILLOW | PERKER, M.K.	$17.99/$21.99 CAN | TP
9781401225469	OCT100317	THE CHILL	STARR, JASON | BERTILORENZI, MICK	$12.99/$14.99 CAN | TP
9781401233853	JAN120331	CINDERELLA: FABLES ARE FOREVER	ROBERSON, CHRIS | MCMANUS, SHAWN	$14.99/$16.99 CAN | TP
9781401262754		CLEAN ROOM VOL. 1	SIMONE, GAIL | DAVIS-HUNT, JON	$14.99/$17.99 CAN | TP
9781401248871	FEB140285	COFFIN HILL VOL. 1: FOREST OF THE NIGHT	KITTREDGE, CAITLIN | MIRANDA, INAKI	$9.99/$11.99 CAN | TP
9781401250843	OCT140394	COFFIN HILL VOL. 2: DARK ENDEAVORS	KITTREDGE, CAITLIN | MIRANDA, INAKI	$14.99/$17.99 CAN | TP
9781401254360	JUN150319	COFFIN HILL VOL. 3: HAUNTED HOUSES	KITTREDGE, CAITLIN | MIRANDA, INAKI	$14.99/$17.99 CAN | TP
9781401215347	MAR110378	COWBOYS	PHILLIPS, GARY | HURTT, BRIAN	$19.99/$22.99 CAN | HC
9781401253363	APR150315	VERTIGO CMYK	MOON, FÁBIO | JOCK; SIMON, SHAUN; AKINS, TONY; CHU, AMY	$19.99/$23.99 CAN | TP
9781401224295	MAY100259	DARK ENTRIES	RANKIN, IAN | DELL'EDERA, WERTHER	$12.99/$14.99 CAN | TP
9781401241438		DARK NIGHT: A TRUE BATMAN STORY	DINI, PAUL | RISSO, EDUARDO	$22.99/$27.99 CAN | HC
9781401229696	NOV100268	DAYTRIPPER	MOON, FÁBIO; BÁ, GABRIEL | MOON, FÁBIO; BÁ, GABRIEL	$19.99/$23.99 CAN | TP
9781401245115	DEC130340	DAYTRIPPER DELUXE EDITION	MOON, FÁBIO; BÁ, GABRIEL | MOON, FÁBIO; BÁ, GABRIEL	$34.99/$41.99 CAN | HC
9781401248895	MAR140290	DEAD BOY DETECTIVES VOL. 1: SCHOOLBOY TERRORS	LITT, TOBY | BUCKINGHAM, MARK	$9.99/$11.99 CAN | TP
9781401250867	OCT140396	DEAD BOY DETECTIVES VOL. 2: GHOST SNOW	LITT, TOBY | BUCKINGHAM, MARK; ERSKINE, GARY	$14.99/$17.99 CAN | TP
9781401234805	FEB120290	DEADENDERS	BRUBAKER, ED | BOND, PHILIP J.	$29.99/$34.00 CAN | TP
9781401247164	DEC130341	DEATH	GAIMAN, NEIL | VARIOUS	$19.99/$23.99 CAN | TP
9781563899386	FEB078187	DEATH: AT DEATH'S DOOR	THOMPSON, JILL | THOMPSON, JILL	$9.99/$11.99 CAN | TP

ISBN	DIAMOND CODE	TITLE	AUTHOR	ARTIST	US$	FORMAT
9781401247096	APR140295	DJANGO UNCHAINED	TARANTINO, QUENTIN	GUERA, R.M.; LATOUR, JASON	$16.99/$19.99 CAN	TP
9781401210625	OCT118125	DMZ VOL. 1: ON THE GROUND	WOOD, BRIAN	BURCHIELLI, RICCARDO	$12.99/$15.99 CAN	TP
9781401212476	JAN138241	DMZ VOL. 2: BODY OF A JOURNALIST	WOOD, BRIAN	BURCHIELLI, RICCARDO	$14.99/$17.99 CAN	TP
9781401214760	JAN138242	DMZ VOL. 3: PUBLIC WORKS	WOOD, BRIAN	BURCHIELLI, RICCARDO	$14.99/$17.99 CAN	TP
9781401216627	DEC070294	DMZ VOL. 4: FRIENDLY FIRE	WOOD, BRIAN	BURCHIELLI, RICCARDO	$12.99/$14.99 CAN	TP
9781401218331	JUL108009	DMZ VOL. 5: THE HIDDEN WAR	WOOD, BRIAN	BURCHIELLI, RICCARDO	$14.99/$17.99 CAN	TP
9781401221300	NOV080228	DMZ VOL. 6: BLOOD IN THE GAME	WOOD, BRIAN	BURCHIELLI, RICCARDO	$12.99/$15.99 CAN	TP
9781401224301	JUN090262	DMZ VOL. 7: WAR POWERS	WOOD, BRIAN	BURCHIELLI, RICCARDO	$14.99/$17.99 CAN	TP
9781401227265	APR100271	DMZ VOL. 8: HEARTS AND MINDS	WOOD, BRIAN	BURCHIELLI, RICCARDO	$16.99/$19.99 CAN	TP
9781401229962	NOV100272	DMZ VOL. 9: M.I.A.	WOOD, BRIAN	BURCHIELLI, RICCARDO	$14.99/$17.99 CAN	TP
9781401231507	FEB110260	DMZ VOL. 10: COLLECTIVE PUNISHIMENT	WOOD, BRIAN	BURCHIELLI, RICCARDO	$14.99/$17.99 CAN	TP
9781401233891	DEC110321	DMZ VOL. 11: FREE STATES RISING	WOOD, BRIAN	BURCHIELLI, RICCARDO	$19.99/$22.99 CAN	TP
9781401234799	MAR120276	DMZ VOL. 12: FIVE NATIONS OF NEW YORK	WOOD, BRIAN	BURCHIELLI, RICCARDO	$14.99/$17.99 CAN	TP
9781401261351		DMZ BOOK ONE	WOOD, BRIAN	BURCHIELLI, RICCARDO	$24.99/$29.99 CAN	TP
9781401263577		DMZ BOOK TWO	WOOD, BRIAN	BURCHIELLI, RICCARDO	$24.99/$29.99 CAN	TP
9781401250003	AUG140357	DMZ THE DELUXE EDITION BOOK THREE	WOOD, BRIAN	BURCHIELLI, RICCARDO; KELLY, RYAN	$29.99/$35.00 CAN	HC
9781401254117	MAR150305	DMZ THE DELUXE EDITION BOOK FOUR	WOOD, BRIAN	BURCHIELLI, RICCARDO	$29.99/$35.00 CAN	HC
9781401258436	AUG150291	DMZ THE DELUXE EDITION BOOK FIVE	WOOD, BRIAN	BURCHIELLI, RICCARDO	$29.99/$35.00 CAN	HC
9781401237424	SEP120264	DOMINIQUE LAVEAU, VOODOO CHILD VOL. 1: REQUIEM	HINDS, SELWYN SEYFU	COWAN, DENYS	$14.99/$17.99 CAN	TP
9781401229481	FEB110213	DONG XOAI VIETNAM 1965	KUBERT, JOE	KUBERT, JOE	$19.99/$22.99 CAN	TP
9781401245627	MAR140282	THE DOOM PATROL OMNIBUS	MORRISON, GRANT	VARIOUS	$150.00/$172.00 CAN	HC
9781401263126	NOV150304	DOOM PATROL BOOK ONE	MORRISON, GRANT	CASE, RICHARD	$24.99/$29.99 CAN	TP
9781401263799		DOOM PATROL BOOK TWO	MORRISON, GRANT	CASE, RICHARD	$24.99/$29.99 CAN	TP
9781401247027	JAN140382	FLEX MENTALLO: MAN OF MUSCLE MYSTERY	MORRISON, GRANT	QUITELY, FRANK	$14.99/$17.99 CAN	TP
9781401256852	MAY150262	EFFIGY VOL. 1: IDLE WORSHIP	SEELEY, TIM	ZARCONE, MARLEY	$14.99/$17.99 CAN	TP
9781401261368	NOV140299	EGYPT	MILLIGAN, PETER	DILLON, GLYN	$19.99/$23.99 CAN	TP
9781401251314	SEP140338	ENIGMA (NEW EDITION)	MILLIGAN, PETER	FEGREDO, DUNCAN	$17.99/$20.99 CAN	TP
9781401228217	FEB110253	THE EXECUTOR	EVANS, JON	MUTTI, ANDREA	$12.99/$14.99 CAN	TP
9781401244989	OCT130291	EX MACHINA BOOK ONE	VAUGHAN, BRIAN K.	HARRIS, TONY	$19.99/$23.99 CAN	TP
9781401246914	FEB140292	EX MACHINA BOOK TWO	VAUGHAN, BRIAN K.	HARRIS, TONY; SPROUSE, CHRIS	$19.99/$23.99 CAN	TP
9781401250034	JUN140307	EX MACHINA BOOK THREE	VAUGHAN, BRIAN K.	HARRIS, TONY; LEON, JOHN PAUL	$19.99/$23.99 CAN	TP
9781401250027	OCT140387	EX MACHINA BOOK FOUR	VAUGHAN, BRIAN K.	HARRIS, TONY	$19.99/$23.99 CAN	TP
9781401254223	FEB150282	EX MACHINA BOOK FIVE	VAUGHAN, BRIAN K.	HARRIS, TONY	$19.99/$23.99 CAN	TP
9781401237554	FEB120285	FABLES VOL. 1: LEGENDS IN EXILE	WILLINGHAM, BILL	MEDINA, LAN	$12.99/$15.99 CAN	TP
9781401200770	DEC138056	FABLES VOL. 2: ANIMAL FARM	WILLINGHAM, BILL	BUCKINGHAM, MARK	$14.99/$17.99 CAN	TP
9781401202569	JAN128247	FABLES VOL. 3: STORYBOOK LOVE	WILLINGHAM, BILL	BUCKINGHAM, MARK	$17.99/$20.99 CAN	TP
9781401202224	OCT058021	FABLES VOL. 4: MARCH OF THE WOODEN SOLDIERS	WILLINGHAM, BILL	BUCKINGHAM, MARK	$17.99/$20.99 CAN	TP
9781401204860	SEP128332	FABLES VOL. 5: THE MEAN SEASONS	WILLINGHAM, BILL	BUCKINGHAM, MARK	$17.99/$20.99 CAN	TP
9781401205003	JAN148352	FABLES VOL. 6: HOMELANDS	WILLINGHAM, BILL	BUCKINGHAM, MARK	$17.99/$20.99 CAN	TP
9781401210007	MAR060384	FABLES VOL. 7: ARABIAN NIGHTS (AND DAYS)	WILLINGHAM, BILL	BUCKINGHAM, MARK	$14.99/$17.99 CAN	TP
9781401210014	SEP060313	FABLES VOL. 8: WOLVES	WILLINGHAM, BILL	BUCKINGHAM, MARK	$17.99/$20.99 CAN	TP
9781401213169	MAR070271	FABLES VOL. 9: SONS OF EMPIRE	WILLINGHAM, BILL	BUCKINGHAM, MARK	$17.99/$20.99 CAN	TP
9781401216863	FEB080297	FABLES VOL. 10: THE GOOD PRINCE	WILLINGHAM, BILL	BUCKINGHAM, MARK	$17.99/$20.99 CAN	TP
9781401219130	AUG080229	FABLES VOL. 11: WAR AND PIECES	WILLINGHAM, BILL	BUCKINGHAM, MARK	$17.99/$20.99 CAN	TP
9781401223168	MAY090236	FABLES VOL. 12: THE DARK AGES	WILLINGHAM, BILL	BUCKINGHAM, MARK	$17.99/$20.99 CAN	TP
9781401225728	NOV090228	FABLES VOL. 13: THE GREAT FABLES CROSSOVER	WILLINGHAM, BILL	BUCKINGHAM, MARK	$17.99/$20.99 CAN	TP
9781401228804	SEP100304	FABLES VOL. 14: WITCHES	WILLINGHAM, BILL	BUCKINGHAM, MARK	$17.99/$20.99 CAN	TP
9781401230005	JAN110422	FABLES VOL. 15: ROSE RED	WILLINGHAM, BILL	BUCKINGHAM, MARK	$17.99/$20.99 CAN	TP
9781401233068	SEP110221	FABLES VOL. 16: SUPER TEAM	WILLINGHAM, BILL	BUCKINGHAM, MARK	$14.99/$17.99 CAN	TP
9781401235161	APR120282	FABLES VOL. 17: INHERIT THE WIND	WILLINGHAM, BILL	BUCKINGHAM, MARK	$14.99/$17.99 CAN	TP
9781401237691	OCT120296	FABLES VOL. 18: CUBS IN TOYLAND	WILLINGHAM, BILL	BUCKINGHAM, MARK	$16.99/$19.99 CAN	TP

ISBN	DIAMOND CODE	TITLE	AUTHOR	ARTIST	US$	FORMAT
9781401242480	SEP130305	FABLES VOL. 19: SNOW WHITE	WILLINGHAM, BILL	BUCKINGHAM, MARK	$16.99/$19.99 CAN	TP
9781401245160	MAY140403	FABLES VOL. 20: CAMELOT	WILLINGHAM, BILL	BUCKINGHAM, MARK	$19.99/$23.99 CAN	TP
9781401251321	JAN150397	FABLES VOL. 21: HAPPILY EVER AFTER	WILLINGHAM, BILL	BUCKINGHAM, MARK	$17.99/$21.99 CAN	TP
9781401252335	APR150316	FABLES VOL. 22: FAREWELL	WILLINGHAM, BILL	BUCKINGHAM, MARK	$17.99/$21.99 CAN	TP
9781401224806	JUL130260	FABLES: WEREWOLVES OF THE HEARTLAND	WILLINGHAM, BILL	FERN, JIM	$14.99/$17.99 CAN	TP
9781401203696	DEC070297	FABLES: 1001 NIGHTS OF SNOWFALL	WILLINGHAM, BILL	VARIOUS	$14.99/$17.99 CAN	TP
9781401225377	SEP100303	PETER & MAX: A FABLES NOVEL	WILLINGHAM, BILL	LEIALOHA, STEVE	$14.99/$17.99 CAN	TP
9781401224271	MAY090235	FABLES THE DELUXE EDITION BOOK ONE	WILLINGHAM, BILL	BUCKINGHAM, MARK	$29.99/$35.00 CAN	HC
9781401228798	JUL100251	FABLES THE DELUXE EDITION BOOK TWO	WILLINGHAM, BILL	BUCKINGHAM, MARK	$29.99/$35.00 CAN	HC
9781401230975	APR110244	FABLES THE DELUXE EDITION BOOK THREE	WILLINGHAM, BILL	BUCKINGHAM, MARK	$29.99/$35.00 CAN	HC
9781401233907	OCT110292	FABLES THE DELUXE EDITION BOOK FOUR	WILLINGHAM, BILL	BUCKINGHAM, MARK	$29.99/$35.00 CAN	HC
9781401234966	JAN120330	FABLES THE DELUXE EDITION BOOK FIVE	WILLINGHAM, BILL	BUCKINGHAM, MARK	$29.99/$35.00 CAN	HC
9781401237240	OCT120295	FABLES THE DELUXE EDITION BOOK SIX	WILLINGHAM, BILL	BUCKINGHAM, MARK	$29.99/$35.00 CAN	HC
9781401240400	APR130253	FABLES THE DELUXE EDITION BOOK SEVEN	WILLINGHAM, BILL	BUCKINGHAM, MARK	$29.99/$35.00 CAN	HC
9781401242794	OCT130286	FABLES THE DELUXE EDITION BOOK EIGHT	WILLINGHAM, BILL	BUCKINGHAM, MARK	$29.99/$35.00 CAN	HC
9781401250041	JUN140304	FABLES: THE DELUXE EDITION BOOK NINE	WILLINGHAM, BILL	BUCKINGHAM, MARK	$29.99/$35.00 CAN	HC
9781401255213	JAN150396	FABLES: THE DELUXE EDITION BOOK TEN	WILLINGHAM, BILL	BUCKINGHAM, MARK; HAMILTON, CRAIG	$29.99/$35.00 CAN	HC
9781401258269	JUN150322	FABLES: THE DELUXE EDITION BOOK ELEVEN	WILLINGHAM, BILL	BUCKINGHAM, MARK	$29.99/$35.00 CAN	HC
9781401261382	JAN160352	FABLES: THE DELUXE EDITION BOOK TWELVE	WILLINGHAM, BILL	BUCKINGHAM, MARK	$29.99/$35.00 CAN	HC
9781401256845	JUL150340	FABLES: THE WOLF AMONG US VOL. 1	STURGES, MATTHEW	JUSTUS, DAVE; MCMANUS, SHAWN	$19.99/$23.99 CAN	TP
9781401261375		FABLES: THE WOLF AMONG US VOL. 2	STURGES, MATTHEW	NGUYEN, ERIC	$19.99/$23.99 CAN	TP
9781401243951	JUN130286	FABLES ENCYCLOPEDIA	WILLINGHAM, BILL	VARIOUS	$39.99/$47.99 CAN	HC
9781401252816	AUG140365	FABLES COVERS: THE ART OF JAMES JEAN (NEW EDITION)	JEAN, JAMES; WILLINGHAM, BILL	JEAN, JAMES	$49.99/$58.00 CAN	HC
9781401235505	AUG120283	FAIREST VOL. 1: WIDE AWAKE	WILLINGHAM, BILL	JIMENEZ, PHIL	$14.99/$17.99 CAN	TP
9781401240219	APR130255	FAIREST VOL. 2: HIDDEN KINGDOM	WILLINGHAM, BILL; BEUKES, LAUREN	MIRANDA, INAKI	$14.99/$17.99 CAN	TP
9781401245931	FEB140288	FAIREST VOL. 3: THE RETURN OF THE MAHARAJA	WILLIAMS, SEAN E.	SADOWSKI, STEPHEN; JIMENEZ, PHIL	$14.99/$17.99 CAN	TP
9781401250058	JUL140278	FAIREST VOL. 4: CINDERELLA - OF MEN AND MICE	ANDREYKO, MARC; WILLINGHAM, BILL	MCMANUS, SHAWN	$14.99/$17.99 CAN	TP
9781401254261	MAY150265	FAIREST VOL. 5: THE CLAMOR FOR GLAMOUR	BUCKINGHAM, MARK	BRAUN, RUSS	$14.99/$17.99 CAN	TP
9781401245573	AUG140364	FAIREST: IN ALL THE LAND	WILLINGHAM, BILL	VARIOUS	$14.99/$17.99 CAN	TP
9781401245108	FEB158452	FBP: FEDERAL BUREAU OF PHYSICS VOL. 1: THE PARADIGM SHIFT	OLIVER, SIMON	RODRIGUEZ, ROBBI	$14.99/$11.99 CAN	TP
9781401250676	JUN140306	FBP: FEDERAL BUREAU OF PHYSICS VOL. 2: WISH YOU WERE HERE	OLIVER, SIMON	RODRIGUEZ, ROBBI	$14.99/$17.99 CAN	TP
9781401254346	JUL150340	FBP: FEDERAL BUREAU OF PHYSICS VOL. 3: STANDING ON SHOULDERS	OLIVER, SIMON	RODRIGUEZ, ROBBI	$14.99/$17.99 CAN	TP
9781401258450	OCT150273	FBP: FEDERAL BUREAU OF PHYSICS VOL. 4: END TIMES	OLIVER, SIMON	PONTICELLI, ALBERTO	$14.99/$17.99 CAN	TP
9781401200138	APR128207	THE FILTH	MORRISON, GRANT	WESTON, CHRIS	$24.99/$28.99 CAN	TP
9781401255459	DEC140414	THE FILTH DELUXE EDITION	MORRISON, GRANT	WESTON, CHRIS; ERSKINE, GARY	$29.99/$35.00 CAN	HC
9781401211851	MAY100260	FILTHY RICH	AZZARELLO, BRIAN	SANTOS, VICTOR	$12.99/$14.99 CAN	TP
9781401258122	SEP150325	FLINCH BOOK ONE	AZZARELLO, BRIAN	MAHNKE, DOUG	$16.99/$19.99 CAN	TP
9781401261399		FLINCH BOOK TWO	QUITELY, FRANK; ENNIS, GARTH; AZZARELLO, BRIAN	LEE, JIM	$14.99/$17.99 CAN	TP
9781401200589	AUG060290	THE FOUNTAIN	ARONOFSKY, DARREN	WILLIAMS, KENT	$19.99/$23.99 CAN	TP
9781401242411	MAY150258	FREE COUNTRY: A TALE OF THE CHILDREN'S CRUSADE	GAIMAN, NEIL	VARIOUS	$24.99/$29.99 CAN	HC
9781401228286	FEB130242	GET JIRO!	BOURDAIN, ANTHONY; ROSE, JOEL	FOSS, LANGDON	$14.99/$17.99 CAN	TP
9781401252267	JUN150315	GET JIRO: BLOOD AND SUSHI	BOURDAIN, ANTHONY	ROSE, JOEL	$22.99/$27.99 CAN	HC
9781401242862	JAN140369	THE GIRL WITH THE DRAGON TATTOO	MINA, DENISE	MUTTI, ANDREA; MANCO, LEONARDO	$24.99/$28.99 CAN	HC
9781401255503	FEB150274	THE GIRL WHO PLAYED WITH FIRE	MINA, DENISE	MANCO, LEONARDO; MUTTI, ANDREA	$19.99/$23.99 CAN	TP
9781401237592	APR150322	THE GIRL WHO KICKED THE HORNET'S NEST	MINA, DENISE	MUTTI, ANDREA; MANCO, LEONARDO	$29.99/$35.00 CAN	HC
9781401237974	OCT120299	GLOBAL FREQUENCY	ELLIS, WARREN	VARIOUS	$19.99/$23.99 CAN	TP
9781401203047	JAN080244	GOD SAVE THE QUEEN	CAREY, MIKE	BOLTON, JOHN	$12.99/$14.99 CAN	TP
9781401223519	NOV110226	GONE TO AMERIKAY	MCCULLOUGH, RODERICK	DORAN, COLLEEN	$24.99/$27.99 CAN	HC
9781401226985	FEB100245	NEIL YOUNG'S GREENDALE	DYSART, JOSH	CHIANG, CLIFF	$19.99 CAN	TP
9781401245184	JAN140379	HINTERKIND VOL. 1: THE WAKING WORLD	EDGINTON, IAN	TRIFOGLI, FRANCESCO	$9.99/$11.99 CAN	TP
9781401250706	AUG140369	HINTERKIND VOL. 2: WRITTEN IN BLOOD	EDGINTON, IAN	TRIFOGLI, FRANCESCO	$14.99/$17.99 CAN	TP

ISBN	DIAMOND CODE	TITLE	AUTHOR	ARTIST	US$	FORMAT
9781401254353	MAR150308	HINTERKIND VOL. 3: THE HOT ZONE	EDGINTON, IAN	TRIFOGLI, FRANCESCO	$14.99/$17.99 CAN	TP
9781401236731	FEB130248	HOUSE OF SECRETS OMNIBUS	SEAGLE, STEVEN T.	KRISTIANSEN, TEDDY H.	$75.00/$85.00 CAN	HC
9781401222345	JUN110354	HOW TO UNDERSTAND ISRAEL IN 60 DAYS OR LESS	GLIDDEN, SARAH	GLIDDEN, SARAH	$19.99/$23.99 CAN	TP
9781401226664	OCT090298	HUMAN TARGET	MILLIGAN, PETER	BIUKOVIC, EDVIN	$14.99/$18.99 CAN	TP
9781401230616	NOV100270	HUMAN TARGET: SECOND CHANCES	MILLIGAN, PETER	PULIDO, JAVIER	$19.99/$22.99 CAN	TP
9781563892677	SEP068118	THE INVISIBLES VOL. 1: SAY YOU WANT A REVOLUTION	MORRISON, GRANT	YEOWELL, STEVE	$19.99/$23.99 CAN	TP
9781563897023	OCT058209	THE INVISIBLES VOL. 2: APOCALIPSTICK	MORRISON, GRANT	THOMPSON, JILL	$19.99/$23.99 CAN	TP
9781563897283	JUN058158	THE INVISIBLES VOL. 3: ENTROPY IN THE U.K.	MORRISON, GRANT	JIMENEZ, PHIL	$19.99/$23.99 CAN	TP
9781563894442	DEC118104	THE INVISIBLES VOL. 4: BLOODY HELL IN AMERICA	MORRISON, GRANT	JIMENEZ, PHIL	$14.99/$17.99 CAN	TP
9781563894893	AUG058062	THE INVISIBLES VOL. 5: COUNTING DOWN TO NONE	MORRISON, GRANT	JIMENEZ, PHIL	$19.99/$23.99 CAN	TP
9781563896002	FEB068103	THE INVISIBLES VOL. 6: KISSING MR. QUIMPER	MORRISON, GRANT	WESTON, CHRIS	$19.99/$23.99 CAN	TP
9781401200190	JAN078237	THE INVISIBLES VOL. 7: THE INVISIBLE KINGDOM	MORRISON, GRANT	BOND, PHILIP J.	$19.99/$23.99 CAN	TP
9781401245023	OCT130287	THE INVISIBLES BOOK ONE DELUXE EDITION	MORRISON, GRANT	VARIOUS	$29.99/$35.00 CAN	HC
9781401245993	APR140299	THE INVISIBLES BOOK TWO DELUXE EDITION	MORRISON, GRANT	VARIOUS	$29.99/$35.00 CAN	HC
9781401249519	OCT140400	THE INVISIBLES BOOK THREE DELUXE EDITION	MORRISON, GRANT	JIMENEZ, PHIL; STOKES, JOHN	$29.99/$35.00 CAN	HC
9781401254216	MAR150306	THE INVISIBLES BOOK FOUR DELUXE EDITION	MORRISON, GRANT	WESTON, CHRIS	$39.99/$47.99 CAN	HC
9781401234591	APR120288	THE INVISIBLES OMNIBUS	MORRISON, GRANT	VARIOUS	$150.00/$172.00 CAN	HC
9781401229658	DEC100299	IZOMBIE VOL. 1: DEAD TO THE WORLD	ROBERSON, CHRIS	ALLRED, MIKE	$14.99/$17.99 CAN	TP
9781401232962	JUN110353	IZOMBIE VOL. 2: UVAMPIRE	ROBERSON, CHRIS	ALLRED, MIKE	$14.99/$17.99 CAN	TP
9781401233709	NOV110232	IZOMBIE VOL. 3: SIX FEET UNDER AND RISING	ROBERSON, CHRIS	ALLRED, MIKE	$14.99/$17.99 CAN	TP
9781401236977	SEP120261	IZOMBIE VOL. 4: REPOSSESSED	ROBERSON, CHRIS	ALLRED, MIKE	$19.99/$23.99 CAN	TP
9781401262037	SEP150327	IZOMBIE OMNIBUS	ROBERSON, CHRIS	ALLRED, MICHAEL	$75.00/$85.00 CAN	HC
9781401262709		JACKED VOL. 1	KRIPKE, ERIC	HIGGINS, JOHN	$16.99/$19.99 CAN	TP
9781401212223	NOV060300	JACK OF FABLES VOL. 1: THE (NEARLY) GREAT ESCAPE	STURGES, MATTHEW; WILLINGHAM, BILL	AKINS, TONY	$14.99/$18.99 CAN	TP
9781401214555	JUL070305	JACK OF FABLES VOL. 2: JACK OF HEARTS	STURGES, MATTHEW; WILLINGHAM, BILL	AKINS, TONY	$14.99/$18.99 CAN	TP
9781401218546	MAR080229	JACK OF FABLES VOL. 3: THE BAD PRINCE	STURGES, MATTHEW; WILLINGHAM, BILL	AKINS, TONY	$14.99/$16.99 CAN	TP
9781401219796	SEP080219	JACK OF FABLES VOL. 4: AMERICANA	STURGES, MATTHEW; WILLINGHAM, BILL	AKINS, TONY	$14.99/$18.99 CAN	TP
9781401221386	DEC080210	JACK OF FABLES VOL. 5: TURNING PAGES	STURGES, MATTHEW; WILLINGHAM, BILL	AKINS, TONY	$14.99/$18.99 CAN	TP
9781401225001	JUL090281	JACK OF FABLES VOL. 6: THE BIG BOOK OF WAR	STURGES, MATTHEW; WILLINGHAM, BILL	AKINS, TONY	$14.99/$18.99 CAN	TP
9781401229825	OCT100327	JACK OF FABLES VOL. 8: THE FULMINATE BLADE	STURGES, MATTHEW; WILLINGHAM, BILL	AKINS, TONY	$14.99/$16.99 CAN	TP
9781401231552	APR110245	JACK OF FABLES VOL. 9: THE END	STURGES, MATTHEW; WILLINGHAM, BILL	AKINS, TONY	$17.99/$19.99 CAN	TP
9781401231798	FEB110214	JEW GANGSTER	KUBERT, JOE	KUBERT, JOE	$14.99/$16.99 CAN	TP
9781401237479	DEC120365	JOE THE BARBARIAN	MORRISON, GRANT	MURPHY, SEAN	$19.99/$23.99 CAN	TP
9781401230067	DEC100302	JOHN CONSTANTINE, HELLBLAZER VOL. 1: ORIGINAL SINS	DELANO, JAMIE	RIDGWAY, JOHN	$19.99/$23.99 CAN	TP
9781401233020	SEP110218	JOHN CONSTANTINE, HELLBLAZER VOL. 2: THE DEVIL YOU KNOW	DELANO, JAMIE	LLOYD, DAVID	$19.99/$23.99 CAN	TP
9781401235192	MAR120279	JOHN CONSTANTINE, HELLBLAZER VOL. 3: THE FEAR MACHINE	DELANO, JAMIE	BUCKINGHAM, MARK	$24.99/$28.99 CAN	TP
9781401236908	AUG120288	JOHN CONSTANTINE, HELLBLAZER VOL. 4: THE FAMILY MAN	VARIOUS	LLOYD, DAVID	$19.99/$23.99 CAN	TP
9781401238025	JAN130335	JOHN CONSTANTINE: HELLBLAZER VOL. 5: DANGEROUS HABITS	DELANO, JAMIE	ENNIS, GARTH	$19.99/$23.99 CAN	TP
9781401240431	MAY130258	JOHN CONSTANTINE, HELLBLAZER VOL. 6: BLOODLINES	ENNIS, GARTH	SIMPSON, WILLIAM	$19.99/$23.99 CAN	TP
9781401243036	OCT130283	JOHN CONSTANTINE, HELLBLAZER VOL. 7: TAINTED LOVE	ENNIS, GARTH	DILLON, STEVE	$19.99/$23.99 CAN	TP
9781401247492	MAR140283	JOHN CONSTANTINE, HELLBLAZER VOL. 8: RAKE AT THE GATES OF HELL	ENNIS, GARTH	DILLON, STEVE	$19.99/$23.99 CAN	TP
9781401250720	JUL140283	JOHN CONSTANTINE, HELLBLAZER VOL. 9: CRITICAL MASS	JENKINS, PAUL	CAMPBELL, EDDIE; PHILLIPS, SEAN	$19.99/$23.99 CAN	TP
9781401251376	NOV140338	JOHN CONSTANTINE HELLBLAZER VOL. 10: IN THE LINE OF FIRE	JENKINS, PAUL	PHILLIPS, SEAN	$19.99/$23.99 CAN	TP
9781401255299	MAY150266	JOHN CONSTANTINE, HELLBLAZER VOL. 11: LAST MAN STANDING	JENKINS, PAUL	PHILLIPS, SEAN	$24.99/$29.99 CAN	TP
9781401258108	OCT150281	JOHN CONSTANTINE, HELLBLAZER VOL. 12: HOW TO PLAY WITH FIRE	JENKINS, PAUL	PLEECE, WARREN	$19.99/$23.99 CAN	TP
9781401261412		JOHN CONSTANTINE: HELLBLAZER VOL. 13: HAUNTED	ENNIS, GARTH	JENKINS, PAUL	$19.99/$23.99 CAN	TP
9781401263737		JOHN CONSTANTINE, HELLBLAZER VOL. 14: GOOD INTENTIONS	VARIOUS	VARIOUS	$19.99/$23.99 CAN	TP
9781401210038	JAN060378	JOHN CONSTANTINE, HELLBLAZER: PAPA MIDNITE	JOHNSON, MAT	AKINS, TONY	$12.99/$17.50 CAN	TP
9781401214531	JUN070273	JOHN CONSTANTINE, HELLBLAZER: THE GIFT	CAREY, MIKE	MANCO, LEONARDO	$14.99/$17.99 CAN	TP
9781401204853	MAR050480	JOHN CONSTANTINE, HELLBLAZER: RED SEPULCHRE	CAREY, MIKE	DILLON, STEVE	$12.99/$17.50 CAN	TP
9781401203177	APR060290	JOHN CONSTANTINE, HELLBLAZER: ALL HIS ENGINES	CAREY, MIKE	MANCO, LEONARDO	$14.99/$19.99 CAN	TP

VERTIGO SELECTED BACKLIST

ISBN	DIAMOND CODE	TITLE	AUTHOR	ARTIST	US$	FORMAT
9781401216511	NOV070297	JOHN CONSTANTINE, HELLBLAZER: JOYRIDE	DIGGLE, ANDY	MANCO, LEONARDO	$14.99/$16.99 CAN	TP
9781401220396	NOV100274	JOHN CONSTANTINE, HELLBLAZER: PANDEMONIUM	DELANO, JAMIE	JOCK	$17.99/$19.99 CAN	TP
9781401225018	AUG090230	JOHN CONSTANTINE, HELLBLAZER: SCAB	MILLIGAN, PETER	CAMMUNCOLI, GIUSEPPE	$14.99/$18.99 CAN	TP
9781401240936	MAR130304	JOHN CONSTANTINE, HELLBLAZER: DEATH AND CIGARETTES	MILLIGAN, PETER	CAMUNCOLI, GIUSEPPE; BISLEY, SIMON	$19.99/$23.99 CAN	TP
9781401247485	DEC130344	JOHN CONSTANTINE, HELLBLAZER: SHOOT	ELLIS, WARREN; AARON, JASON	JIMENEZ, PHIL; MURPHY, SEAN	$14.99/$17.99 CAN	TP
9781401247157	JAN140383	JONAH HEX: SHADOWS WEST	LANSDALE, JOE	TRUMAN, TIMOTHY	$24.99/$28.99 CAN	TP
9781401258115	AUG150294	KID ETERNITY DELUXE EDITION	MORRISON, GRANT	FEGREDO, DUNCAN	$24.99/$29.99 CAN	HC
9781401261429	OCT150282	KILL YOUR BOYFRIEND/VINAMARAMA DELUXE	MORRISON, GRANT	BOND, PHILIP	$19.99/$23.99 CAN	HC
9781401257736	AUG150292	THE KITCHEN	MASTERS, OLLY	DOYLE, MING	$16.99/$19.99 CAN	TP
9781563898587	MAY118167	THE LEAGUE OF EXTRAORDINARY GENTLEMEN VOL. 1	MOORE, ALAN	O'NEILL, KEVIN	$16.99/$19.99 CAN	TP
9781401201180	MAY118168	THE LEAGUE OF EXTRAORDINARY GENTLEMEN VOL. 2	MOORE, ALAN	O'NEILL, KEVIN	$16.99/$19.99 CAN	TP
9781401203078	JUL080193	THE LEAGUE OF EXTRAORDINARY GENTLEMEN: BLACK DOSSIER	MOORE, ALAN	O'NEILL, KEVIN	$19.99 CAN	TP
9781401240837	MAY130257	THE LEAGUE OF EXTRAORDINARY GENTLEMEN OMNIBUS	MOORE, ALAN	O'NEILL, KEVIN	$29.99/$35.00 CAN	TP
9781401204280	NOV100265	THE LITTLE ENDLESS STORYBOOK	THOMPSON, JILL	THOMPSON, JILL	$14.99/$16.99 CAN	TP
9781401229238	MAY100275	THE LOSERS BOOK TWO	DIGGLE, ANDY	JOCK	$24.99/$28.99 CAN	TP
9781401240264	FEB130247	LUCIFER BOOK ONE	CAREY, MIKE	GROSS, PETER; HAMPTON, SCOTT	$29.99/$35.00 CAN	TP
9781401242602	JUL130266	LUCIFER BOOK TWO	CAREY, MIKE	GROSS, PETER	$29.99/$35.00 CAN	TP
9781401246044	DEC130345	LUCIFER BOOK THREE	CAREY, MIKE	GROSS, PETER	$29.99/$35.00 CAN	TP
9781401246051	MAY140408	LUCIFER BOOK FOUR	CAREY, MIKE	GROSS, PETER	$29.99/$35.00 CAN	TP
9781401249458	SEP140346	LUCIFER BOOK FIVE	CAREY, MIKE	GROSS, PETER; KELLY, RYAN	$29.99/$35.00 CAN	TP
9781401261931		LUCIFER VOL. 1	BLACK, HOLLY	GARBETT, LEE	$14.99/$17.99 CAN	TP
9781401259037	MAR150292	MAD MAX: FURY ROAD INSPIRED ARTISTS DELUXE EDITION	BERMEJO, LEE	$24.99/$29.99 CAN	HC
9781401259051	MAY150271	MAD MAX: FURY ROAD	MILLER, GEORGE	VARIOUS	$14.99/$17.99 CAN	TP
9781401261436		MANIFEST ETERNITY	LOBDELL, SCOTT	NGUYEN, DUSTIN	$19.99/$23.99 CAN	TP
9781401229597	JUL110278	MARZI	SOWA, MARZENA	SAVOIA, SYLVAIN	$17.99/$19.99 CAN	TP
9781401251420	MAY140410	MR. PUNCH - 20TH ANNIVERSARY EDITION	GAIMAN, NEIL	MCKEAN, DAVE	$34.99/$41.99 CAN	HC
9781563891892	STAR18959	MYSTERY PLAY	MORRISON, GRANT	MUTH, JON J	$12.95/$21.95 CAN	TP
9781401252434	MAY150268	THE NAMES	MILLIGAN, PETER	FERNANDEZ, LEANDRO	$16.99/$19.99 CAN	TP
9781401234577	MAR120280	NEIL GAIMAN'S MIDNIGHT DAYS DELUXE EDITION	GAIMAN, NEIL	MCKEAN, DAVE	$24.99/$27.99 CAN	HC
9781401210076	NOV060304	NEIL GAIMAN'S NEVERWHERE	CAREY, MIKE	FABRY, GLENN	$19.99/$23.99 CAN	TP
9781563894701	FEB058028	NEIL GAIMAN AND CHARLES VESS' STARDUST	GAIMAN, NEIL	VESS, CHARLIE	$19.99/$23.99 CAN	TP
9781401228224	JUN130298	NEIL YOUNG'S GREENDALE	DYSART, JOSH	CHIANG, CLIFF	$14.99/$17.99 CAN	TP
9781401263515		NEW ROMANCER VOL. 1	MILLIGAN, PETER	PARSON, BRETT	$14.99/$17.99 CAN	TP
9781401263317		NORTHLANDERS BOOK 1	WOOD, BRIAN	GIANFELICE, DAVIDE	$29.99/$35.00 CAN	TP
9781401251451	OCT140401	NORTH 40 (NEW EDITION)	WILLIAMS, AARON	STAPLES, FIONA	$14.99/$17.99 CAN	TP
9781401255343	NOV140339	OCEAN/ORBITER DELUXE EDITION	ELLIS, WARREN	SPROUSE, CHRIS; DORAN, COLLEEN	$29.99/$35.00 CAN	HC
9781401219024	DEC090263	OTHER LIVES	BAGGE, PETER	BAGGE, PETER	$24.99/$29.99 CAN	HC
9781401215354	OCT100316	NOCHE ROJA	OLIVER, SIMON	LATOUR, JASON	$19.99/$22.99 CAN	HC
9781401240455	MAR130303	PREACHER BOOK ONE	ENNIS, GARTH	DILLON, STEVE	$19.99/$23.99 CAN	TP
9781401242558	JUN130299	PREACHER BOOK TWO	ENNIS, GARTH	DILLON, STEVE	$19.99/$23.99 CAN	TP
9781401245016	OCT130293	PREACHER BOOK THREE	ENNIS, GARTH	DILLON, STEVE	$19.99/$23.99 CAN	TP
9781401230944	MAR140292	PREACHER BOOK FOUR	ENNIS, GARTH	DILLON, STEVE	$19.99/$23.99 CAN	TP
9781401250744	MAY140409	PREACHER BOOK FIVE	ENNIS, GARTH	DILLON, STEVE	$19.99/$23.99 CAN	TP
9781401252793	JUL140282	PREACHER BOOK SIX	DILLON, STEVE	ENNIS, GARTH	$19.99/$23.99 CAN	TP
9781401264413	JAN160353	ABSOLUTE PREACHER VOL. 1	ENNIS, GARTH	DILLON, STEVE	$172.00	HC
9781401203153	FEB118119	PRIDE OF BAGHDAD	VAUGHAN, BRIAN K.	HENRICHON, NIKO	$14.99/$17.99 CAN	TP
9781401248949	AUG140360	PRIDE OF BAGHDAD DELUXE EDITION	VAUGHAN, BRIAN K.	HENRICHON, NIKO	$24.99/$28.99 CAN	HC
9781563896675	APR108106	PROMETHEA BOOK 1	MOORE, ALAN	WILLIAMS III, J.H.	$17.99/$20.99 CAN	TP
9781401200947	AUG128046	PROMETHEA BOOK 2	MOORE, ALAN	WILLIAMS III, J.H.	$17.99/$20.99 CAN	TP
9781563896675	AUG128047	PROMETHEA BOOK 3	MOORE, ALAN	WILLIAMS III, J.H.	$17.99/$20.99 CAN	TP
9781401200312	OCT098137	PROMETHEA BOOK 4	MOORE, ALAN	WILLIAMS III, J.H.	$17.99/$20.99 CAN	TP

ISBN	DIAMOND CODE	TITLE	AUTHOR	ARTIST	US$	FORMAT
9781401206208	DEC138192	PROMETHEA BOOK 5	MOORE, ALAN	WILLIAMS III, J.H.	$17.99/$20.99 CAN	TP
9781401237684	JAN130330	PUNK ROCK JESUS	MURPHY, SEAN	MURPHY, SEAN	$16.99/$19.99 CAN	TP
9781401251468	JUN140309	PUNK ROCK JESUS DELUXE EDITION	MURPHY, SEAN	MURPHY, SEAN	$39.99/$47.99 CAN	HC
9781401204006	JUL060250	THE QUITTER	PEKAR, HARVEY	HASPIEL, DEAN	$12.99/$17.50 CAN	TP
9781401263614		RED THORN VOL. 1	BAILLIE, DAVID	HETRICK, MEGHAN	$14.99/$17.99 CAN	TP
9781401222420	APR110251	REVOLVER	KINDT, MATT	KINDT, MATT	$19.99/$22.99 CAN	TP
9781401229443	MAY130262	RIGHT STATE	JOHNSON, MAT	MUTTI, ANDREA	$16.99/$19.99 CAN	TP
9781401231903	JUL110281	ROAD TO PERDITION 2: ON THE ROAD	COLLINS, MAX ALLAN	GARCIA-LOPEZ, JOSE LUIS	$14.99/$16.99 CAN	TP
9781401223847	AUG120296	RETURN TO PERDITION	COLLINS, MAX ALLAN	BEATTY, TERRY	$14.99/$17.99 CAN	TP
9781401250546	SEP140347	THE ROYALS: MASTERS OF WAR	WILLIAMS, ROB	COLEBY, SIMON	$14.99/$17.99 CAN	TP
9781401220839	JAN120343	SAGA OF THE SWAMP THING BOOK ONE	MOORE, ALAN	BISSETE, STEPHEN	$19.99/$23.99 CAN	TP
9781401225445	JUN120283	SAGA OF THE SWAMP THING BOOK TWO	MOORE, ALAN	BISSETE, STEPHEN	$19.99/$23.99 CAN	TP
9781401227678	OCT120301	SAGA OF THE SWAMP THING BOOK THREE	MOORE, ALAN	BISSETE, STEPHEN	$19.99/$23.99 CAN	TP
9781401240462	APR130262	SAGA OF THE SWAMP THING BOOK FOUR	MOORE, ALAN	BISSETTE, STEPHEN; WOCH, STAN	$19.99/$23.99 CAN	TP
9781401230968	SEP130310	SAGA OF THE SWAMP THING BOOK FIVE	MOORE, ALAN	VEITCH, RICK	$14.99/$17.99 CAN	TP
9781401246921	FEB140293	SAGA OF THE SWAMP THING BOOK SIX	MOORE, ALAN	VEITCH, RICK; ALCALA, ALFREDO	$19.99/$23.99 CAN	TP
9781401243043	OCT130292	SWAMP THING BY BRIAN K. VAUGHAN VOL. 1	VAUGHAN, BRIAN K.	PETERSON, ROGER; CHIANG, CLIFF	$19.99/$23.99 CAN	TP
9781401245986	APR140296	SWAMP THING BY BRIAN K. VAUGHAN VOL. 2	VAUGHAN, BRIAN K.	PETERSEN, ROGER; CAMUNCOLI, GIUSEPPE	$19.99/$23.99 CAN	TP
9781401252410	APR150325	SWAMP THING: THE ROOT OF ALL EVIL	MORRISON, GRANT; MILLER, MARK	HESTER, PHIL	$19.99/$23.99 CAN	TP
9781401261450		SWAMP THING BY MARK MILLAR	MILLAR, MARK	VARIOUS	$19.99/$23.99 CAN	TP
9781401258283	AUG150296	SWAMP THING: DARKER GENESIS	PFEIFER, WILL	WOODS, PETE	$19.99/$23.99 CAN	TP
9781401263379		SWAMP THING VOL. 3: TRIAL BY FIRE	MILLAR, MARK	VARIOUS	$19.99/$23.99 CAN	TP
9781401248963	JUL158372	THE SANDMAN: OVERTURE DELUXE EDITION	GAIMAN, NEIL	WILLIAMS III, JH	$24.99/$29.99 CAN	HC
9781401225759	JUL100259	THE SANDMAN VOL. 1: PRELUDES & NOCTURNES	GAIMAN, NEIL	KIETH, SAM	$19.99/$23.99 CAN	TP
9781401227999	JUL100260	THE SANDMAN VOL. 2: THE DOLL'S HOUSE	GAIMAN, NEIL	DRINGENBERG, MIKE	$19.99/$23.99 CAN	TP
9781401229351	JUL100261	THE SANDMAN VOL. 3: DREAM COUNTRY	GAIMAN, NEIL	JONES, KELLEY	$19.99/$23.99 CAN	TP
9781401230425	OCT100330	THE SANDMAN VOL. 4: SEASON OF MISTS	GAIMAN, NEIL	JONES, KELLEY	$19.99/$23.99 CAN	TP
9781401230432	JAN110431	THE SANDMAN VOL. 5: A GAME OF YOU	GAIMAN, NEIL	MCMANUS, SHAWN	$19.99/$23.99 CAN	TP
9781401231231	MAY110297	THE SANDMAN VOL. 6: FABLES & REFLECTIONS	GAIMAN, NEIL	TALBOT, BRYAN	$19.99/$23.99 CAN	TP
9781401232634	SEP110177	THE SANDMAN VOL. 7: BRIEF LIVES	GAIMAN, NEIL	THOMPSON, JILL	$19.99/$23.99 CAN	TP
9781401234027	NOV110233	THE SANDMAN VOL. 8: WORLDS' END	GAIMAN, NEIL	ALLRED, MIKE	$19.99/$23.99 CAN	TP
9781401235451	FEB120298	THE SANDMAN VOL. 9: THE KINDLY ONES	GAIMAN, NEIL	HEMPEL, MARC	$19.99/$23.99 CAN	TP
9781401237547	AUG100292	THE SANDMAN VOL. 10: THE WAKE	GAIMAN, NEIL	ZULLI, MICHAEL	$19.99/$23.99 CAN	TP
9781401224288	JUN100280	THE SANDMAN: THE DREAM HUNTERS	GAIMAN, NEIL	RUSSELL, P. CRAIG	$19.99/$23.99 CAN	TP
9781401242336	JUL130264	THE SANDMAN: ENDLESS NIGHTS	GAIMAN, NEIL	VARIOUS	$19.99/$23.99 CAN	TP
9781563893872	STAR07911	THE SANDMAN: THE COLLECTED DUSTCOVERS	MCKEAN, DAVE	MCKEAN, DAVE	$24.95/$38.00 CAN	TP
9781401233327	AUG110277	THE ANNOTATED SANDMAN VOL. 1	GAIMAN, NEIL	VARIOUS	$49.99/$58.00 CAN	HC
9781401235666	JUN120271	THE ANNOTATED SANDMAN VOL. 2	GAIMAN, NEIL	VARIOUS	$49.99/$58.00 CAN	HC
9781401241025	APR140291	THE ANNOTATED SANDMAN VOL. 3	KLINGER, LESLIE S.; GAIMAN, NEIL	VARIOUS	$49.99/$58.00 CAN	HC
9781401243227	JUL150334	THE ANNOTATED SANDMAN VOL. 4	GAIMAN, NEIL	KLINGER, LESLIE	$49.99/$58.00 CAN	HC
9781401250652	JUL140270	DREAM STATES: THE COLLECTED DREAMING COVERS	MCKEAN, DAVE	MCKEAN, DAVE	$49.99/$58.00 CAN	HC
9781401250669	JUL140271	DUST COVERS: THE COLLECTED SANDMAN COVERS	MCKEAN, DAVE	MCKEAN, DAVE	$49.99/$58.00 CAN	HC
9781401218553	MAY080258	THE SANDMAN PRESENTS: DEAD BOY DETECTIVES	BRUBAKER, ED	TALBOT, BRYAN	$12.99/$14.99 CAN	TP
9781401263270		SANDMAN MYSTERY THEATRE BOOK 1	WAGNER, MATT	DAVIS, GUY	$29.99/$35.00 CAN	TP
9781401235499	AUG120295	SAUCER COUNTRY VOL. 1: RUN	CORNELL, PAUL	KELLY, RYAN	$14.99/$17.99 CAN	TP
9781401240479	MAY130259	SAUCER COUNTRY VOL. 2: THE RETICULAN CANDIDATE	CORNELL, PAUL	BROXTON, JIMMY; LAPHAM, DAVID	$16.99/$19.99 CAN	TP
9781401213176	APR108251	SCALPED VOL. 1: INDIAN COUNTRY	AARON, JASON	GUERA, R.M.	$14.99/$17.99 CAN	TP
9781401216542	NOV070301	SCALPED VOL. 2: CASINO BOOGIE	AARON, JASON	GUERA, R.M.	$14.99/$17.99 CAN	TP
9781401219192	JUN080304	SCALPED VOL. 3: DEAD MOTHERS	AARON, JASON	GUERA, R.M.	$17.99/$20.99 CAN	TP
9781401221799	JAN090288	SCALPED VOL. 4: THE GRAVEL IN YOUR GUTS	AARON, JASON	GUERA, R.M.	$14.99/$17.99 CAN	TP
9781401224875	JUL090293	SCALPED VOL. 5: HIGH LONESOME	AARON, JASON	GUERA, R.M.	$14.99/$17.99 CAN	TP

ISBN	DIAMOND CODE	TITLE	AUTHOR	ARTIST	US$	FORMAT
9781401227173	FEB100266	SCALPED VOL. 6: THE GNAWING	AARON, JASON	GUERA, R.M.	$14.99/$17.99 CAN	TP
9781401230197	NOV100278	SCALPED VOL. 7: REZ BLUES	AARON, JASON	GUERA, R.M.	$17.99/$20.99 CAN	TP
9781401232887	AUG110288	SCALPED VOL. 8: YOU GOTTA SIN TO GET SAVED	AARON, JASON	GUERA, R.M.	$17.99/$20.99 CAN	TP
9781401235055	APR120293	SCALPED VOL. 9: KNUCKLE UP	AARON, JASON	GUERA, R.M.	$14.99/$17.99 CAN	TP
9781401237349	JUL120253	SCALPED VOL. 10: TRAIL'S END	AARON, JASON	GUERA, R.M.	$14.99/$17.99 CAN	TP
9781401250911	OCT140402	SCALPED DELUXE EDITION BOOK ONE	AARON, JASON	GUERA, R.M.	$29.99/$35.00 CAN	HC
9781401254254	APR150324	SCALPED DELUXE EDITION BOOK TWO	AARON, JASON	GUERA, R.M.	$29.99/$35.00 CAN	HC
9781401258580	AUG150295	SCALPED DELUXE EDITION BOOK THREE	AARON, JASON	GUERA, R.M.	$29.99/$35.00 CAN	HC
9781401261443		SCALPED DELUXE EDITION BOOK FOUR	AARON, JASON	GUERA, R.M.	$29.99/$35.00 CAN	HC
9781401263638		SCALPED DELUXE EDITION BOOK FIVE	AARON, JASON	GUERA, R.M.	$29.99/$35.00 CAN	HC
9781401200466	AUG090239	SHADE, THE CHANGING MAN VOL. 1: AMERICAN SCREAM	MILLIGAN, PETER	BACHALO, CHRIS	$17.99/$22.99 CAN	TP
9781401225391	AUG090240	SHADE, THE CHANGING MAN VOL. 2: EDGE OF VISION	MILLIGAN, PETER	BACHALO, CHRIS	$19.99/$24.99 CAN	TP
9781401227685	MAR100311	SHADE, THE CHANGING MAN VOL. 3: SCREAM TIME	MILLIGAN, PETER	HEWLETT, JAMIE	$19.99/$23.99 CAN	TP
9781401222154	DEC110314	SHOOTERS	JERWA, BRANDON	LIEBER, STEVEN	$22.99/$25.99 CAN	HC
9781401210496	SEP080229	SILVERFISH	LAPHAM, DAVID	LAPHAM, DAVID	$17.99/$21.99 CAN	TP
9781401262778		SLASH & BURN VOL. 1	SPENCER, SI	PARKS, ANDE	$16.99/$19.99 CAN	TP
9781401223601	MAR090210	SLEEPER: SEASON ONE	BRUBAKER, ED	PHILLIPS, SEAN	$24.99/$28.99 CAN	TP
9781401238032	OCT120298	THE SLEEPER OMNIBUS	BRUBAKER, ED	PHILLIPS, SEAN	$75.00/$85.00 CAN	HC
9781401203689	AUG080238	SLOTH	HERNANDEZ, GILBERT	HERNANDEZ, GILBERT	$14.99/$16.99 CAN	TP
9781401242701	NOV130269	SPACEMAN	AZZARELLO, BRIAN	RISSO, EDUARDO	$19.99/$23.99 CAN	TP
9781401243937	NOV130276	STRANGE ADVENTURES	VARIOUS	VARIOUS	$14.99/$17.99 CAN	TP
9781401258641	SEP150326	STRANGE SPORTS STORIES	AZZARELLO, BRIAN	POPE, PAUL	$14.99/$17.99 CAN	TP
9781401248970	JUL150341	SUICIDERS VOL. 1	BERMEJO, LEE	BERMEJO, LEE	$22.99/$27.99 CAN	HC
9781401259808		SUICIDERS: KINGS OF HelLA	BERMEJO, LEE	BERMEJO, LEE	$22.99/$27.99 CAN	HC
9781401226961	AUG108007	SWEET TOOTH VOL. 1: OUT OF THE DEEP WOODS	LEMIRE, JEFF	LEMIRE, JEFF	$12.99/$15.99 CAN	TP
9781401228545	OCT118099	SWEET TOOTH VOL. 2: IN CAPTIVITY	LEMIRE, JEFF	LEMIRE, JEFF	$14.99/$17.99 CAN	TP
9781401231705	MAR110392	SWEET TOOTH VOL. 3: ANIMAL ARMIES	LEMIRE, JEFF	LEMIRE, JEFF	$14.99/$17.99 CAN	TP
9781401233617	OCT110296	SWEET TOOTH VOL. 4: ENDANGERED SPECIES	LEMIRE, JEFF	LEMIRE, JEFF	$16.99/$19.99 CAN	TP
9781401237233	JUL120259	SWEET TOOTH VOL. 5: UNNATURAL HABIT	LEMIRE, JEFF	LEMIRE, JEFF	$14.99/$17.99 CAN	TP
9781401240295	MAR130305	SWEET TOOTH VOL. 6: WILD GAME	LEMIRE, JEFF	LEMIRE, JEFF	$16.99/$19.99 CAN	TP
9781401258719	MAY150269	SWEET TOOTH DELUXE EDITION BOOK ONE	LEMIRE, JEFF	LEMIRE, JEFF	$29.99/$35.00 CAN	HC
9781401261467	DEC150368	SWEET TOOTH DELUXE EDITION BOOK TWO	LEMIRE, JEFF	LEMIRE, JEFF	$29.99/$35.00 CAN	HC
9781401242800	OCT130294	TERRA OBSCURA: S.M.A.S.H. OF TWO WORLDS	MOORE, ALAN; HOGAN, PETER	PAQUETTE, YANICK	$24.99/$28.99 CAN	TP
9781401226800	DEC090253	TOM STRONG DELUXE VOL. 2	MOORE, ALAN	SPROUSE, CHRIS	$39.99/$49.99 CAN	HC
9781401246457	MAR140291	TOM STRONG AND THE PLANET OF PERIL	HOGAN, PETER	SPROUSE, CHRIS; STORY, KARL	US$14.99/$17.99 CAN	TP
9781401254933	JAN150410	TOP 10	MOORE, ALAN	HA, GENE; CANNON, ZANDER	$24.99/$28.99 CAN	TP
9781401220846	DEC080220	TRANSMETROPOLITAN VOL. 1: BACK ON THE STREET	ELLIS, WARREN	ROBERTSON, DARICK	$14.99/$17.99 CAN	TP
9781401222611	FEB090264	TRANSMETROPOLITAN VOL. 2: LUST FOR LIFE	ELLIS, WARREN	ROBERTSON, DARICK	$14.99/$17.99 CAN	TP
9781401223120	DEC098262	TRANSMETROPOLITAN VOL. 3: YEAR OF THE BASTARD	ELLIS, WARREN	ROBERTSON, DARICK	$14.99/$17.99 CAN	TP
9781401224905	JUL090291	TRANSMETROPOLITAN VOL. 4: THE NEW SCUM	ELLIS, WARREN	ROBERTSON, DARICK	$14.99/$17.99 CAN	TP
9781401228194	SEP090228	TRANSMETROPOLITAN VOL. 5. LONELY CITY	ELLIS, WARREN	ROBERTSON, DARICK	$14.99/$17.99 CAN	TP
9781401228187	DEC090284	TRANSMETROPOLITAN VOL. 6: GOUGE AWAY	ELLIS, WARREN	ROBERTSON, DARICK	$14.99/$17.99 CAN	TP
9781401228156	FEB100264	TRANSMETROPOLITAN VOL. 7: SPIDER'S THRASH	ELLIS, WARREN	ROBERTSON, DARICK	$14.99/$17.99 CAN	TP
9781401229368	JUN100282	TRANSMETROPOLITAN VOL. 8: DIRGE	ELLIS, WARREN	ROBERTSON, DARICK	$14.99/$17.99 CAN	TP
9781401230494	JAN110435	TRANSMETROPOLITAN VOL. 9: THE CURE	ELLIS, WARREN	ROBERTSON, DARICK	$14.99/$17.99 CAN	TP
9781401231248	MAY110296	TRANSMETROPOLITAN VOL. 10: ONE MORE TIME	ELLIS, WARREN	ROBERTSON, DARICK	$19.99/$23.99 CAN	TP
9781401254308	OCT140403	ABSOLUTE TRANSMETROPOLITAN VOL. 1	ELLIS, WARREN	ROBERTSON, DARICK; RAMOS, RODNEY	$125.00/$144.00 CAN	HC
9781401254308	OCT150280	ABSOLUTE TRANSMETROPOLITAN VOL. 2	ELLIS, WARREN	ROBERTSON, DARICK	$125.00/$144.00 CAN	HC
9781401249007	MAY140407	TRILLIUM	LEMIRE, JEFF	LEMIRE, JEFF	$16.99/$19.99 CAN	TP
9781401262457		THE TWILIGHT CHILDREN	HERNANDEZ, JAMIE	COOKE, DARWYN	$22.99/$27.99 CAN	HC
9781401243944	JUL130271	THE UNEXPECTED	VARIOUS	VARIOUS	$14.99/$17.99 CAN	TP

ISBN	DIAMOND CODE	TITLE	AUTHOR	ARTIST	US$	FORMAT
9781401262747		UNFOLLOW VOL. 1	WILLIAMS, ROB	DOWLING, MICHAEL	$14.99/$17.99 CAN	TP
9781401244170	NOV130277	UNKNOWN SOLDIER (NEW EDITION)	ENNIS, GARTH	PLUNKETT, KILLIAN	$14.99/$17.99 CAN	TP
9781401223113	MAY090251	UNKNOWN SOLDIER VOL. 1: HAUNTED HOUSE	DYSART, JOSHUA	PONTICELLI, ALBERTO	$9.99/$12.99 CAN	TP
9781401226008	DEC090283	UNKNOWN SOLDIER VOL. 2: EASY KILL	DYSART, JOSHUA	PONTICELLI, ALBERTO	$17.99/$22.99 CAN	TP
9781401228552	AUG100276	UNKNOWN SOLDIER VOL. 3: DRY SEASON	DYSART, JOSHUA	PONTICELLI, ALBERTO	$14.99/$17.99 CAN	TP
9781401231767	FEB110269	UNKNOWN SOLDIER VOL. 4: BEAUTIFUL WORLD	DYSART, JOSHUA	PONTICELLI, ALBERTO	$14.99/$16.99 CAN	TP
9781401225650	APR128238	THE UNWRITTEN VOL. 1: TOMMY TAYLOR AND THE BOGUS IDENTITY	CAREY, MIKE	GROSS, PETER	$14.99/$17.99 CAN	TP
9781401228736	MAY100283	THE UNWRITTEN VOL. 2: INSIDE MAN	CAREY, MIKE	GROSS, PETER	$12.99/$15.99 CAN	TP
9781401230463	DEC100305	THE UNWRITTEN VOL. 3: DEAD MAN'S KNOCK	CAREY, MIKE	GROSS, PETER	$14.99/$17.99 CAN	TP
9781401232924	JUL110296	THE UNWRITTEN VOL. 4: LEVIATHAN	CAREY, MIKE	GROSS, PETER	$14.99/$17.99 CAN	TP
9781401233594	OCT110301	THE UNWRITTEN VOL. 5: ON TO GENESIS	CAREY, MIKE	GROSS, PETER	$14.99/$17.99 CAN	TP
9781401235604	JUL120262	THE UNWRITTEN VOL. 6: TOMMY TAYLOR AND THE WAR OF WORDS	CAREY, MIKE	GROSS, PETER	$16.99/$19.99 CAN	TP
9781401238063	DEC120368	THE UNWRITTEN VOL. 7: THE WOUND	CAREY, MIKE	GROSS, PETER	$14.99/$17.99 CAN	TP
9781401243012	OCT130295	THE UNWRITTEN VOL. 8: ORPHEUS IN THE UNDERWORLDS	CAREY, MIKE	GROSS, PETER	$16.99/$19.99 CAN	TP
9781401246945	APR140302	THE UNWRITTEN VOL. 9: THE UNWRITTEN FABLES	CAREY, MIKE	GROSS, PETER; BUCKINGHAM, MARK	$14.99/$17.99 CAN	TP
9781401250553	JUL140285	THE UNWRITTEN VOL. 10: WAR STORIES	CAREY, MIKE	GROSS, PETER	$14.99/$17.99 CAN	TP
9781401253486	FEB150288	THE UNWRITTEN VOL. 11: APOCALYPSE	CAREY, MIKE	GROSS, PETER	$16.99/$19.99 CAN	TP
9781401229771	JUN140310	THE UNWRITTEN: TOMMY TAYLOR AND THE SHIP THAT SANK TWICE	CAREY, MIKE	GROSS, PETER	$14.99/$17.99 CAN	TP
9781401208417	SEP088030	V FOR VENDETTA	MOORE, ALAN	LLOYD, DAVID	$19.99/$23.99 CAN	TP
9781401261474		VERTIGO QUARTERLY SFX	MILLIGAN, PETER	VARIOUS	$19.99/$23.99 CAN	TP
9781401254919	MAR150313	THE WAKE	SNYDER, SCOTT	MURPHY, SEAN	$17.99/$20.99 CAN	TP
9781401243029	NOV130270	WE3	MORRISON, GRANT	QUIETLY, FRANK	$14.99/$17.99 CAN	TP
9781401257743	JUL150342	WOLF MOON	BUNN, CULLEN	HAUN, JEREMY	$14.99/$17.99 CAN	TP
9781401251512	JUN140312	Y THE LAST MAN BOOK ONE	VAUGHAN, BRIAN K.	GUERRA, PIA	$19.99/$23.99 CAN	TP
9781401254391	DEC140421	Y THE LAST MAN BOOK TWO	VAUGHAN, BRIAN K.	GUERRA, PIA	$19.99/$23.99 CAN	TP
9781401258801	JUN150324	Y THE LAST MAN BOOK THREE	VAUGHAN, BRIAN	GUERRA, PIA	$19.99/$23.99 CAN	TP
9781401261689	NOV150300	Y: THE LAST MAN BOOK FOUR	VAUGHN, BRIAN K.	GUERRA, PIA	$19.99/$23.99 CAN	TP
9781401263720		Y: THE LAST MAN BOOK FIVE	VAUGHAN, BRIAN K.	GUERRA, PIA	$19.99/$23.99 CAN	TP
9781401254292	DEC140420	ABSOLUTE Y THE LAST MAN VOL. 1	VAUGHAN, BRIAN K.	GUERRA, PIA	$125.00/$144.00 CAN	HC
9781401219789	AUG138202	YOUNG LIARS VOL. 1: DAYDREAM	LAPHAM, DAVID	LAPHAM, DAVID	$14.99/$17.99 CAN	TP

BATMAN: THE A[...]
THE BA[...]

ALL CHARACTERS, THEIR DISTINCTIVE LIKENESSES AND RELATED ELEMENTS ARE TRADEMARKS OF AND © DC COMICS.
PRODUCTS MAY VARY FROM IMAGES SHOWN.

IMATED SERIES
MOBILE

* Batman sold seperately

COLLECT
THEM ALL!

ONLY FROM

"A masterful return."
—IGN.com
"Lives up to the hype."
—WASHINGTON POST
"Defies expectations."
—COMICBOOKRESOURCES.COM
"For fans of Miller's DARK KNIGHT series, this is vital reading."
—NY DAILY NEWS
DKIII
THE MASTER RACE
AN EIGHT-ISSUE LIMITED SERIES
WRITTEN BY FRANK MILLER BRIAN AZZARELLO
ART BY ANDY KUBERT KLAUS JANSON
DC COMICS™
TM & © DC Comics